PAPER 24

D0274547

000898

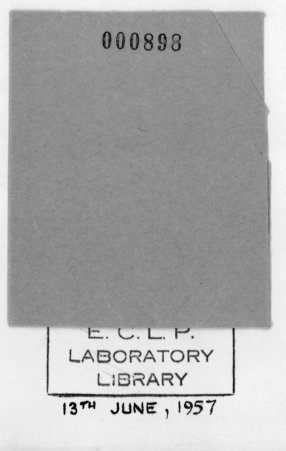

000898

E. C. L. P.
LABORATORY
LIBRARY
13TH JUNE, 1957

£ 3/15/-

SPECIALTY PAPERS

Their Properties and Applications

Prepared by a Staff of Specialists
under the Editorship of

ROBERT H. MOSHER

Manager of Manufacturing
The Holyoke Card & Paper Company

formerly
Technical Director,
The Marvellum Company

1950
REMSEN PRESS
BROOKLYN N. Y.

Copyright
1950
REMSEN PRESS
BROOKLYN   N. Y.

PRINTED IN THE UNITED STATES OF AMERICA

CONTRIBUTORS

AIKEN, WILLIAM H. Assistant Manager, Chemicals Division, Goodyear Tire and Rubber Co., Akron, Ohio. Previous experience as Project Leader in Quartermaster Corps, Project on Coated Fabric and Films, The Brooklyn Polytechnic Institute. Studied at Texas A and M College and The Institute of Paper Chemistry.

ARIES, ROBERT S. Adjunct Professor of Chemical Engineering at Brooklyn Polytechnic Institute, and Technical Director of the Northeastern Wood Utilization Council. Studied at Columbia University, Yale University, The University of Minnesota, and Brooklyn Polytechnic Institute.

AUSTIN, JOSEPH J. Austin Industries, Concord and Sudbury, Massachusetts. Previously connected with Dewey and Almy Chemical Company. Studied at Boston University and Massachusetts Institute of Technology.

BARR, F. A. Vice-President, The Holyoke Card and Paper Co.

BLAKESLEE, ROBERT B. Chemist, Wallpaper Division, The Imperial Paper and Color Corporation, Glens Falls, New York. Studied at University of Cincinnati.

BLOUNT, RUFUS. Treasurer, The Hampden Glazed Paper and Card Company, Holyoke, Massachusetts. Studied at Yale University.

BRACEWELL, RUSSELL S. Vice-President, The Marvellum Company, Holyoke, Massachusetts. Previously connected with The American Writing Paper Company. Studied at The University of Kansas and The University of Illinois.

DAVIES, JOHN H. Manager of Foil-Paper Division, Standard Rolling Mills, Inc.

DOWNS, MARTIN C. Technical Director, Thilmany Pulp and Paper Co., Kaukauna, Wisconsin. Previously connected with The Mead Corporation. Studied at Pennsylvania State College and The Institute of Paper Chemistry.

FARRELL, FRED W. Technical Director, The McLaurin-Jones Co., Brookfield, Massachusetts. Previously connected with Emerson Laboratory and The Bureau of Chemistry, U. S. Department of Agriculture. Studied at The Massachusetts Institute of Technology.

HEYWOOD, FRANCIS C. President, The Marvellum Company, Holyoke, Massachusetts. Previously connected with The Whitmore Manufacturing Company, The Chemical Paper Co., and The American Writing Paper Company. Studied at Cornell University.

MOSHER, ROBERT H. Manager of Manufacturing, The Holyoke Card and Paper Company, Springfield, Massachusetts. Formerly Technical Director, The Marvellum Company, Holyoke, Massachusetts and previously connected with Monsanto Chemical Company and various paper mills. Studied at The University of Massachusetts and The Institute of Paper Chemistry.

PARK, MAURICE A. Pacific Coast District Manager, W. C. Hamilton and Sons. Previously connected with Holyoke Card and Paper Company and The Marvellum Company. Studied at Columbia University.

PICKERING, JOHN C., JR. Vice-President, The Pervel Corporation. Previously connected with The Brown Paper Co. Studied at Brown University.

SCHMID, GEORGE. Chemist, The Cellutin Corporation, Holyoke, Massachusetts. Previously connected with The Michigan Paper Company, Falulah Paper Company, and The Institute of Paper Chemistry. Studied at University of Wisconsin.

SIMMONS, ROBERT H. Chemist, United States Government Printing Office, Washington, D. C. Previously connected with The Oxford Paper Co. Studied at Colgate University, Columbia University, and The Brooklyn Polytechnic Institute.

THOMSON, C. E. GEDDES. President, North Shore Blue Print Co. Previously connected with Charles Bruning Company. Studied at McGill University.

WISSINGER, ROBERT R. Plant Manager, Copyright Carbon Corporation, Chardon, Ohio. Previously connected with Moore Business Forms and The Ault-Wiborg Carbon and Ribbon Company. Studied at Kenyon College.

WORTHINGTON, ARTHUR M. Technical Superintendent, The American Tissue Mills, Holyoke, Massachusetts. Previously connected with Fraser Paper, Ltd., The Acme Paper Board Company, and The Beach and Arthur Paper Company. Studied at The Massachusetts Institute of Technology.

FOREWORD

by R. S. Aries

THE steady growth of the American pulp and paper industry has not been accompanied by a commensurate increase in our technical literature on the subject. While the Technical Association of the Pulp and Paper Industry, as well as some trade papers, have made scattered articles available, we have not had the profusion of reference works on the subject which many other industries are fortunate enough to already possess. This is especially true of the field of converted papers, including decorative, specialty, functional, and protective papers and their manufacture and use. This volume, under the editorship of Mr. Robert H. Mosher, has set as a goal for itself the filling of this gap and has uniquely succeeded in this respect. The importance and magnitude of the task can best be realized by indicating that this volume is the first book on the subject in the English language and marks a milestone in the development of the specialty paper industry.

This book should serve the needs of both the technically trained graduates who enter the industry and the older and more experienced technologists who are already a part of it. The specialty paper industry is in the process of transition. Its growth has been a development of the arts and "secrets" but now the industry is on the threshold of becoming more scientific. The newer advancements in synthetic resins, pigments, and solvents as well as in processing equipment are the results of research in pure science which have been made applicable to the needs of the industry. In recent years, naturally occurring substances have been replaced by a multiplicity of synthetic ones and their use is rapidly expanding. When one consults the German equivalent work on this subject, published a number of years ago, one cannot help marvelling at the tremendous strides which the American industry has made in the last two decades. Over one-half of the various chapters in this book deal with topics and products which were completely unknown then, while new developments in the other chapters far outweigh the know-how which today's technologists have acquired from the men of yesterday.

In preparing this book on the materials and processes of the specialty paper industry, Mr. Mosher has been fortunate in securing the collaboration of a number of distinguished specialists in various branches of the subject who have been successful and practical technologists, engaged in the industry for a number of years. Mr. Mosher himself has had a unique background, which well qualifies him to edit the book and write the major part of it. His association with the Institute of Paper Chemistry and his work in various paper mills has given him a broad background in the paper industry. His work with resins and plastics in the research and development departments of the Monsanto Chemical Company has resulted in familiarity with the many phases of the synthetic resin industry as well as a knowledge of the many problems involved in resin utilization. As Technical Director of the Marvellum Company and a member of various chemical and converting industry committees which permitted him to obtain a good over-all picture of the problems of the industry, he is well qualified to undertake this pioneering work. His efforts will undoubtedly contribute to the further development of the American specialty paper industry by outlining its present status and facilitating the exchange of valuable know-how that until now could be obtained only after very laborious personal efforts on the part of the individual researcher.

This book, which has been several years in preparation and

to which the technologists of our industry have unselfishly devoted their time, energy, and knowledge, should be of service for a considerable length of time. Men in the industry can look to it for guidance and information. It fills the need for a general reference book which organizes the scattered body of facts and theories on specialty papers into a coherent and inclusive whole thus providing the basis upon which newer developments can be indicated and classified. Few great developments are the result of chance or sheer inspiration. They are more often the result of chance plus a long course of study, training, and work. Each new discovery or improvement builds on the foundation of the past and the overall picture has a distinctly perceptible continuity.

The keen competition ahead in the decorative, specialty, packaging, and protective branches of the paper industry will necessitate many improvements in the materials and methods utilized at the present time. It is believed that this volume will make a distinct contribution in this regard.

ACKNOWLEDGMENT

WHEN the project of the preparation of this volume was first undertaken, its magnitude and the wide range of specific subjects which had to be covered were not fully realized. Upon sketching out a detailed outline of the desirable subject matter, however, it was readily discovered that no one man or organization was in a position to supply complete coverage due to the tendency in the paper converting industry for specialization of individual mill units. It then became the policy of the editor to invite various men who were active in specific phases of the industry to prepare those sections of the book which dealt with their specialty. The response was surprising and the editor is deeply grateful to these collaborators since it was their cooperation that made possible the completeness of this work. These men were all busy with their own problems but gave freely of their time and effort to complete this volume which all felt to be a worth-while contribution both to the literature and to the industry.

The purpose of the authors was to compile the information available on the different products of the specialty paper converting industry, on the raw materials which go into them, on the techniques used in their manufacture, and on the tests used in their evaluation. The language of the book, although often necessarily technical in nature, is such as to reach the widest possible group of readers, from the technical specialists to the nontechnical sales and consuming groups. This volume should particularly serve as a source book for the young men now coming up in the ranks of the industry. Wherever possible, the man who was invited to prepare the section on a given subject, was actively engaged in the production or utilization of such papers so that the theoretical aspects of most of the subjects are in general subordinated to the practical ones.

The selection of the list of authors was difficult since in many cases there were several men each of whom would be fully qualified to do the job. Where this was true, the invitation was issued to the one who was closer geographically and who, it was felt, would be in a position to prepare the section with the minimum of delay. Many of the authors contributed additional time in reading and commenting on the sections prepared by other contributors.

The procedure of using a number of contributing authors posed the problem of uniformity of style and structure and continuity of thought, but the use of the editor's perogative along with consultation and discussion with the individual authors permitted the result to be reasonably uniform. It was necessary to examine carefully all submitted material and to make some changes and deletions and to even transpose some material from one chapter to another. This was, in general, readily agreed to by the specific authors, however, and the compromises all worked out in a satisfactory manner. Some authors explained their subject in great detail while others only covered the essentials of their specific field, especially where the technology varies from standard practice, and left the basic information to the companion volume which includes such material.

In addition to the contributing authors, there are many other individuals in the industry and among the paper and chemical supply houses who have given freely of their time and effort in reading, commenting, and offering criticisms on the various individual manuscripts as well as submitting additional data and special notes. The list is very lengthy and it is impossible to give full credit, but representative members include S. Johnson, John W. Clark, and J. J. Thomas of S. D. Warren Co.; Victor O. Lemieux of American Tissue Mills; F. B. Hilmer of Shell

Development Co.; Walter L. Hardy of Shellmar Corp.; Norris Sutherland of the Perfect Safety Paper Co.; Byron Wehmhoff of the West Virginia Pulp and Paper Co.; Prof. B. E. Proctor of M.I.T.; Gerald A. Fitzgerald of The Frozen Food Foundation; Dr. A. C. Fay of H. P. Hood and Sons; A. B. Brackett of General Foods Corp.; C. H. Shackelford of Great Atlantic and Pacific Food Co.; Mason T. Rogers of The Packaging Institute; Dr. J. T. R. Nickerson of the National Association of Frozen Food Packers; Richard S. Fay, William Schramm, and Robert C. Adams of The Marvellum Company; James Cronk of The Hampden Glazed Paper and Card Co.; M. A. Krimmel of the Hammermill Paper Co.; and George J. Blake of the Holyoke Card and Paper Co.

As the editor of this book, I wish to particularly acknowledge not only the work of the contributing authors which can be visibly judged, but also the data and information contributed on the various subjects by men who wish to remain anonymous because of their particular position in the industry. Where it was not possible to find a suitable person who would be free to prepare a given section, it was often possible for the editor to prepare a rough draft of the subject matter which was then carefully gone over and corrected by men who were for one reason or another not in a position to have their names attached to the work.

The aid and efforts of Philip C. Whiting, Jr. are very gratefully acknowledged, as he not only offered much advice and help, both in the preparation and proofreading of the various chapters, but also prepared several of the tables and checked the reliability of certain data in the laboratory. I also wish to acknowledge the assistance of Hazen P. Chase, George W. Rothmyer, and Whiting S. Houston of the Technical Department of The Marvellum Company for their comments and efforts in proofreading much of the material and for their constant faith that the work will be completed.

There has been very little literature previously available on most of the various specialized subjects covered in this book and as a result, the literature references are fewer than are normally met in this type of publication. It is the earnest hope of those who have cooperated in the preparation of these volumes that at a later date, revised and enlarged editions can be prepared by other people thus increasing the data and information which has been accumulated here.

I wish to thank Mrs. Claire Kane and Miss Barbara Cruickshank for their efforts in typing and proofreading much of the manuscript.

ROBERT H. MOSHER

TABLE OF CONTENTS

Chapter I

INTRODUCTION

by R. H. Mosher

T HE development of the specialty or converted paper industry has closely paralleled the overall developments in the paper-making industry since the convertors are dependent upon this industry for their basic raw material. Prior to 1800, when paper was produced only by hand and limited to single sheets, printing and coating operations were simple and as primitive as the paper-making technique.

The hand-made paper, which was produced in small volume in Europe beginning with the 12th century, was used from the earliest days of its development as a base for printing. All books and documents were, of course, hand written or printed prior to the development in 1456 of movable block type by Johann Gutenberg at Mainz, Germany. Previously, the use of woodcuts or engravings was the only method of commercial printing. The early inks were formulated from carbon black and vegetable oil and later from vegetable and mineral oil mixtures. Colored inks were made, using vermilion, cinnabar, indigo, cobalt, and copper oxide as the pigmenting or coloring medium.[2]

The printing of the surface of hand-made paper was a real problem, using the shallow wood cuts and even shallower wood engravings available at that time since the paper surface was

relatively coarse. This difficulty was overcome to a certain extent by burnishing the surface of each sheet with some sort
of smooth glossy stone, but the process was slow and cumbersome. About 1540, the glazing hammer was developed and
this caused a feud between the stone glazers and hammer glazers,
which lasted for more than 150 years, but as in most cases the
mechanically operated device finally won out. This process in
turn was superceded about 1720 when the Dutch developed a
method of calendering the sheets using a pair of polished copper
rolls and this technique led to the invention of the sheet plating
machine.[1, 2, 6]

The main object of all of these processes was to smooth down
the surface of the paper so that fine engravings and letter press
block printing could be produced using the paper which was
available at the time. The printed paper was used for its legendary or pictorial value and could not be considered as a part
of the specialty paper industry as we think of it today.

The real start of the paper-converting industry began with
the development of wallpaper, or paper "hangings" as they
were then termed. This development must apparently be cred-
ited to the Chinese, who also invented paper, but it was brought
to the western world about 1620 when paper "hangings" were
first made in France. The sheet was produced in its earliest
stages by block printing upon plain paper, but it was soon found
that some sort of "grounding" or base coating was needed which
would be capable of holding up the color and preserve the
brilliancy of its hues. A coating was developed from glue and
pigments and this was applied with a brush to supply a "ground"
or "color" for the printing process. It was later discovered that
the coated surface could be smoothed mechanically and used as
a base for other types of printing operations.[6] This was the
first purely decorative application of paper, other than as an
artists' medium, and marked the beginning of the specialty
paper industry, even though the paper was still only available
in sheet form.

About 1800, the basic invention which changed the paper-making industry was brought to light and this was the machine for the production of paper in a continuous sheet. The first machine, invented by Louis Robert in 1798, was developed by Henry and Sealy Fourdrinier and involved the same basic fundamentals which had been in use for 2000 years. The machine, which bears the name of the two brothers who lost a fortune in its exploitation, was based on an endless wire screen which allowed the water to run through and form a felt or sheet of paper on its surface. This sheet was continuously stripped off the end of the wire and either cut into strips which were hung up to dry, or wound up in a partially dried state and later redried. A second type of paper-making unit, the cylinder machine, was independently developed in 1806. It contained a wire-covered cylinder which rotated in a vat of stock, with the water again running through the screen and the fiber mat remaining on the surface. The two types were introduced to this country in 1816 and 1827 respectively, and soon both were in production. These same type machines, although modified, improved, enlarged, and speeded up, are still used today although the early papermakers would scarcely believe their senses if they could see them in their present form.[3, 4, 5]

The availability of paper in continuous form instead of sheets soon led to the development of web calenders for smoothing the surface of the paper to produce good printing surfaces, but it was not until the middle 1800's that equipment was developed for coating the paper by a continuous operation. The use of coated papers had been increasing and coated labels, fancy papers, and wallpapers were gradually attaining reasonable volume. Gravure printing using copper plates had been introduced about 1650 with the mezzotint process, and lithography was developed by Alois Senefelder in the early 1800's. Coated and printed playing cards were developed prior to 1500. All these products and processes had been limited by the lack of continuous machinery for their production.[1]

One of the first companies formed for the express purpose of coating fancy and box papers was the firm of Alois Dessauer

which was set up in 1810. By 1865 it had grown so that the
employment had risen to 300 people and a sizable volume of
paper was being handled. The continuous coating process was
introduced into Germany at the Plant of E. Kretzchmar in
Dresden by a Frenchman named Möglin in 1866. A similar
machine appeared in England at approximately the same time
and apparently independently of the French development. The
first machines faithfully reproduced the hand brushing operation by the use of the so-called "sun and planets" design
smoothing unit in which the coating was smoothed out by
brushes which revolved in a motion imitating the hand operation. The German machine was horizontally operated while the
English machine was a vertical unit. These machines had
obvious disadvantages, however, and in 1874 a cam-driven
oscillating-brush unit, similar to those used today in the converting industry, was developed at the plant of E. Kretzschmar
in Dresden. The development of the method of making paper in
a continuous web and the subsequent adaption of the hand
coating technique to the continuous machine coating operation
was the basis for the specialty paper industry of today. Continuous methods of printing, staining, embossing, brushing and
otherwise decorating paper for the fancy and decorative trade
followed in relatively short time.[1, 2, 4]

The development of the specialty paper industry in the United
States followed along the same lines, but with a time lag of
several years after the European developments. As noted previously, the first Fourdrinier paper-making machine was set up
in this country in 1816 and the first cylinder machine in 1827.
The wallpaper industry was a going business at that time,
however, since the first factories had been set up in 1775, and
by 1795 there were mills producing this type of decorative sheet
in Pennsylvania, New Jersey, and Massachusetts. The early
papers were made in sheets about 30 inches long.[6] As early
as 1824, a wallpaper with a coated and glazed background for
the usual block printing was produced and the development was
rapidly picked up by the fancy paper producers. Aside from

wallpapers, there were two other growing industries, the label printers and the paper box manufacturers, and they all were rapidly developing the art of coloring, glazing, and printing paper for both decorative and legendary applications. In 1839, the firm of Pollack and Doty was formed in Philadelphia for the express purpose of producing coated label papers. These papers were coated and plated and then printed in the form of labels for print works, cotton mills, and proprietary medicines. According to Wheelwright,[6] "The paper was coated sheet by sheet, the color being brushed on it by girls, whose aprons were covered with blotches of all sorts of colors; the sheets were then hung on laths which rested on wooden racks, where they remained overnight—sometimes longer—to dry."

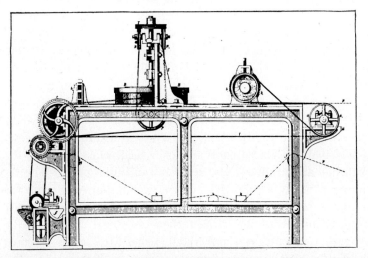

FIGURE 1. *Wallpaper coating machine of about 1860* (Courtesy of Paper Museum of M. I. T.)

The industry showed a slow but steady development with formation of new converting companies at Albany, N. Y. and Nashua, N. H., both of which did large and prosperous business. In 1845, the firm of Doty and Bergen was started in New York and was later changed to Doty and Scrimgour and the plant moved to Reading, Pa. In 1846, the firm of J. & L. DeJonge was formed at Staten Island and was set up to produce glazed fancy papers. This firm in 1852 bought a coating machine from the firm of John Waldron Co., which had been producing coating machines since 1832 for the wallpaper industry, for the purpose of making glazed paper on a continuous basis, an art which was to revolutionize this phase of the industry. The machine, which was of the "sun and planet" design was bought for $225.00.[6] The web of paper was coated and festoon-dried before being rolled up. The rolls were then friction-calendered or flint-glazed and sold, either plain or embossed, for labels and box coverings. As time went on rotary brushes for color application and oscillating brushes for smoothing the surface gradually supplemented and replaced the older designs, but the flinting and friction-calendering operations remained practically the same as when they were first developed.

In 1875, a new field of application of coated papers was developed when Theodore Low DeVinne conceived the idea of using such paper for printing purposes where good color reproduction was desired.[6] Up to this time, paper had only been coated on one side but for such an application two-side coating was a necessity. Charles M. Gage, who was manufacturing one-side coated and glazed paper in Springfield, Mass. accepted the challenge and produced 100 reams as an initial order. The resulting paper was printed from fine wood engravings and the results were very satisfactory. The idea was then temporarily dropped until 1881 when Gage, then associated with the S. D. Warren Company at Cumberland Mills, Me., again accepted the challenge and produced another quantity of the paper. The resulting printing work was so superior over the supercalendered paper then in use for gravure printing that soon afterward, when the photoengraving process was developed, it became the standard paper for fine half-tone printing.

In more recent years many further developments have been forthcoming in this industry. Improved adhesives of starch, casein, soya protein, and synthetic resins have been developed to take the place of the glue which was used in early work. Better and more lightfast dyes and pigments have been constantly introduced and these have raised the standards of the resulting coatings.

FIGURE 2. *Early drum-type brush-coating machine* (Courtesy of John Waldron Corp.)

Dull- or matte-finished papers, gummed papers, mica-coated papers, and finally the varnished and then the lacquered or plastic-coated papers were introduced. New methods of coating, which eliminate the need of the brush coater and based on roll or spray applications and the use of an air knife instead of brushes for smoothing the coated surface, have been developed and brought to a high degree of efficiency. The old festoon lines are being gradually replaced by enclosed tunnel driers which increase the speed and efficiency of drying. All these developments have tended to improve the quality and reduce the unit cost of coated papers.

FIGURE 3. *Early flat-bed brush-coating machine* (Courtesy of John Waldron Corp.)

The coated paper industry began as a converting business, purchasing paper as one of its raw materials and coating and processing the sheet according to its own requirements. The production of coated printing papers has now developed into such a volume business, however, that many large printing paper mills have installed their own coating departments running on relatively standard items which can be produced in large volume at reduced costs. This has resulted in the converting industry turning its energies to the coating of fancy, box, cover, and other specialty papers and leaving most of the printing paper field to the big mills. These larger mills have even gone a step farther and at the present time many of the coated printing papers are made directly on the paper machine. The resulting product was rapidly adopted by the book and magazine trade and at the present time it is even finding applications in the job printing field.[6] It is too early to predict just how machine-coated and off-the-machine-coated printing papers will finally divide the available market, but intensive studies are being made in this field and the printing industry is doing its share in the development and adaptation of processes for better printing.

FIGURE 4. *Early inclined-bed brush-coating machine; improvement over the flat-bed type* (Courtesy of John Waldron Corp.)

The paper converters in this time have not been setting aside and watching their volume diminish without making definite advances in their own field. The wallpaper industry, still strong and healthy, has had its techniques altered so that paper drapes, shelfpapers, lamp shades, and many other decorative items are now produced using similar methods and equipment. The simulated leather finishes originally used in the box paper industry has led to the development of synthetic leather cover papers made from heavy and laminated papers and synthetic-resin and rubber saturated papers. Such sheets are used for book, brochure, and menu covers, inner linings for shoes, displays, chair and seat coverings, and handbags and belts. The fancy and box papers, originally used only for decorative packaging, have been tremendously expanded so that literally thousands of different types, patterns, and designs are available and the use of plastic coatings and laminants has opened the tremendous new fields of functional packaging. These and similar items have all developed from the basic products of the early converting industry. In addition to these developments, there are dozens of new specialty applications where the paper is only a carrier for some coating or material whose properties are required for some specific purpose. Photographic paper, blueprint paper, pressure-sensitive tapes, magnetic recording and conducting papers, abrasive papers, carbon and stencil papers are examples of some of these new and diversified products which are today manufactured by the same specialty paper company which yesterday or the day before was complacently making glazed box coverings only.

FIGURE 5. *Typical boxes covered with fancy papers* (Courtesy of Modern Packaging Magazine)

This development of new and specialized sheets, which no longer even possess the common denominator of being based on paper, since foil, films, and even cloth are used in their makeup, has extended the boundaries of the converting industry to such a degree that many of the coaters and treaters no longer even consider themselves to be a part of the paper industry. The development of complex synthetic resin coatings and the techniques involved in their application, have resulted in some companies being formed for the expressed purpose of applying these coatings to paper, film, and foil. The connection of these firms with the paper industry is that they merchandise their products through paper industry channels.

A list of the specific places where the converting industry has expanded and where other industries are now invading into the paper field would touch practically any of us in our daily lives. Papers of distinctive appearance or unique characteristics are constantly sought by the package designers and others who create the appealing products and packages which are demanded by a quality-minded purchasing public. The more useful papers have, in many instances, replaced cloth, coated fabrics, leather, or wood. There is a most lucrative market for papers with unusual properties.[10] A look at the diversified utility of paper, and paper products is persuasive evidence that they represent a rare combination of potential characteristics whose commercial acceptance is the result of a similar pattern in each instance—the most practical way to achieve a group of difficult specifications, unusual features, or special properties.

Immediately at the command of the manufacturer seeking to dress up his product are literally thousands of fancy box, packaging, and decorative papers which run the gamut of the rainbow in their range of colors. By starting with the color of the product to be packaged and adding complementary or harmonizing colors, it is possible to utilize these new, modern, and refreshing papers to make the product and the package blend into a single effect, each contributing to the overall impression.[9] The range of colors, printed designs, surface finishes, and embossed patterns is so wide that the problem is not one of seeking a suitable packaging medium, but rather one of making a choice from among innumerable specific sheets all of which could do the proper job. Where one of the various stock papers is not suitable for the specific job or where a definite individuality is desired, special and unique papers can be designed to designate the source of the package and to emphasize the product. The so-called "packaging papers" of today may be made from a coated or printed paper, but they may also be formed from printed or stained metal foil, printed plastic or cellophane film, or some combination of the three. Special inks and coatings are used extensively where needed to do a given job. These sheets are designed to draw attention to the product and to sell.

Another group of packaging papers is used to protect the contents of the package from change and deterioration due to outside influence. These are classified as protective and functional papers. Such papers, while they may possess decorative features, are generally designed to do a given job with more of an eye to the performance characteristics than to the visual sales appeal of the unit. Such sheets are produced by coating and laminating paper with synthetic resins, waxes, asphalts, and other barrier materials and combining paper with plastic films and metal foils. The resulting barrier sheet may possess any or all of the following characteristics: water and/or water vapor resistance; grease resistance; gas resistance; heat or pressure sealability; acid, alkali, and chemical resistance; insect, rodent, and fungus resistance; or abrasion and scuff resistance. It is possible, by the proper use of synthetic resins and barrier films and foils, to build into a given sheet any desirable combination of properties but there are only a limited number of combinations which will do a given job at the lowest price. In the competitive days to which our economy has always returned, the necessary criterion is the best job for the lowest unit cost.

The field of decorative papers has expanded into many areas formerly sacred to wood, glass, cloth, metal, as well as holding their own in their established markets. Wallpapers, which do the same job today as they did one hundred years ago, are now made truly washproof and with lightfast colors. If desirable they can be produced with waterproof, greaseproof top coatings which will withstand the abuse of even the toughest youngster as long as his armament does not contain a blowtorch or a set of sharp edged tools. Synthetic oilcloth, table and shelf coverings, flexible and fade-resistant paper drapes, exquisite and sturdy lampshades, attractive display papers, sturdy photo mountings, and other specialties are available from numerous sources and again the problem is to make the correct choice rather than to have to go seeking a given material.

Great advancements have been made in the field of cover and synthetic leather papers. The older casein-coated, laminated, and embossed sheets are available in improved form while the plastic-coated and synthetic-resin and rubber-impregnated synthetic leather covers possess many of the desirable properties of real leather. The coated papers are used in the book-binding trade, as brochure and menu covers, for upholstery, table tops, wall coverings, luggage and belts. The uncoated stock is used for shoe inner soles and gaskets. The use of synthetic resins in this phase of the industry has completely revolutionized the earlier products and the properties which can now be built into a sheet have resulted in an extensive expansion of the boundaries of their previous area of application.

The various items listed above cover most of the traditional area of the paper convertor, but at the present time the products of this industry are entering and have entered many other fields where they are offering a strong challenge to established products of long standing. Pressure-sensitive coated papers and films are entering areas where cloth-backed material reigned for many years. Paper tapes which have been provided with a magnetic coating are competing with wire in the sound-recording and automatic controls and equipment field. Photographic papers, both plain and colored, are well established and blueprint and dry-print papers are being used in large quantities. Conducting papers for use with the new facsimile printing techniques are introducing a new concept in the news reporting field. Abrasive papers of many types are essential items in our manufacturing industries. Carbon papers are the basis of our accounting business. These items will illustrate the extent to which the converting industry has enlarged the scope of its activities from the original premise of taking paper from a manufacturer and coating it for the printing or fancy box industry.

Many of the new products which are listed in this book owe

their existence to the fact that during World War II, paper was considered the substitute beyond which there appeared to be no further substitutes. The industry developed many products, particularly in the functional packaging and specialty fields, which started out as substitutes, but which have now come into their own as valuable new items. Where the application of many of these materials has survived and grown, it has usually been at the expense of glass, steel, tin, rubber, textiles, wood, aluminum, and other such commodities. The product which will survive will once again be the best one which can be obtained at the lowest price. The converting industry is interested in supplying a demand and they will not be primarily interested in evangelizing any particular material. The properties of all kinds of papers, films, foils, synthetic resins, cloth, and other components of each product must be thoroughly known and understood and a knowledge of the drawbacks and faults of a material are as or more important than its advantages. The paper-converting industry is fortunate in its knowledge that a union of paper and other products can meet many use requirements. This opens a great field for products which are decorative, functional, or a combination of both, as each item can be made in several different ways by any number of different companies yet since there is such a diversity of materials, techniques, and processes with which to work, many can come up with a product which will do the given job.[8]

The result of this analysis seems to indicate that the future offers great promise to the specialty paper and converting industry. According to Macdonald,[7] however, it will require great resourcefulness on the part of the paper-use promotors. The enormously expanding field of plastic products can become predominantly a branch of the chemical or the paper industry depending upon which makes the greater promotional efforts. The opportunity for development and promotion is further dependent on the quality and intensity of technical effort. Between these two industries is the convertor who takes paper and additive materials and combines them to create products which have a specific value.[7] The ultimate user will buy the best products available at a price and will care little about how, or of what they are made. If the independent convertor can direct his efforts along similar lines he will be able to create products to meet the unsatiable demand of the consuming public.

With all its past history of development, growth, and diversification, the converting industry in this country has had one great drawback and this is lack of documentation and free interchange of information. According to Macdonald[8] the average converting company has been a relatively small business enterprise which has not been a large employer of technical men. The industry, in general, has also held its men with the result that each organization tended to feel that they had developed certain techniques and formulations to do a given job in the best and most efficient manner and that they alone possessed the knowledge. In many respects this may be the truth since the industry is based upon specialties and many mills have developed certain items over which they exercise a practical monopoly. This is probably due to the fact that many of these items require a number of different operations to obtain the finished product and since most of the mills have certain equipment which might not be exactly duplicated elsewhere, they would be the only ones to have the correct combination to do the specific job. A second possibility may be that there is a limited market for many of these specialty items with the result that the first one in the market, if his product is good enough and the price is fair, is able to more or less cover the field so as to make a second producer unnecessary or, by dividing the market, to make it unprofitable for both.

Against the production of specialties, however, can be contrasted the normal types of pigment-coated papers of the glossy and matte types for the fancy paper field and the enormous quantities of coated stock for the printing-paper industry. In these fields there are only a limited number of adhesives available, a relatively few standard pigments, and only a half dozen methods of economic application. This part of the in-

dustry is still almost as secretive with its coating formulations
and technology as are the highly specialized portions. In
recent years, the Coating Committee of T.A.P.P.I., has undertaken the massive job of assembling some of this closely held
information so as to make it available to the rest of the industry. Secret questionnaires circulated to the industry, which were
filled in and returned with the names withheld so as not to
identify the individual mills, indicated that many mills were
operating under very similar formulae and the spread between
deadly competitors was so small in many cases so as to be
negligible!

The information which has been available on the subject
of converting formulae and operations has been general in
nature and has mainly come from the various suppliers, con-
sultants, and machinery producers and very little from the
mills themselves. Where technical information and data have
been interchanged, it has generally been at the management
and high technical levels, and even at this point cross visitation
at the mills themselves has often been strongly discouraged.
Each mill has developed its own techniques and know-how and
each feels it advisable to retain that knowledge within its own
group.

It is against this overall background that the editor has
attempted to evaluate and documentize the available information and knowledge of the paper-converting industry. The
scope of the subject and its ramifications are far too large to
be handled well by any one man. Therefore, to attain completeness, accuracy, and the ability to present detailed information, each specific section of the industry has been covered by
a different author. These men have all had a wide experience
with their subject and, practically without exception, each is
considered an authority in that specific field. In most cases,
there is a great deal more which could be said on the various
subjects and the information presented could be more detailed
and specific, but the overall reticence of the industry must be
kept in mind, since in many cases it was the limiting factor.

In certain cases it was not possible to find a man in an operating capacity in the industry who was in a position to prepare the section and in those cases someone who had previously been connected with the industry and who now was active in some other phase or connected with it in a consulting capacity consented to do the work. The overall response of those men contacted to do the work was very gratifying and the extent to which they covered, and were permitted to cover, their subjects on the whole was very satisfactory. It is not the purpose of this work to expose the "know-how" which any specific organization considers to be its private property or stock in trade but the intention is to cover that information on materials and processes which is fairly well known and which represents fairly uniform practice throughout the field. The types of machinery and equipment used by most organizations is generally well known and the general formulation of the compounds used is also common knowledge. There are small variations in equipment; the technique of operation, and the materials and methods of application are different in the individual mills, and no attempt has been made to publicize this knowledge.

The overall purpose has been to assemble as accurately and as completely as possible the known data on the materials used in the converting operations, on the equipment and techniques used in actual production in the varied phases of the industry, and the applications of the various items. No claim is made that the work is complete, even to date, but an attempt has been made to correlate as much information as is available and condense it into one volume with the hope that others will carry on from this point.

References

1. August Weichelt. *Buntpapier-fabrication*. Carl Hofmann-Verlag für Papier-Zeitung, Berlin.
2. Carlton Ellis. *Printing Inks*. Reinhold Publishing Co., New York, 1940.
3. R. Canfield. "The Paper Industry." *Think*, May 1947.
4. Anon. *The History and Story of Paper Making*. Kalamazoo Vegetable Parchment Co. Roycrafters, East Aurora, N. Y.

5. Anon. *Paper: Pacemaker of Progress.* F. C. Huyck and Sons. C. Lynn Summer Co. The Marchbanks Press, 1946.

6. W. B. Wheelwright. "The Coating of Paper." *The Papermaker* No. 1: 1–5, February 1948.

7. R. G. Macdonald. "Postwar Possibilities of the Paper Industry." *Barrell's Paper Annual,* 1944–1945, p. 3.

8. R. G. Macdonald. "Paper Products Face the Future." *Barrell's Paper Annual,* 1945–1946, p. 9.

9. J. T. Cronk. "Glazed and Fancy Papers." *Packaging Catalogue,* Breskin and Charlton Publishing Corp., New York, 1938, p. 158.

10. J. K. Speicher and F. K. Shankweider. "Creative Coatings—Lacquers for Papers." *The Papermaker* No. 1: 7–11, February 1948.

Chapter II

GIFT WRAPS, FANCY BOX AND PACKAGING PAPERS

by R. H. Mosher

SOME of the earliest products of the specialty paper converting industry were the flint glazed papers which were used as box coverings in Germany and Austria starting with the late 1790's. From this beginning the industry has grown to its present proportions where the sales appeal of gift and seasonal items as well as a wide range of competitive merchandise is achieved by clever package design and the use of decorative packaging papers. A wide variety of packaging materials are available and they range in color from white through literally thousands of different shades and from a matte, dull satiny appearance to a high-gloss finish. The surface may be plain or printed and decorated with as many as twelve different colors and/or embossed in a wide range of patterns. If the proper effect cannot be obtained by using a paper or coated paper surface, plain or laminated films, foils, or cloth products are available to meet the exacting requirements of the packaging industry.

From the standpoint of the specialty converting industry these products can be divided into two classes: (1) the fancy and decorative box and packaging papers, and (2) the gift wraps. The first class contains those products which are used in the manufacture of setup boxes and for wrapping packages

19

so as to catch the public eye and serve as an identification
of the product. The second group includes those materials
which are used as seasonal outer wrappings and to dress up
gift items and represent one of the few products of the industry
which are used by the ultimate consumer as well as by the
packaging industry. Such papers also find widespread use as
box and envelope linings and as specialties in the papeterie field.

FANCY BOX AND PACKAGING PAPERS

The main purpose of attractively packaging a product for
today's market is to increase sales. If a packaged product can
stand out sharply on a store shelf containing many competitive
products it has a good chance of arresting the attention of the
passing shopper and so arouse interest. According to one estimate 54% of all purchases is made on the spur of the moment
and more than 90% of all purchases is made by women.[1] A
suitable wrapper can be used to transform a plain product or
simple box into a beautiful package which arouses the desire
to purchase the item. Impulse buying has become an important
factor in today's marketing picture and without "eye appeal"
a competitive product may find its sales lagging in an alarming
manner.

In creating a paper for packaging purposes, it must be designed with several specific requirements in mind. The finished
paper must allow the manufacturer of the product to be packaged to label or identify the contents properly, both from the
standpoint of necessary sales information and to meet any legal
requirements. The surface, therefore, must be printable and
the surface decoration must be so laid out that space is available to receive the necessary legendary printing. If the product
is to be a part of a merchandizing plan which necessitates
affixing a label or price tag to the surface, the characteristics
of the surface must be such that it will hold a gummed, pressure
sensitive, or special adhesive coated label. The sheet must be
flexible enough so that it can be folded around the product, and

take the 90° or even the 180° folds necessary in a box fabricating operation without cracking or tearing. If the package is likely to be exposed to sunlight, it must possess more or less fade or discoloration resistance, and the degree required may greatly influence the cost of the paper. The package surface should be more or less abrasion resistant, depending upon the expected usage, and this may be a very important characteristic if the package has reuse possibilities. If there is a chance that the package will be carried in the open where it may become wet, wet abrasion resistance and resistance to color bleeding are necessary properties to prevent smearing of the package surface and possible discoloration of surfaces with which it comes into contact. The sheet must not embrittle upon aging and must not block, either in the rolls or the sheets supplied by the convertor or in the form of the final fabricated product. The sheet must be nontoxic and should not possess any odor in its basic form, although these decorative products are often formulated so as to emit a synthetic odor such as a perfumed, leathery, or fruity smell, or other distinct odor which will assist the package in creating an overall effect. The surface of the sheet should not mark or discolor upon handling, and a certain amount of water, grease, and chemical resistance may be desirable. It should be understood that all of these properties are not necessary in every single decorative packaging paper but some are always required and others depend upon the economics of the package. As a general rule, the final choice of the sheet properties will be a compromise and the more of these properties can be built into a given sheet, the wider is the expected use. For many applications it is the decoration and appearance which sell the sheet, but its performance is what sells and resells the packaged product. In the following chapters many types of finishes and surface effects are described and technically classified and it is the purpose at this point only to outline briefly what is available in this field.

In the development of a given specialty decorative packaging or fancy paper, the convertor first carefully selects the proper

base paper since this sheet is the basis for all the later processing operations. The finish, color, and use requirements of the
finished product must be taken into consideration. For the usual
type of setup box covering a ground-wood-base paper is a common choice, since the sheet will be coated and thus cover up
any deficiency in the appearance of the base stock. In such a
case, strength and finish would not be of too great importance.
In no case would such a sheet be planned for use in a folding
box, bag, or flexible packaging applications. In these cases,
a kraft, sulfate-, or sulfite-base paper would be indicated since
such papers possess higher physical strength and have better
folding qualities. The weight of the base paper is extremely
important and the usual sheet has a basis weight of about 45
pounds on a 24 x 36—500 ream size.

The cost of the finished product will many times, and more
often than necessary, govern the composition of a fancy paper.
When the question of cost reduction is introduced, the manufacturer may substitute cheaper base stocks, less costly raw
materials, and less expensive processing operations since the
diversity of processes and the wide variety of raw materials
usually permit such action. This process might involve substitution of ground-wood-base paper for a sulfite sheet, a friction-glazing process for a flint-glazing operation, or a lithocoated printing base sheet for a matte coated fancy paper. The
amount of light-fast pigments or dyestuffs can be reduced or
they can be replaced with cheaper and less resistant materials
and the amount of high-priced metallic inks can also be reduced. Water-base coatings can be used in place of organic
solvent soluble varieties. Such substitutions will often reduce
the price by one third or one half of the original estimate, but
at the same time the customer necessarily receives a reduction
in finish, quality, and general appearance. Reduction is sometimes necessary, but it can turn out to be a false economy since
the few pennies, or even fraction of a penny, which are saved
on the unit cost of the final package, may make the difference
between wide customer acceptance of the packaged product and

a poor position in a competitive market. The basic premise remains that the convertor must design a product to meet the specific needs and cost budget of the consumer and this is the problem of the industry.

Many types of papers are used in this field and a wide variety of finishes are available. The glossy papers may be flint-glazed, friction-glazed, super-calendered, or cast-coated types. The medium- and matte-finished papers are extensively used and these may also be later top coated or varnished using casein, shellac, varnishes, lacquers, water dispersions, hot melts, or organosol or plastisol types of coatings where the specific properties which these materials offer are needed. Such coatings can be applied as clears on a wide range of colors and where multiple coating operations are used, the pigmentation or coloring can be done in any of the applied coatings.

In the field of printed fancy papers the most popular printing technique is the gravure process which is fairly low in cost and enables the manufacturer to bring out details and clarity in the design by using properly etched rolls. It is also possible by this process to make many extra color shades by over-printing or using half-tone engraved rolls. Aniline printing is also popular and although the clarity of print is not as satisfactory as with the gravure method, the cheaper roll cost and ease of multiple roll printing offer advantages. Surface printing is used to some extent and the letterpress process is useful where special effects are desired. Some lithographic or offset printed papers are produced for this trade, but the general practice is to subcontract this work. The type of printing used is often a question of expediency, as some plants are set up with one type of press and another, bidding on the same job, with a different type; yet both will produce a sheet which is very similar, if not identical in appearance. A wide range of printed designs are used and include large floral patterns, small flower arrangements, wide to narrow stripes, a wide variety of spotted, speckled, and irregular designs, small figures of babies, animals, Christmas figures, stars, houses, trees, birds, fish, and countless other products of the brain of the artist and designer. The actual printed product of any converting plant is only limited by the type of presses available and the number of color stations on the presses. The desired rolls for printing a given design can be easily procured if they can be run on the available press.

FIGURE 6. *Typical seasonal packages; gifts wrapped with attractively decorated tissues* (Courtesy of Tuttle Press Co.)

The third major method of decoration is by embossing the sheet, and a wide variety of embossing patterns is available. The designs may be exclusive or common depending upon the requirements of the package. The common designs, such as certain leather grains, moire, basket weave, swirls, and skytogen are supplied by practically any convertor since these patterns are very popular and most mills own or can obtain rolls which will produce these designs. The exclusive patterns, however, are the property of the manufacturer who owns or originates the design. Most manufacturers have certain designs of their own and many of these are protected by the U. S. Patent Office. Where it is desirable to carry the decoration even farther, print embossing, topping, or spanishing techniques can be utilized as their application permits attractive color combinations as well as the light and shadow effect produced with embossing units.

Where the use of plain or colored coated papers, which are later printed and/or embossed will not produce a sufficiently decorative or unique sheet for some applications, there are other special products of the paper converting industry which may be used. Films and foils, both plain and laminated to paper can be decorated in various ways to make striking and brilliant box coverings. Decorated cloth and cloth-paper laminations also can be utilized to produce very attractive wrappers. Metallic coated papers in various shades of gold, silver, copper, and colors; velour or flock coatings; crystal and iridescent finishes; marble finish; mica-coated papers; and plastic coatings of many types can be used to produce a sheet which is just a little, or to a great extent, different from its competition.

The question of consumer preference in design and color is one which plagues every manufacturer of fancy papers. Every company has had the unfortunate experience more than once of developing a new line of papers encompassing a number of printed patterns and a base color line of several shades and then finding that the trade practically unanimously chooses three different patterns and wants them printed upon two of the available base color shades. This problem is less acute in the development of a special paper for a given application but here again there is often a problem since in many cases the convertor does not know exactly what the boxmaker will do with his product and even less as to what the final package will be. Some of the larger consumers of fancy box papers are the stationery, candy, jewelry, and cosmetic manufacturers and jobbers, but large quantities are also used in general gift boxing and the packaging of any type of competitive items where women are the probable buyers. The artists and designers of the industry spend many hours and produce dozens of individual sketches before they determine the exact pattern which will be the basis of the coming line. In normal times the average fancy paper manufacturer will introduce 8 to 12 new printed patterns and 4 to 5 new embossing patterns per year.[2] The older designs are retained and may be renewed again at 5 to 10 year intervals.

A recent development which has aroused a great deal of interest in the box trade is the extensive use of brand identity and trademarked papers. The use of such papers which definitely identify the origin of the product has been rapidly growing and has been found very successful by the large and progressive stores. In some cases the organization name is imprinted directly on the paper, and in other instances the design is used to identify the source. This type of boxpaper can be manufactured only in large quantities, however, due to the cost of the art work, preparation of the printing rolls, and other special production costs.

The remaining problem confronting the fancy paper manufacturer is that of insuring that his product will handle in a

FIGURE 7. *S & S automatic tight-wrapping machine for packages*
(Courtesy of Stokes & Smith Co.)

satisfactory manner on package fabricating machinery. Standard and specialized types of box-wrapping machinery are both
used. They include tight-wrapping units where the box covering is glued to the preformed package as well as the specialized
machinery for the production of set-up paper boxes which are
covered with the proper wrapping prior to shipment; collapsible
or folding boxes which are produced flat and are then set up
when filled in the packaging plant; and the special types such as
the bag-in-box, fitted box, and cut out box.

FIGURE 8. *S & S paper-box wrapping and automatic gluing machine* (Courtesy of Stokes & Smith Co.)

Specialized package forming and wrapping units which do
not involve a box as the basic unit are also finding wide application. The package design may be simple and thus simplify
the problem of the paper manufacturer, but where special folding requirements, gluing specifications, and functional characteristics are demanded, the paper manufacturer should be
notified of these before the paper is produced or serious difficulties may arise which may not only cause rejection of the
paper but also can slow up the entire packaging setup.

GIFT WRAPPINGS

The idea of decorated tissue papers for use as wrappers originated in Europe during the seventeenth century. From this early usage as a wrapper around women's hand boxes it has widened out in its applications until today it is widely used as a seasonal overwrapper for gifts of all types, for envelope and box linings, and as a fancy or decorative packaging medium.[2] Well wrapped and attractive packages have tremendous appeal from the standpoint of impulse sales, but a pretty package has also become a necessity with most gifts, and gift wrapping has developed into an art in itself. Most large stores will now gift wrap packages for the customer, not only during the holiday season but at any time during the year.

The usual gift wrapping sheet is based upon a sulfite tissue paper, whose basis weight ranges from 18 to 30 pounds (24 x 36—480) and the recent trend has been toward the heavier papers. Some bleached kraft and rag-content sheets are utilized where special requirements are necessary, but the rag-base sheet is rather expensive for this field of application. The heavier-weight papers, running about 24 to 26 pounds are often used for gravure printing, but the lighter weights can be handled without trouble where they are desirable.

The base paper may be coated or printed and even embossed and further decorated in some special cases. The printing is done in bright or pastel colors using aniline and gravure techniques for most jobs. The most expensive papers are usually produced by the surface-printing or the silk-screen process in order to give the effect of handmade or block-print products. The printing may be done as a direct print, or by a choke-roll process so that a solid background color is used to outline the design. The colors most commonly used depend upon the seasonal application. For Christmas the blues, reds, and greens along with gold and silver are most popular since the designs are all cheery and colorful and reflect the holiday spirit. For

Easter the pastel spring colors are naturally called for, the most popular shades being the violets, lavender, yellow, green, and pink. Reds and white are the common Valentine colors. Films, foils, and other special-base sheets are used.

The designs used cover a wide range, depending upon the specific season for which the paper is designed. Snowflakes, Christmas trees, miniature Santa Claus', bells, and holly are usual designs for the Christmas season, while hearts and lovers are the Valentine motif, and flowers and rabbits are usually the center of attraction in Easter wraps.

These papers are generally merchandized through specialty channels which cater to the packaging trade and they are also packaged for direct sale to the consuming public by specialty houses. These companies put their offerings up in nicely packaged assortments complete with wrapping paper, labels, tags, and ribbon. The packaged merchandise is then distributed through department stores, stationery stores, gift shops, and the chain stores.

REFERENCES

1. N. Eastern. "All Wrapped Up in Fancy Wraps." *Packaging Systems.* **4,** No. 5: 10–13 (June 1948).
2. *Modern Packaging Encyclopedia (1948).* Packaging Catalogue Corp., New York, N. Y.
3. F. T. Day. "Current Fancy Box Papers and Trends." *British Packer.* **10,** No. 7: 24–5 (July 1948).

Chapter III

DECORATIVE PAPERS

by R. H. Mosher

THERE is a large volume production of specialty papers which, although they may have some functional characteristics, are basically utilized for their decorative value. Such papers are wall papers, display papers, lampshade stocks, and paper drapes. Other papers which are decorative, but should also possess some functional characteristics are those used for table cloths, napkins, and shelf papers. These sheets are utilized in the home, and in business as expendable products which have a predicated life span and then are replaced by new material. These papers are generally printed in bright colors and fancy patterns and may be coated or specially treated according to their use requirements.

SHELF PAPERS, TABLE CLOTHS, AND NAPKINS

The shelf papers, table cloths, and napkins manufactured by the specialty converting industry have been developed over a period of years from the original printed tissue papers, which are still utilized as items for one time use to the plastic-coated, treated, and printed materials of today which can be reused in a similar manner to oilcloth or regular treated cloth. All the pigments used in either inks or coatings must be fade resistant and must not bleed when water or alcohol is spilled on their surface. All ingredients should be nontoxic, odorless, and contain no components which could migrate to the surface and cause discoloration of the sheet.

The earliest shelf papers and table cloths or napkins were manufactured by printing suitable designs on plain or creped tissue, or other light-weight paper by gravure, aniline, or surface printing techniques. Such sheets possessed little or no reuse value and were purchased as disposable items. The inks were only partially resistant to water, and most of them possessed practically no resistance to alcohol. The inks have been improved over the years so that these items now possess excellent water and alcohol resistance. Machines have been developed which print the paper, emboss the sheet in a fine pattern and then slit and sheet it to size. The printed designs cover a wide range from overall patterns to small individual designs spotted on the corners or in the center of the individual items.

There has been a tendency toward more permanent papers in this field, however, and the better shelf papers and table coverings now manufactured are based upon a strong-fibered paper: usually either a bleached kraft or a sulfite sheet which has had a wet-strength treatment or a rubber- or resin-saturated sheet with high tear resistance and folding strength. When properly treated and/or coated, such a sheet has the life expectancy and many of the properties of oilcloth. Another base for these sheets is the nonwoven cloth now commercially produced, although this product is even more expensive than the treated papers. Napkins are manufactured from tissue and nonwoven cloth, as the heavier treated paper base products do not have sufficient softness and flexibility. The cost is also a factor in selecting the base paper.

The various papers or nonwoven-cloth bases are prepared for use by printing directly on the surface and then coating with a clear, synthetic-resin-base plastic as a protective film to facilitate cleaning, to provide grease and solvent resistance, and to prevent scuffing and abrasion of the sheet surface. Where a more light-stable and/or colored base is desired, the sheet may be coated with a pigment composition of the synthetic-resin-base type. This is used plain, or a printed design may be applied to the surface using special resistant inks. The coatings may be applied by roll, knife, or gravure-coating equipment and the printing is generally done on a gravure unit. The plastic coatings may be of the solvent, dispersion, hot-melt, or organosol type. A major requirement with this type of sheet is to formulate the coating so that it will not become brittle upon aging and crack and flake off the paper surface.

In the manufacture of papers for shelf coverings D.D.T. or other insecticides, as well as fungicides are often incorporated in the coating or the base paper. This has been proved to be very effective and is a strong selling point with such papers. In some cases, clean scents such as wintergreen, cedar, or pine, or even perfumes are added to the coating or printing ink for shelf papers which are designed for bathroom or closet use.

One very popular shelf paper and table cloth material which recently has been on the market is made from a special resin-saturated base paper, which has been printed and/or coated with a heavy film of a vinyl-resin organosol. This sheet possesses high strength and flexibility and excellent aging resistance. Much of these properties are contributed by the relatively thick resin film on the surface. It is available in a wide range of colors and plain or printed patterns.

DISPLAY PAPERS AND LAMPSHADE STOCK

These sheets are purely decorative in character and possess practically no functional characteristics. The pigments used in coatings or printing inks must be completely lightfast and bonded to the sheet by an agent which will not age and crack off. There is very little requirement for scuff and abrasion resistance in display materials, but lampshade papers do need this property to some extent.

Display Materials

The basic function of these materials is a visual one; the attraction of attention and the delivery of a message, either by legendary means or by the creation of an image which by direct or abstract association will put across the basic concept. Many materials are used in this work and crepe and other papers, cloth, foil, all types of coated and printed papers and boards and films find application. The sheets may be plain or colored, coated or noncoated, embossed or printed, and include plain whites and colors, imitation leathers, printed paper with textile or wood-grain designs as well as a wide range of fancy and box paper designs.

Creped papers are widely used because of the ease with which they can be handled, their relatively low cost, and the wide range of colors and varieties in which they may be obtained. Foils and metallic coated papers are popular because of their brilliance and eye-catching color and rich appearance. Printed papers, especially lithographs, are always popular, although silk screened papers are now also very extensively used.

There are a few special papers which are produced for the display trade. Papers coated or printed with fluorescent or phosphorescent inks or coatings make displays which are startling and attract wide attention. Show-card paper must be made with nonbleeding dyestuffs or pigments in the coatings so that the water-soluble show-card inks will not bleed out from the base color. Some special papers for show-card work are made with a pressure-sensitive or gummed backing so that they can be pasted directly on the desired surface.

These materials belong to the advertising and merchandising industry and as such are constantly in a state of flux. Materials of great importance one month will be completely superseded the following. The overall result is that, aside from creped paper which is a standby in this work, the converting industry supplies the materials which are required at any one time, and goes on producing these same materials for their regular uses the remainder of the time.

Lampshade Stock

Plain or coated paper or laminated-foil- or cloth-base materials are printed, embossed or otherwise decorated by the specialty convertor and are then fabricated into the desired shades by the customer. A wide variety of materials is used, and they fall into two main classes: 1. translucent; 2. opaque. Transparent sheets are not generally used since they would not reduce the glare from the incandescent lamps or hide the lamp structure. The purposes of the shades are (1) decoration, (2) to cut down direct glare from the light source and either to channel it to the ceiling for reflection to the room or send it directly to the desired surface, and (3) to hide the structure of the lamp and the light source. The shade should be preferably flame-retarding in case of the overheating of a lamp.

Translucent Stock

Translucent shades are generally made from treated paper; parchment; laminated glassine; or woven or nonwoven cloth, either plain or laminated to a tissue or glassine. The base material is often impregnated with a flame-retarding compound to guard against the possibility of overheating by the lamp. In the case of laminated products, a nonthermoplastic laminant is desirable since the heat generated in the illuminating system may melt the laminant. Where a treated paper is used, it is saturated with an oily, waxy, or resinous compound which tends to transparentize or semitransparentize the sheet. Such compounds may be wax- or resin-base hot melts, solutions of synthetic resins, and in many cases, oils and petrolatum.

The base sheet is usually decorated by embossing and/or printing with a suitable design which will show up when a light source is placed inside the shade. When embossing is the method of decoration, a roll setup which will compress that portion of the sheet under the pattern without deeply embossing it is preferred. In this way, the design will show up darker when the light is turned on behind the shade while the surface of the sheet will still appear relatively smooth. Lightfast pigments and a binder which will not age fast and crack off are used for decorating shades. Surface, gravure, aniline, and lithographic printing processes have all been used, each for a specific type of design, and all have been successful.

The finished paper is generally sheeted to rather large dimensions, in terms of the usual specialty paper sizes, i.e., the sheets range from 30 inches x 40 inches, to 44 inches x 92 inches. This is necessary since the customer wishes to have the minimum amount of waste, and small size sheets, in general, produce high waste ratios.

Translucent shades are often pleated and the sheet must possess sufficient flexibility for this operation. The material may also be pasted or stapled to make the shade cone, perforated to take ribbons or threads, and sewed where a fancy binding or trimming is applied. The sheet must be suitable for these fabricating steps.

Opaque Stocks

Opaque shades are generally produced from coated and printed papers, foil or woven or nonwoven cloth laminated to paper, glassine laminated to paper, or film laminated to paper. In the last three cases, the paper is on the inside to produce the opacity while the foil, film, or cloth is the outer, visible portion of the shade. A black colored laminant is generally used in order to reduce light transmission.

1. **Coated and printed papers.** The outer surface of such sheets may have a glossy or a matte surface in a wide range of colors and may be printed with a decorative design or a pictorial representation. The finished surface is usually given a protective coating of a synthetic resin, plastic or varnish. Instead of a plastic coating for protection, a cellophane or cellulose acetate film may be laminated to the sheet surface to provide both gloss and protection. The pigments and adhesives used in both inks and coatings must be fast to light and resistant to aging. The sheet is often treated with a flame-retarding agent to reduce danger from overheating.

2. **Foil laminations.** Foil, either plain or colored, may be laminated to the surface of heavy paper to provide a brilliant and eye-catching shade. Dull-surfaced foil is generally used to reduce excessive surface glare. Such foil shade stock may be printed to produce the desired effect and the backing paper can be treated to produce fire-retardent properties.

3. **Cloth laminations.** The material is handled similarly to the foil and may be printed as desired. The finished product can be made to closely resemble expensive handmade multi-layer cloth shades. The new nonwoven cloth offers some unique possibilities in these applications.

4. **Laminated glassine or film.** The use of laminated glassine which is backed by a glossy coated paper as a lampshade material is a recent development. The surface of the glassine is printed with an overall design which contrasts with the background coated sheet. The overall sheet is opaque, even though the glassine portion is translucent. Similar effects can be produced by films laminated to coated paper, with the printing done on the reverse side of the film before lamination. The print is protected by the layer of film, and the glossy surface of the film is fully utilized.

These stocks may be embossed, but as a general rule, the natural surface is left untouched. The product is sheeted and shipped to the customer. The shade blank may be stapled, glued, pleated, or decorated and its properties must permit these operations to be easily performed.

Many complex and expensive printed papers of the brocade type, and special gravure or surface printed designs are produced for lampshade applications. Metallic printing is common, and some flocked surfaces are also made. The size of the runs of individual, special or complex designs are usually relatively small, but plain colors and simple overall patterns with popular appeal can be large enough to be very desirable business.

PAPER DRAPERIES
by J. C. Pickering, Jr.

The concept of making window curtains or hangings from paper is not new. However, in order to get a practical, decorative, and salable paper drapery, it was necessary for the paper industry to reach a point in its development where it could furnish a web which, when suitably processed, could be made into such an item.

The result of paper industry development work was an absorbent, wet-strength web, first produced about 1930 and primarily utilized in towels. Such a material was capable of being plasticized, and since cellulose plasticizers are humectants, the ability to retain a certain percentage of strength at high humidities was vital. Using a well-known plasticizer, such as glycerin as a saturant, a web could be produced which had cloth-like characteristics. It would drape, it was soft, had a smooth, silky "hand" or feel, had sufficient tensile strength to be handled and could even be sewn. Several products were made from this paper, included bed-sheets, pillow cases, dental bibs, and various types of medical examination sheets. Further experimentation showed that a highly plasticized paper, under the proper conditions, had excellent printing properties. This immediately opened up the field of decorative papers, and suggested the possibility of a durable paper window hanging. Such a product could not be laundered or dry cleaned. It was to be used and thrown away and replaced with other hangings at the next cleaning season, hangings of new patterns and color schemes. This would certainly be a radical departure from the conventional scheme of reusing the same fabric draperies year after year. Another drapery product which has come into more recent use is made from the nonwoven cloths which do not require plasticizing and can be handled with normal converting equipment.

Paper draperies were first offered to the public late in 1938.

Consumer acceptance was slow in coming, partly because of the novelty of the idea and the reluctance to try anything new and partly because the word "paper" created the fear that the hanging was fragile and not durable. Yet there was sufficient

FIGURE 9. *Photograph of paper drapery* (Courtesy of Pervel Corp.)

interest aroused to warrant the continuance of promotional sales work. With the coming of the second World War, there was soon a shortage of fabrics and in the hunt for materials to replace cloth hangings, the public found a limited quantity of paper draperies available. As time passed and further allocations of paper for draperies were curtailed, users found, that with proper care the hangings were decorative and durable. Their old paper draperies could be saved and put up for another season. The product, because of its low price and proven acceptability, soon became another one of the "nylon" items and was eagerly sought after by long queues of anxious shoppers. The end of the war brought an end to the restrictions on production which had practically stopped the manufacture of paper hangings and manufacture was expanded as new producers entered the field and a rapid growth of the infant industry ensued.

The Technology of Drape Manufacture

The manufacture of paper draperies may, for convenience, be divided into three steps; (1) plasticizing the base sheet, (2) printing the plasticized paper, and (3) fabricating the drape from the printed paper.

Plasticizing

This operation is usually one of impregnation, and it imparts to the base sheet the cloth-like qualities previously mentioned. The web is unwound from the roll and first passes through a bath containing the softener in water solution. The impregnated web then is passed between a pair of squeeze rolls so that the excess of plasticizer is removed. It is finally passed over drying drums where the excess of water is removed and the finished paper is then rewound in roll form. The base paper now contains the predetermined amount of plasticizer, usually calculated as a percentage by weight of the web. This process is sometimes carried out as a size tub operation on the paper machine, but it is more often run as a secondary converting procedure. Extreme care is necessary in handling a limp sheet of this kind, because of the tendency to form wet wrinkles when tension is applied. The use of spreader rolls or bars will normally correct this tendency.

In the past few years, much time has been devoted to the theory of cellulose fibre plasticizing and undoubtedly a great deal more time will be given to it in the future, for it is a fascinating subject and the occasion for a considerable amount of controversy. One only need to be concerned here with the fact that in order to make a paper drape which would "drape," it has been found necessary to employ hygroscopic, water-soluble compounds or mixtures. There are certain characteristics which the drape plasticizing agent should possess:

1. A narrow humectant range
2. Nonvolatility
3. Freedom from objectionable odor
4. Nontoxicity
5. Lack of color

Glycerin has been about the best-known, most effective, and most readily available plasticizer for cellulose. It has been used in the paper industry for many years even though it has its limitations, particularly with respect to humectant range. During the second World War it was not available for use in such a nonessential product as window drapes and the search for a substitute or a combination of materials which might replace it was, therefore, quite desperate. Since the end of the war, severe shortages and consequent high prices of glycerin have stimulated further work to find more plentiful and cheaper plasticizers. Some of the glycerin substitutes or extenders currently being used include the glycols, particularly ethylene glycol; sorbitol; invert sugar; sodium lactate; and potassium acetate.

A fairly new development has been to incorporate into the web a flame retardent which will prevent or retard the propagation of a flame. A stable and nonvolatile flame retardent will remain in the paper drape, since it will not be subject to laundering or dry-cleaning.

The most logical place to introduce the flame retardent is in combination with the plasticizer during the impregnation operation. Therefore, the substance or combination of substances used must be compatible with the plasticizer. Such a material should not volatilize or migrate from the paper, should not materially affect the stiffness of the web, and should not destroy the feel or "hand." Aluminum sulfate, ammonium sulfate, borax, ammonium and diammonium phosphate, and recently the salts of sulfamic acid (particularly the ammonium salt) have all been employed. Some of the hygroscopic inorganic salts used as plasticizers also have flame-retardent properties which make them of interest.

Printing

When the paper has been properly plasticized and conditioned, the next step is printing. Either one of two processes is generally used in the printing of paper-drapery material: surface printing or intaglio (engraved-roller) printing. The character of the design produced will depend to some extent upon the method used. Since the visual appeal of the product will be very largely the initial determining factor in selling it, choice of design and coloring is of paramount importance. A paper window hanging, although it is destined for a shorter useful life than cloth, must have a design which will give the illusion of cloth and not paper.

The inks employed naturally depend upon the method of printing used. If it is surface printing, water-base inks with the proper vehicles and dispersable pigments are utilized. Many different formulas have been studied for this type of ink, in order to obtain coatings which will have a maximum resistance to the hygroscopic action of the plasticizer. Care must also be taken that the coating does not have the effect of stiffening up the previously softened base paper. In connection with the engraved roller method for gravure printing, spirit-soluble inks are normally used. Precautions must be observed in the choice of the proper vehicle and particularly in obtaining sufficient coverage. In all cases, colors should be picked with emphasis first on light stability and second on quality and range of shades.

The design of specialized window-drapery patterns is the work of skilled artists. There is a limit on available designs, but there are many variations of standard patterns. Many designs are created but most of them do not get beyond the artist's sketch. In this connection public preference will be the decisive factor. If there were any method known by which it could reasonably be determined which patterns and color combinations would sell and which ones would definitely not, an enormous amount of human energy, to say nothing of money, could be more profitably utilized elsewhere.

After a pattern has been accepted as having reasonable possibilities, the sketch is then submitted to the roll maker. The design is broken down into its component colors according to the artist's sketch, and one roller is cut for each of the colors to be used. The set of rollers for printing a design will consist of four to twelve rollers. The completed set of rollers is delivered to the printer and the pattern must be sampled. This consists of taking the artist's basic conception of coloring and then experimenting with various combinations of colors for harmony and visual appeal, until a series of colorings has been obtained, with an eye to current color trends and tastes.

Fabrication

This final part of the operation has to be dealt with as briefly as possible, because there are many kinds of window hangings for a multiplicity of windows in rooms used for different purposes. Basically, the industry employs two methods of fabricating the printed plasticized paper into draperies (1) sewing or stitching, and (2) pasting.

Since the paper has certain cloth-like characteristics, it is possible to sew it on power sewing machines in a manner similar to cloth. The method simulates cloth fabrication, and when properly done, gives additional strength, as well as decoration to the product. Side, top and bottom hems, and rod pockets can all be fabricated by ordinary sewing. Even shirring and ruffling can be sewn into the paper to give added decorative effects.

The pasting method of fabrication requires the use of edge gumming equipment to fold over and secure with paste the side hems. Reinforcing tape and thread are often employed to give additional strength to the side hems. Rod pockets in most cases are stitched to give security to the hanging. Since the plasticizer is hygroscopic, the adhesive used must be one which is not materially affected by moisture. Several synthetic resin glues are being employed.

Future Developments

In any new product such as the paper draperies, growing pains have been inevitable. Considerable work is being carried out by the industry with a view toward bettering the product. Mechanical softening as a means of rendering the sheet pliable instead of the use of a hydroscopic plasticizer is one trend of future improvement. Ways and means of incorporating more strength into the web are also worthy of concentrated study so as to produce a more durable product. This is, however, rather a problem of the base-paper manufacturer and not of the converter. Although the product has been accepted as something worth while, it will require constant diligence and continuing improvements to keep the industry a dynamic force in the paper converting field.

WALLPAPERS

by Robert Blakeslee

The term "specialty paper," when applied to wallpaper, is particularly appropriate because wallpaper possesses almost all of the characteristics which place a product in the "specialty" class. It is a finished consumer product designed and produced for one purpose only—that of decorating the walls of a home. Its manufacture involves coating, embossing and printing—printing not with one, two or three colors, but with as many as thirteen colors on one paper. Finally, these colors must be fast to water, soap, light, acid, alkali and organic solvents.

In volume, also, wallpaper rates well up in the "specialty papers." During each of the three years prior to the second

World War, just short of 400,000,000 rolls of wallpaper were manufactured in the United States. In paper trade terms, this amounts to better than five million reams (24 x 36-480) or about 125,000 tons of raw stock. The manufacture of wallpaper is largely an "art," yet many technological improvements have been made in recent years and undoubtedly some of the methods developed by the wallpaper industry to solve their problems may be adapted to the manufacture of unrelated specialty papers.

History of Wallpaper

Since the first caveman made a crude sketch on the walls of his cave, mankind had been relieving the monotony of four walls by decorating them in some manner. The first use of wall coverings in recorded history was by the Chinese, although these were not made of paper but of fabric. The Romans and early Europeans also used fabric wall coverings or tapestries over the cold stone walls of their homes for the dual purpose of decoration and insulation. Such luxury was only for the very wealthy, however, and inevitably someone discovered that the same decorative effect could be obtained much more cheaply by substituting paper for fabric. The first historical reference to the use of wallpaper was around the beginning of the 16th century. These papers were hand painted and the first guild of painters for decorating wallpaper was formed in 1586. During the 17th century, the use of wallpaper became very fashionable. Large quantities of hand-painted papers were imported from China, and the influence of these Chinese papers is still to be seen in modern wallpaper designs 300 years later.

It was during the 17th century, also, that the first beginnings of modern wallpaper printing developed. Instead of free-hand painting, the pattern outline was printed from a carved wooden block and the colors were painted in by hand. In the light of modern jurisdictional disputes between labor unions, an interesting footnote is that the Printers' Guilds were successful in making the wallpaper printers cease putting legends in their designs, since it was considered an infringement on the printing trade.

Eventually, the painting by hand was replaced by using multiple blocks instead of one outline block. A flat, wooden block was carved for each color in the design and these blocks were printed in succession to complete the pattern. This method is still used today in hand-blocked papers, and the same principles are used in machine printing, except that the blocks have been bent into a cylinder so the process could be made continuous. This development came early in the 19th century and there has been no basic change in the manufacturing equipment since that time, except the use of the coating machine for the background color. Like so many artistic forms, the mechanization of wallpaper printing led to its temporary downfall as a decorative medium. The designers could not keep up with the mechanical presses and the distasteful patterns of the Victorian period resulted in wallpaper falling into disfavor. Another good reason for wallpaper's loss in popularity was the development of colors from coal-tar derivatives, which were brilliant but very fugitive, and the faded walls produced an unfavorable reaction.

With the beginning of this century, wallpaper started to come back into its rightful place as the most versatile of wall decorations. The principal reason for the current popularity which it enjoys was the development of washable and fast-to-light wallpaper. Not only do these qualities make a more practical decorating medium for the householder, but no longer is a complex pattern required to disguise faded colors and accidental spotting. Thus the artists are given greater latitude in designing the tasteful patterns available in modern wallpaper.

Manufacturing Operations

1. **Background Coating.** Practically all the better-grade wallpapers are completely covered with an opaque "ground" coating and then dried before printing the top colors. This ground coating has a dual function of providing a proper

background color on which to print the top colors and also to make the paper fast to light. The raw stock from which most wallpaper is made is a ground-wood sheet and will yellow on exposure to light. Consequently, the ground coating must be opaque enough to hide this discoloration. This means coating weights ranging from 14 to 22 pounds per ream (24 x 36-480) which must be carefully controlled to insure that the papers are fast to light.

Almost all of the conventional types of coating machines can be, and are, used for applying the background color. These machines will not be discussed here only as they particularly apply to wallpaper. In choosing a coating machine for wall-paper manufacture, there are two factors which are not always encountered in other coating fields. The first is that the coating machine is generally run in tandem with the print machines. This means that its operation may be interrupted frequently, and a machine which requires special attention to prevent color drying on the equipment is at a disadvantage. Similarly, usually a number of trials have to be made at the start of a run to adjust the shade, and the time of running one color may be relatively short; so that the ease with which the color may be drawn from the pan and the machine washed up is an important feature in its design. The other factor not common to other coating fields is that very uniform application from edge to edge is a requisite. On the wall, the left-hand edge of the sheet butts against the right-hand edge of the adjoining strip. A slight difference in the lay of the coating from edge to edge becomes noticeable under these conditions, and very close control on the coating machine is required. It is for this reason that the air-knife and reverse-roll coater are gaining favor despite the fact that these machines are less adapted to intermittent operation and frequent wash-ups.

As mentioned previously, the usual practice is to operate the ground machine in tandem with the printing machine. In this arrangement, the paper from the coating machine is festooned and dried with circulating hot air. At the end of the drying rack the paper is pulled from the sticks and carried back on an endless canvas to the printing machine which is placed in front of the coating machine. After printing, the paper is refestooned in another rack placed above the ground drying rack.

2. **Printing Procedures and Equipment.** There are at least three methods of reproducing the design on paper to transform it into wallpaper. These are surface printing, intaglio or engraved printing, and screen printing. The latter two methods are used only by a few manufacturers today and account for but a fraction of the total rollage produced. The surface printing method is the method used for the common type of wallpaper with which everyone is familiar. This method will be discussed in detail.

FIGURE 10. *Wallpaper printing machine* (Courtesy of Imperial Paper & Color Corp.)

Careful examination of a piece of wallpaper will disclose that the design is composed of a number of distinct colors. The apparent shading of a pink rose with a deep red center, for example, is achieved by printing three or four shades of pink side by side, and the eye receives the impression of a gradual shading. Each of these colors requires a separate cylinder, called a "block" or "roller," on the face of which a portion of the complete design is in relief. In the days of hand-blocked papers, the designs contained as many as twenty-four different colors but, with machines, the number rarely exceeds thirteen and is usually from eight to twelve. The preparation of these printing blocks, which is called "cutting," takes time and skill. The original artist's design is first traced in its entirety without regard to color. This tracing is then transferred to rock maple cylinders—as many cylinders as there are colors in the design. One of these cylinders is to print a green leaf, let us say. That part of the design which is to be green is painted to distinguish it from the rest of the design, and a craftsman outlines this area with thin brass strips. These strips are cut and bent to follow the intricacies of the design and then pounded into the wooden block about ¼ inch, leaving about ¼ inch of brass exposed. This space enclosed in brass is filled with a special thick felt of the type used on piano hammers. Smaller areas are shaped from solid brass which is filed and bent to the desired shape. The same process is repeated for each of the rollers in the complete design.

The above process is obviously a tedious and expensive one, and efforts have been made to cheapen it. Aluminum alloy cylinders are used in which the design is reproduced by routing out the unwanted metal, leaving the design in relief. This type of block is widely used for smaller designs, but the quality of printing from the alloy surface is inferior to that from brass and felt which are generally used for the larger designs in higher-class papers.

As we have seen, the wallpaper design contains up to thirteen colors which must be printed in proper sequence and register to make the complete reproduction. The printing machine or surface printer, in which this is accomplished, consists of a drum around the periphery of which are placed the printing rollers. As the paper is carried around by the drum, each roller prints its portion of the design. To keep the blocks in proper register, they are all geared to a master gear of the

FIGURE 11. *Cutting the wallpaper printing roll* (Courtesy of Imperial Paper & Color Corp.)

same diameter as the drum which may be as large as 10 feet in diameter. Each roller is a part of a color unit which includes, in addition to the roller, a color pan, a felt sleeve, and a doctor blade. The color pan is a wooden or metal pan with an applicator roll rotating in a bath of color. The color is picked up by a felt sleeve, known as "sieve cloth," and a doctor blade scrapes off the excess. The sieve cloth then makes contact with the pattern surface of the block transferring the wet color which is, in turn, transferred to the paper. While each color unit considered individually is relatively simple, when multiplied by thirteen, the printing machine becomes a complex machine requiring the full time attention of a skilled craftsman.

3. **Converting or Waterproofing.** Since water colors are

generally used in surface-printed wallpaper, the binder must be soluble in water when applied, but insoluble in the finished paper, if it is to be washable. To accomplish this, one more step is required which is known as converting or treating. Essentially, this involves applying a solution to the paper which renders the binder insoluble. The method varies with the materials used and the peculiarities of individual mills. It ranges from a simple spray, through a squeeze roll applicator, to a complete immersion bath. Because the different colors vary in absorbency due to differences in pigment-binder ratios, the ideal converter is one which completely saturates the paper with a dilute reagent which renders all the binder insoluble and leaves no excess. Such an ideal converter, however, would require a drying rack larger than the coating-machine drying racks. The converting operation has been developed after most wallpaper mills were built, and there is no provision for such drying facilities. Compromise is, therefore, required which calls for more concentrated solutions and shorter periods of exposure to the solution. In most mills, the converter consists of an applicator roll and a squeeze roll to remove the excess. The distance of travel between these rolls determines the amount of solution picked up by the paper and is limited by the drying capacity available.

4. **Embossing and Cutting.** A major portion of the wallpaper is completed as it leaves the converter dryer except for cutting into commercial rolls. Some patterns, however, require an additional embossing operation. There are two general types of embossing, the more common of which is known as plain embossing and merely imparts a texture to the wallpaper such as a weave, rib, etc. The other type is ink embossing in which a part or all of the design is supplied by the embossing roll and its ink. The embossing frames are the conventional type used in most converting operations. When ink is used, it is applied from a pan roller to a composition roller and from there to the embossing roll. In some papers, two or more colors are used, in which case, the applicator rolls must be

routed out so that they ink only the desired areas. The inks used are generally pigment in varnish, although water vehicles can also be used.

The final step is the cutting of the paper into commercial rolls. This is done either by hand or by machine. The machine is much speedier than hand rolling but it does not permit good inspection and hand rolling is generally used on higher-grade papers.

Coating and Printing-Ink Sampling and Color Matching

The preceding section has covered the conversion of the raw stock to the finished paper, but it has ignored the very important and highly interesting subject of the preparation of the wet colors or inks. To a technical or production man from another field, one of the most baffling things about wallpaper manufacture is that all of the color matching is done without the benefit of formulae. Except for the basic, pure color mixes from which they are compounded, each of the thousands of colors used is matched by eye; and this is true whether the amount is forty barrels or one pail. The reason for this situation is apparent when one considers that each machine may be applying a dozen different colors; and, when ten or twenty machines are in operation, the disposal of the surplus colors at the end of a printing is a problem. In practice, the color mixers take such dead heads and blend them off in succeeding batches, which would not be practical if formulae were used. The color mixers are supplied with a base white mixed with binder and the various colored pigments mixed with binder which are called "stainers." There are usually six to a dozen pigments used and the color mixers blend any or all of these with white to obtain the desired shade in the same manner as a painter would match a paint for woodwork. The difference is that the painter is concerned with only one color while the color mixer may be mixing a dozen. Since one color mixer serves as many as three or more machines with several colors in each, he must be very skilled, and it is amazing to see how closely and quickly he can mix the right amount of the right shade.

Raw Materials

A. **Raw Stock.** The consumer who purchases a roll of wallpaper is not in the least concerned with the paper itself, since she is purchasing a decorating medium and the paper is merely incidental. To the paperhanger and the manufacturer, however, the raw stock has other important attributes beyond acting merely as a carrier for the design. Among these are:

a. *Wet and dry strength.* These are important to the manufacturer since the paper must hold together through the various manufacturing processes. The wet strength is especially important to the paperhanger, since he does most of his handling of the paper while it is soaked with paste.

b. *Expansion and contraction.* The paperhanger requires a paper which will stretch while wet so that he can match the pattern exactly despite irregularities of the wall. Upon drying however, the paper must shrink with the paste to give a tight smooth surface.

c. *Sizing and density.* These factors are interrelated somewhat since either or both will cause curling if too high, which is troublesome to both the paperhanger and the manufacturer. Conversely, if they are too low, they will cause trouble for the manufacturer during the ground-coating operation and for the paperhanger by soaking up too much paste. The above desirable attributes are to be found in a ground-wood sheet, known as "#2 hanging." This paper is similar to newsprint except for being heavier in weight and having around 20% sulfite pulp and also somewhat higher sizing.

Two other more or less standard grades of raw stock are used by some manufacturers for special papers. These are "#1 hanging" and "semi #1 hanging." The first is a 100% chemical pulp sheet, while the second is in between the #1 and #2 grades in sulfite content. The only advantages of sulfite containing sheets are somewhat greater strength and better light-fastness. They have the disadvantage of having less satisfactory handling characteristics from both the paperhanger's and the manufacturer's standpoint. A few other special grades of raw stock are used by some manufacturers, the principal one of which is a special stock for heavily embossed papers which contains bleached kraft pulp for greater strength.

B. **Pigments.** Except for special effects, wallpaper generally has a dull, matte surface which enhances its decorative value. For this reason the clay used as the base white for backgrounds is a relatively coarse filler clay of the air-floated type. For top colors, however, better hiding power is required for printing light colors on dark backgrounds and the finer grades of coating clay are used for this purpose. For highlights and the finest printing, the coating clays must be improved by adding whiter and brighter pigments such as titanium dioxide, lithopone, and calcium carbonate.

When light-fast wallpaper was first proposed, its manufacture seemed relatively simple, if one applied sufficient ground coating to hide the raw stock and used pigments which were fast to light in the fadeometer. Experience has shown, however, that it is not quite so simple because the fadeometer only tells a part of the story as to the stability of a pigment over a variety of wall conditions. While one would not think of exposure inside a house as an extreme condition, experience has shown that some pigments suitable for outside paints are not stable enough for wallpaper. The reason seems to be that the paint vehicle which protects the surface also protects the pigment from the destructive action of light, air, and moisture. In wallpaper, the pigment is not protected by a paint vehicle and pigment failure due to the combined action of light and moisture can occur. In addition to being stable under light and moisture, the pigment must have other properties. For example, it must be fast to both mild acids and alkalis. Further, it is desirable that the pigment is fast to organic solvents to allow removal of grease spots from the wallpaper, and it should be clean, bright, and strong. Obviously there are no pigments which completely fill these specifications and the manufacturer is forced to compromise, utilizing those pigments which he feels will give him the optimum combination of properties. Among the pigments used by the various manufacturers we find the inorganic iron oxide reds, yellows, browns, and black, the chrome yellows and oranges, the cadmium reds and yellows, acid-resistant ultramarine, and iron blues. Among the organics are alizarine, rubines, hansa yellows, thio-indigo red, pigment green B, and phthalocyanine blue and green. Prior to the advent of washable wallpapers, most pigments were purchased in pulp form and merely mixed with sufficient binder or size to hold them on the paper. Washability, however, requires much higher sizing ratios and, in order to maintain high solids for good printing, the use of dry pigments has largely been required. In present practice, the dry pigments are dispersed in the adhesive either in ball mills or colloid mills to insure maximum color development.

C. **Adhesives.** It has been mentioned previously that wallpaper is printed with water colors containing a binder which must be rendered insoluble to make the paper washable. The almost universal method is to use a protein binder which can be made insoluble either by aldehyde or aluminum fixation, or both. Prior to the second World War casein with formaldehyde or aluminum fixation was widely used in the production of washable wallpaper. With proper control of pH it is possible to incorporate formaldehyde directly in the wet mixes, and upon drying and aging, the reaction between the formaldehyde and casein continues until the colors are insoluble. In actual practice, the formaldehyde is usually not incorporated in the colors, but subsequently a dilute solution of formaldehyde or alum is applied.

The casein was generally used as a size solution of about 15% concentration which was combined with the pigments in ball mills. The sizing ratios varied with the pigments and ranged from 8 to 12 pounds of casein per 100 pounds of clay to as high as 100 pounds of casein per 100 pounds of the finer, lower specific gravity pigments. The alkalis used to dissolve the casein were usually caustic soda, soda ash, borax, ammonia, etc. The choice was largely a matter of preference on the part of the individual manufacturer. In some ways, caustic soda is to be preferred, but very close technical control is required when it is used.

With the shortage of casein during the war years, the wall-paper manufacturers, like all other paper coaters, had to develop other sizing materials. Experimental work with soya flour and the protein isolated from it had been carried on for several years, and much of the preliminary work had already been done. The principal difference between soya protein and casein is that soya protein cannot be completely insolubilized with formaldehyde and requires an application of aluminum salt solution. This meant an additional processing operation and was one of the chief reasons why soya was not more widely used prior to the war. Now that the manufacturers have the necessary equipment, it is doubtful if they will completely revert to casein. Another obstacle which had to be overcome in the successful use of soya flour was a fear of high alkalinity. Unlike casein, soya flour is not harmed by storage in the alkaline state. In fact, a certain minimum alkalinity is necessary to develop the optimum in flow and adhesive strength and maximum stability on aging. In some cases this meant the elimination of pigments which were not fast to alkali; but, once this and other necessary changes had been made, soya flour proved itself a successful substitute for casein.

The alkalis used with soya flour include all those used with casein. Again the choice depends on the preference of the individual manufacturer. In general, the weaker alkalies such as ammonia give greater fluidity but lower adhesive strength than the stronger alkalis such as caustic soda. The choice, therefore, is dictated by balancing such factors as fluidity against economy. Suggested amounts of the various alkalis on the weight of soya flour are:

	%
Caustic Soda	4
Ammonia (28%)	10
Soda Ash	10
Borax	15

It has been mentioned that soya flour must be frequently supplemented by other binders, and it is doubtful whether any manufacturer uses soya flour exclusively. The usual binder for this purpose is protein isolated from soya flour which, in many respects, is similar to casein. Unlike casein, however, isolated soya protein requires aluminum fixation for successful use in making washable wallpaper. Isolated protein will react with formaldehyde when freshly prepared. However, in wallpaper manufacture it is necessary to keep wet mixes a week or longer and under these conditions, the isolated protein cannot be depended upon to give sufficient washability with formaldehyde alone. Where isolated protein is used in combination with soya flour, this is not a serious drawback, since the aluminum fixation is required for the soya flour.

The aluminum fixation required for soya adhesives has been the subject of much study by the manufacturers, and there are probably as many formulae as there are mills. The reason is that, at best, the formula used is a compromise between several opposing considerations and is influenced also by the type of converter used and the amount and kind of alkali in the colors. Theoretically, there should be an optimum aluminum-protein ratio at an optimum pH for minimum solubility. It was pointed out in a previous section that the pigment-protein ratio of the top colors may be widely different from that of the background color, and it is impossible to adjust the fixing solution to produce the optimum conditions throughout the whole sheet. Most of the formulae are based on aluminum sulfate, acetate, or formate with added salts, acids, or bases. Some of the formulae also include formaldehyde which has some hardening effect on soya adhesives even though it does not completely insolubilize them.

Among the protein adhesives used in wallpaper, animal glue must also be mentioned. Its use is by no means as widespread as it used to be, but it is still used by some manufacturers to make both washable and nonwashable paper. The chief virtue of glue lies in its superior printing properties. Another protein adhesive which has been utilized to a small extent is zein, the corn protein.

The space devoted to the protein adhesives might leave the impression that other adhesives are unimportant in wallpaper. This is not the case because a tremendous rollage of wallpaper is still made with the older adhesives used in nonwashable paper such as glue, dextrine, and particularly starch. Prior to the advent of modified, thin-bodied starches, Egyptian gum and pearl and tapioca starches were the principal types used. For easy brushing and good printing, a thinner-bodied starch is desirable, therefore, these starches have been largely replaced by such modified products as chlorinated corn starch.

Among the newer adhesives which are used in wallpaper, are the synthetic resin latices such as butadiene-styrene latex. They are used as an additive to soya flour in place of casein or isolated protein. The flexibility of these sizing agents as contrasted with protein make them promising, particularly in embossed papers. The continued improvements being made in latices, which are capable of yielding insoluble films at ordinary temperatures, make them the most interesting field for future developments in the manufacture of wallpaper. The promise of latices lie in their use as adhesives, and not as surface coatings over the printed paper, as has been suggested by every latex manufacturer. While a surface coating to prevent accidental spotting on the wallpaper seems sensible enough, the industry has tried such treatment in years past and the results were not as good as might be expected. The primary drawback is that a surface treatment protects the colors only from the front but not from the back or at the seams where grease can get into the paper and cannot be removed. The impervious film on the surface also prevents moisture from the paste and the wall from escaping and this is very destructive to the pigment.

It has already been stated that the current popularity of wallpaper is largely due to the technological improvements of washability and light-fastness, and there is no doubt that modern wallpapers are a much more practical decorating medium than those used in the days of our grandmothers. Yet there is still much that can be done through additional research. More permanent pigments, greater resistance to stains and soil, and new decorative effects are all problems which must be solved to keep wallpaper competitive with other forms of wall decoration.

REFERENCES

C. W. Ward. *Wallpaper: Origin and Manufacture.* Putnam, New York (1921).

P. Ackerman. *Wallpaper: Its History, Design and Use.* F. A. Stokes, New York (1923).

N. McClelland. *The Practical Book of Decorative Wall Treatment.* J. B. Lippincott, New York (1926).

R. Staeble. "Wallpaper pigments." *Farben-Chem.* **2**, No. 505–6 (1931).

H. Heinrich. "Requirements for Wallpaper Pigments." *Farbe und Lack.* 43–4, 97–8 (1932).

Ducrou. "Starch in Wallpaper." *Recherches et inventions.* **16**, 254–7 (1935).

R. Louchart. "Accelerated Aging of Wallpaper." *Papier.* **39**, 129–35 (1936).

R. Sansone. "History of Wallpaper in Europe." *Paper Ind.* **18**, 741–4 (1936).

M. C. Neuberger. "Modern Wallpaper Manufacture." *Ciba Review.* **1**, No. 3:102–103 (1937).

M. Weilerswist. "Manufacture of Wallpaper in Historical and Modern Times." *Papier-Ztg.* **64**, No. 45:1008–1010 (1939).

J. A. Ross. *U. S. Patent 1,218,474.* Moisture Resistant Wallpaper Using Glue, Wax Emulsion and Coated with Shellac (1917).

L. Rado. *British Patent 313,550.* Wallpaper Laminated With Cellulose Hydrate Foil (1928).

E. F. Arnold. *U. S. Patent 1,848,686.* Wallpaper Coated with Cellulose Nitrate and Wax or Stearate (1932).

A. E. Vanwirt. *U. S. Patent 1,950,279.* Washable Wallpaper Using Casein Binder and Sprayed with Formaldehyde (1934).

L. C. Fleck. *U. S. Patent 1,955,626.* Washable Wallpaper Using Casein Binder and Formaldehyde (1934).

W. J. H. Hinrichs. *German Patent 610,018.* Preserving Wallpaper by Application of Rubber Latex Film (1935).

I. G. Farbenindustrie. *French Patent 782,42ᵗ.* Urea or Phenol-formaldehyde Esterified with Fatty Acids and Used as Emulsion (1935).

J. R. Hubbard. *U. S. Patent 2,043,324.* Washable Wallpaper Using Protein Binder and Application of Aluminum Salt Solution (1936).

C. J. Wernlund. *U. S. Patent 2,073,666.* Hardening Proteins by Means of Insoluble Aluminum Compound and Acid-forming Ammonium Salt (1937).

R. A. Voet. *U. S. Patent 2,079,780.* Hardening Baths for Proteins.

C. Dangelmajer. *U. S. Patent 2,101,574.* Water Resistant Coating Containing Protein, Hardening Agent and Fatty Acid Amide to Prevent Premature Reaction.

J. W. Close. *U. S. Patent 2,284,800.* Washable Wallpaper Using Corn Protein, Alkaline Resinate and Bleaching Compound (1942).

F. K. Schoenfeld. *Canadian Patent 416,754.* Wallpaper Coated with Plasticized Vinyl Chloride Film (1943).

Chapter IV

FUNCTIONAL AND PROTECTIVE PACKAGING PAPERS

by R. H. Mosher

THE functional and protective papers are a class which possess special properties which are not generally to be found in regular cellulose-base papers. These sheets are used as wrappers over objects or materials to prevent water, grease, vapors, or chemicals from entering or leaving the unit package. Since the specific functions of the wrapper depend, to a great extent, upon the properties of the coating, laminants, or a protective film or foil layer in the sheet, the trend in these papers has been toward better coatings and the use of more laminated structures. By the use of coatings, laminants, plastic films, foils, cellophane, or glassine as barrier layers, almost any type of resistance or proofness to a given compound can be developed. For any specific packaging problem, however, there may be a number of different combinations of these barriers which will give the desired results and the converting equipment available and the unit costs must be balanced to produce a sheet which will give the best protection for the least cost.

FUNCTIONAL PROPERTIES

The functional and protective papers can be classified according to their properties as follows:

   1. Water-resistant
   2. Waterproof
   3. Grease-resistant
   4. Greaseproof
   5. Water-vapor-resistant
   6. Water-vaporproof
   7. Chemical-resistant
   8. Gas-resistant
   9. Gasproof
  10. Heat-sealing

In most cases, as used in the industry today, these terms cover relative properties and there has been very little differentiation between "water-resistant," and "waterproof" papers, for example. Many different tests have been devised, recommended, and used, but in general it is now recognized that no set of laboratory tests can duplicate actual usage requirements. The subject will be discussed from the standpoint of general requirements for protection against water, water vapor, grease, chemicals, and gases. Heat sealability or pressure sensitivity are specific properties which can be built into coatings.

   1. **Water-resistant and Waterproof Papers.** Water-resistant and waterproof sheets have a great many applications. The degree of resistance to the passage of water will depend on the usage to which the sheet will be subjected. In general, there are three types of requirements:

   a. Resistance to staining and absorption in the sheet by a of water under negligible pressure.
   b. Resistance against the penetration of water or aqueous solutions under a substantial head or pressure for a given time, and
   c. Absolute resistance to penetration of water or aqueous solutions under a substantial head or pressure.

In order to develop a sheet which will do the job required, yet not incorporate an expensive, yet unnecessary, degree of resistance, the application should be analyzed so as to determine the proper characteristics needed in the sheet. The type and thickness of coating or laminant must be adequate, yet even the best coated films have a certain number of pinholes or voids, and the degree of water resistance is a function of their number and size, of the thickness of the coating, and the hydrophobic characteristics of the surface. In cases where a film thickness of 0.001 inch, and one coating will be adequate, it is certainly not economical to apply a 0.002 inch film requiring two coatings. The same is true of the required load of laminant, or the use of a specific type and thickness of a laminated film or foil. The composition of the coating is an important factor since an easily wetted surface will permit the water to seek out any pinholes or apertures in the film, while a hydrophobic surface, such as vinyl film, will make wetting and penetration extremely difficult if not impossible for water unless under pressure. The question of economics also enters the picture in another way, since a coating composed of 20 pounds per ream of wax at 7¢ per pound is obviously cheaper than 5 pounds per ream of vinyl lacquer costing 50¢ per pound, assuming that each did a satisfactory job. The problem of equipment in this specialized field also must be taken into account, since the use of the wax in the above comparison might be very sound on the basis of raw materials alone, but if there was a laquer coating machine available and no waxing equipment, this factor would have to be considered. In the development of papers which are resistant to the penetration of water or aqueous solutions, however, the problems are generally not overly complex since water is a simple compound and easily repelled, and the only major factor which must be guarded against is the presence of some of the modern surface-active agents which can cause wetting and penetration of the sheet where plain water is easily resisted.

The question of flexibility of the coating must also be considered, since a sheet built with a 100% safety factor in the flat form, but which cracks on folding, is not much better than a sheet with a 50% deficiency in the overall makeup if an envelope or package must be fabricated from it. The development and testing of these papers requires fine judgment and the proper test conditions are determined only by experience and experiment.

2. **Grease-resistant and Greaseproof Papers.** The development of sheets resistant to the passage of "grease" presents a problem almost diametrically opposite to that posed by water resistant papers. Grease is hydrophobic in character and is a common term for anything from heavy motor oil to light machine oil containing special penetrants, and extending to chocolate, peanut butter, and lard. Instead of a single chemical compound such as water, the technician is faced with an extensive range of chemical compounds and a wide range of physical states including light fluids, viscous oils, and solids. This complexity of composition has forced the technician to evaluate his specific sheet on the same material which will be packaged in it. Most of the industry is now carrying out its evaluation programs in this manner. The various technical associations still base their evaluation tests on turpentine, however, since early specifications of greaseproofness were set up in terms of this compound. This test, although it offers a good control mechanism, does not necessarily predict the resistance the paper will offer to anything besides turpentine and although it is still widely used both in evaluation and control work it is being rapidly superseded by more accurate and specific methods.

There are a few general aspects which may be discussed in connection with grease-resistant sheets and they are concerned with the nature of the transmission of grease or oil through such sheets. Cellulose itself is a good grease-resistant barrier due to its hydrophilic character, and grease or oil penetrates a sheet of paper through the interstices between the individual fibers or along the fibers themselves by capillary action and not through the cellulose. If the sheet can be so altered that there are no intersticial spaces as in the case of glassine and parchment, it will be resistant to the passage of grease or oil.

The use of cellophane, or regenerated cellulose film, also illustrates this point. If a film, foil, or a coating or laminant is used to produce the barrier, the material used for this purpose should be hydrophilic in nature and if this is not possible, it should be insolube or not dissolve in the specific grease or oil being tested. If a coating or laminant is used, it should be applied to a smooth base sheet, since any voids or apertures in the film may permit transmission and any fibers which protrude through the surface may act as wicks and pass the oil or grease through the film to the opposite side.

There are three types of requirements:

a. Resistance to training and absorption in the sheet by a film of grease or oil under negligible pressure.
b. Resistance to penetration of grease or oil through the sheet under a substantial pressure for a given period of time, and
c. Absolute resistance to any penetration of grease or oil over long periods of time and under substantial pressure.

When selecting a sheet for a certain application the test methods which will be applied to the sheet and also its use requirements should be studied.

A very important consideration is how long the barrier must resist the specific material being packaged in it. A perishable food product with a greasy surface, such as doughnuts, may require a sheet possessing only a few days of grease resistance to lard or fats. A lubricating-oil container, on the other hand, might require absolute proofness to the penetration of both hydrocarbons and aromatic oils for a period of 1 or 2 years. A further consideration is the economics of using various alternate barriers for any application. The failure of a grease-proof sheet used on a machine part might not be too serious since a messy package could be the only consequence other than the loss of oil from the part due to its absorption by the package. The failure of a doughnut package would result in an unsalable product, however, and the failure of the oil container could well result in a loss of its contents. The flexibility of the sheet must also be considered.

There are at least three methods of grease penetration:

a. Penetration through pinholes or apertures in the sheet. The viscosity of the material will determine the rate of penetration for a given sheet.
b. Wick action along and through protruding fibers.
c. Solution of the grease in, and consequent diffusion or transmission through, the sheet. The chemical constitution of the grease or oil will determine this for any given sheet.

From this, it can be assumed that the maximum grease-resistance can be obtained when:

a. The barrier film is continuous and free from voids, apertures, or pinholes.
b. The surface of the paper under the coating or laminant is smooth so that no or a minimum of fibers protrude to act as wicks. This condition is, of course, eliminated if the barrier is a film or foil.
c. The components of the film are not soluble in or do not dissolve the grease or oil.

3. **Water-vapor- and Gas-resistant and Water-vapor- and Gasproof Sheets.** There is no absolutely vaporproof barrier since even metal foils which are known to be free from pinholes and apertures transmit minute amounts of water vapor due to the nonhomogeneity of their structure. Water vapor or other gases may also be transmitted through a homogeneous plastic film, if minute amounts can be absorbed by the surface structure, passed through by an absorption-diffusion mechanism, and then desorbed on the far side of the film. The amounts are small in most cases and depend upon the size, polarity, and structure of both gas molecule and the barrier, but it does illustrate the problems which must be faced in this application.

The transmission of water vapor and gases is a function of several factors including the over-all temperature of gas and of the barrier; the difference in pressure on the two sides of the barrier; the type, thickness, composition, and crystallinity of the barrier; and the area exposed to transmission.

Vapor-resistant papers are used for wrapping products to maintain their original moisture or gas content as long as possible. Some frozen meats may have a tendency to dry out in storage, causing "freezer burn" because of moisture diffusion out of the package due to the low moisture content of the low-temperature air outside the package. Dry-packaged cereals, flour, and hygroscopic salts may tend to cake if they absorb moisture and moisture must be kept out of the package. Some foods, such as spices and essential oils lose their flavor if the aromatic odors evaporate and must be packaged so as to retain their odor and flavor. Certain foods require that the package "breathe" moisture, CO_2, and/or O_2. Some foods are packed in nitrogen or are vacuum packed and the specific gas must be retained or the air kept out. In many of these applications, the gas pressure is equal on both sides of the barrier and in others a pressure difference is maintained. In some cases the temperature is normal and in others it is low or excessively high.

The contents of the package may have a tendency to dry out or lose a volatile ingredient, or may tend to pick up moisture, depending upon their nature and on the conditions on either side of the barrier. If the equilibrium vapor pressure of the contents is higher than the vapor pressure outside the package the passage of vapor will be outward. If the opposite conditions exist, the passage will be inward. On the inside of the package, the vapor pressure depends on the temperature and the composition of the contents. On the outside it is a function of the temperature and, in the case of moisture, on the relative humidity.

In setting up specifications for a vapor-resistant barrier, careful consideration must be given to the nature of the contents and the equilibrium vapor pressure, the size of the package and exposed surface area, the critical amount of gas or moisture that can be gained or lost, the length of time that the material will be in the package before being used, and the temperatures at which the package will be stored. The test conditions for the evaluation of such a package are a matter of fine judgment and should be decided upon only after careful consideration of the application. It is not of much value to test a frozen food package at room temperature, for example, or to evaluate a package for use in the tropics under test conditions of 73° and 50% R.H.

No standard requirements for moisture-vapor transmission have been adopted by the paper or packaging industry to this date. It has been proposed, however, that the following classification be used, based on the General Foods Cabinet Test:

Low Permability	0.15 grams or less *
Medium Permeability	0.15–1.0 grams
High Permeability	1.0–3.0 grams
Vapor Breathing	3.0+ grams

Water-vapor permeability of several types of papers and plastic films, tested according to Army-Navy Spec. ANC–67, is given in Table I.[1] The values are reported in grams per 100 square inches, per 24 hours, at 100°F. and 95% relative humidity.

There is one specific problem involved in the utilization of vapor barriers and this is concerned with flexibility and folding properties. When a sheet is folded, either 90°, in fabricating a container or box cover, or completely back upon itself, as when making an envelope, there is an intense stress and stretching at the fold. In some films such stretching causes crystallization and in some cases, a partial rupture or at least a thinning of the film results. This could obviously cause an increase in the vapor-transfer rate at the point of the crease if any diminu-

* Per 100 square inches, per 24 hours.

TABLE I

Water-vapor Permeability of Common Films and Papers

	Thickness in Inches	Permeability *
Plain Glassine	0.00075–0.002	High
Lacquered Glassine	0.0008–0.002	0.2–1.0
Waxed Glassine	0.0008–0.003	0.2–1.0
Pliofilm	0.0008–0.002	0.5–1.0
Moistureproof Cellophane	0.0009–0.0017	0.2–0.6
Ethyl Cellulose Film	0.001–0.2	High
Vinyl Chloride Film	0.001	High
Vinyl Copolymer Film	0.001	High
Vinyl Coated Paper	0.001 (Film Thickness)	High
Saran Film	0.001–0.002	0.2 or less
Vegetable Parchment	0.0017–0.0075	High
Kraft Paper	0.002–0.009	High
Polyethylene	0.004	0.25
Cellophane	0.008–0.0015	High

* Measured as grams of water transmitted per 100 square inches, per 24 hours, at 100°F. and 95% relative humidity.

tion of the film thickness took place, although if crystallization and no rupture occurred in all probability the sheet would become more resistant to passage of vapor at that point. Since most packages contain a number of such potential danger spots, it is generally the safest technique to evaluate the package which will actually be used in making recommendations for any specific application.

4. **Chemical-Resistant Sheets.** There are many applications in the packaging field where the barrier must be resistant to specific materials such as foods, chemicals, drugs, and industrial products. The requirements vary so much, however, depending upon the specific material involved, that no attempt will be made here to make any analysis of individual applications. The coating must be tested in contact with the material that is to be packaged and under conditions as close as possible to those met in actual use. There are some general conditions however, as follows:

a. *High alkalinity or high pH.* In packaging salts, some drugs, soaps, and other alkaline materials, that portion of the barrier which comes into contact with the contents must be resistant to alkali and not be affected by it or change its properties because of any reaction with it.

b. *Acidity or low pH.* When packaging certain salts, drugs, or foods which are acidic in nature, the barrier contacting the material must be resistant to weak and preferably also to strong acids and not be affected by the specific compound being packaged.

c. *Solvents.* The packaging of any compound containing solvents such as nail polish, drug tinctures, liquors, cleaners, etc., invariably presents a problem since most plastic films and synthetic resin coatings and laminates are softened, if not completely dissolved by many solvents. Foil, of course, does not present this problem. Any compound containing solvents must be evaluated against the coating to be used since traces of a solvent other than that tested will often affect the coating.

It is possible to set up some general requirements for sheets to be used with reactive compounds:

a. The sheet should not react chemically with the packaged product.

b. It should not contain any mobile component which could migrate into the packaged product. It should also be formulated so that it cannot absorb any component of the packaged product.

c. It should not impart any odor, particularly objectionable ones, to the product.

d. If the product is used for food, drugs, or any compounds which are taken internally, the barrier must be absolutely free from toxic components which could contaminate the product.

e. If the packaged product is of the type which contains a critical amount of moisture, the coating must be sufficiently water-vapor resistant to maintain it in the proper condition. An example of this would be citric acid which in the dry crystalline form would be easy to package. If the content were in a concentrated solution of citric acid, it might attack and destroy the barrier.

5. **Heat Sealing Papers.** These papers have the property of being self-sealing under the combined action of heat and pressure.[2] The purpose of such a seal is to make a fused closure in a package which will be as resistant to grease, water, water vapor, etc., as is the surface area of the sheet itself. A heat-sealing coating is necessarily thermoplastic, but it must also be sufficiently nontacky and nonblocking so that the face will not block to the back in the roll or in skids. Another problem with this type of sheet is the tendency for the two coated faces, at spots other than at the heat seal, to block since the sheet made into an envelope or sleeve container must be capable of being packed flat for shipment and if the envelopes cannot be opened to insert the product to be packaged, they will have no value.

The mechanism of heat sealability depends upon at least five factors:

a. The temperature of the sealing platen
b. The pressure applied per unit area of the seal
c. The time of contact at the above temperature and pressure
d. The heat transfer characteristics of the barrier, and
e. The softening characteristics of the heat sealing film

When the coated sides of the two sheets, or one sheet and an uncoated surface, as in a lap seal, are pressed together and a heated surface applied to one or both surfaces, heat transfer to the coating takes place. The coating film either melts or becomes viscous and tacky, depending upon the type of coating. A paraffin-wax coating, for example, will melt at 125° to 145°F., depending upon the grade of wax and the composition of the coating, while a coating formulated from a cellulose derivative or a vinyl resin will become viscous and tacky at 185°

to 275°F. A coating that has a sharp melting point and which melts to a low viscosity solution is usually not sticky while in this condition, with the result that it is not able to bond the two sheets together until it is chilled and becomes solid once again. It is apparent, therefore, that when this type of heat-seal coating is used, the two sheets must be held together after contact with the heated platen and preferably in contact with a cooling mechanism until the temperature of the seal drops below the solidification temperature so that a bond can be set up. With a resinous coating, on the other hand, where the coating becomes viscous and tacky when heated, the two layers will fuse and the cohesion between the layers is usually sufficiently strong to bond them and hold them together even at the temperature at which the sealing takes place.

The temperature to which the two layers of coating must be raised in order to bring about activation of the heat seal and a resulting flow and tackiness so that fusion can occur depends upon the formulation of the coating. For different coating compositions the temperatures may range from 150° to 350°F. For any particular coating, there may be a range of 25° to 50°F. over which satisfactory seals can be made. It must be kept in mind that the lower the minimum temperature of fusion, the more subject the coating will be to blocking, unless a compound is found with a sharp melting point which changes the film from a solid to a viscous and tacky melt. Needless to say that this problem is being actively studied and the solution on a commercial scale may come sometime in the future. The higher the minimum temperature of fusion, the higher must be the heating surface temperature and this would probably lead to a reduction in the speed of heat sealing.

The temperature of the heated surface of the platen must, of course, be higher than the fusion temperature of the coating so that a temperature gradient may exist for heat flow to the coating through the sheet. The capacity of the heating unit should be sufficiently high, particularly on a continuous heat-sealing machine, so that this temperature can be maintained at the sealing speeds at which the machine is operated. There are a number of different machines available, some which heat the sheet while the platens are held under sealing pressure, and others which supply the sheet with increasing increments of heat as the package moves through the unit until the pressure area is reached and the seal is made. Where fluid melt type coatings are used, heat and pressure are applied to produce the seal. The heat is then removed and the seal held until its temperature has been lowered to below the solidification point.

Just as there is a lower temperature limit below which fusion will not take place, there is also an upper limit above which either of two undesirable conditions may occur. First, if the temperature is above a certain critical limit it may be high enough to scorch the paper. This affects its strength and may also discolor the sheet. Second, there is a limit, above which the coating will become so fluid that it will squeeze out and not possess sufficient tack to hold the two surfaces together unless they are rapidly chilled. When the coating becomes too fluid, it may strike through the paper causing a discoloration on the outside of the sheet and it may also foul the sealing platens. Where impermeable sheets such as film and foil are being sealed this strike through will not occur, since such barriers will not pass the melt, even at its lowest viscosity.

The pressure applied is very important. The higher the pressure the more intimate contact there is between the heating surface and the paper, and this provides for more rapid and uniform heat transfer. Increased pressure also helps the two layers of coating to flow into each other and form a fusion weld. Where non-continuous sealers are used, a crimp sealing or corrugated platen is often used to produce the maximum of contact and pressure.

The required time of contact is a function of the applied temperature and pressure and decreases as the temperature and/or pressure are increased.

The temperature, pressure, and time relationship for any specific formulation must be determined by experiment, aided by the knowledge of the type of heat-sealing equipment available for the specific application.

Assuming that a satisfactory weld or fusion of the two layers of coating has been effected, the strength of the seal will depend upon two conditions:

    a. The cohesion of the two layers of coating to themselves, and

    b. The adhesion of the coating to the paper, film, or foil base.

If the cohesion of the coating to itself is good and the bond to the sheet is poor, the seal may separate from one or both of the plies. If, on the other hand, the bond to the sheet is good, and the cohesion of the coating is poor, the seal may fail in the coating itself. Obviously both must be satisfactory to obtain a good seal, and the entire seal will only be as good as its weakest component.

Specific Packaging Applications

The previous general description of the properties necessary in packaging papers outlined what they are and how they function, but any specific application must take into account a great deal more than just the basic property. The two general applications in which the major part of these papers is used are food packaging and metal parts packaging. A detailed description of the types of barriers utilized by these two industries and the reasons for their use are given in the following sections.

FOOD PACKAGING*

by J. J. Austin

Packaging is a vital activity in all industries. The art of properly packaging food to give ultimate protection, to retain the highest nutritional value and the maximum in eye appeal started in earnest at the turn of the century.

Practically every known kind of paper is used in some phase or other of the food industry. The basic types in most common use are the various krafts, glassine, vegetable parchment, and parchmentized and waxed papers. To these should be added two widely used films which may be considered, for packaging purposes, first cousins to paper, namely, Cellophane and metal foil. Foil has been included because in most packaging applications its functional properties are used in conjunction with paper, which performs the job of conveying the delicate, unmanageable film. There are many other films which might be included when one discusses food packaging, such as Pliofilm, Saran, Polyethylene, Cry-o-vac, Hycar, and the vinyls.

The major types of packaged foods are: fresh, canned or heat-processed in either glass or metal, smoked, pickled, frozen, and dehydrated. It is estimated that the annual pack in tin and glass, according to U. S. Government statistics, is approximately 640,000,000 cases as follows:

Vegetable Pack	190,000,000
Fruit Pack	80,000,000
Fruit and Vegetable Juices	120,000,000

---

* A series of three articles in the *Food Industries* magazine by John V. Ziemba, Assistant Editor, gives detailed information concerning the setting up of a packaging laboratory. It would be well worth the while of many firms at the present time making food packaging materials and of those contemplating entering into this field to review these articles which were entitled as follows:

"Why a Packaging Laboratory?"—July 1947.
"How to Equip and Organize a Packaging Laboratory"—August 1947.
"How a Food Packaging Laboratory Functions"—September 1947.

Condensed and Evaporated Milk   75,000,000
Miscellaneous Meat, Fish, Pickles, Baby Foods,
    Etc.   175,000,000

This important portion of the food industry, although it uses some paper in certain of its processes and in the form of labels and cases, is one which will not be discussed in detail as the intent of this chapter is to lay out general specifications for that portion of the food industry in which flexible films and papers are commonly used as the packaging materials. In most cases, the consumer-size package will be the unit under consideration.

Ninety per cent of the men engaged in the food industry are so occupied with their own production problems that they rarely have an opportunity to understand or visualize the whole food packaging picture, or borrow ideas from related industries. This presents an opportunity for the men in colleges and research organizations, in cooperative groups, such as the Institute of Food Technologists, the Technical Association of the Pulp and Paper Industry, the Packaging Institute, the American Management Association, and scores of others, to do a real missionary work.

The paper manufacturing and converting industry must cooperate wholeheartedly with the machinery manufacturers servicing the food industry to develop nearly foolproof packages. It should be pointed out that because a film, as manufactured, apparently has all the proper characteristics for the protection of a certain food product, it does not necessarily follow that this film formed into a finished package will actually do the job expected of it. It must be proved that it will stand the creasing, scoring, and glueing operations without breakdown as it should, with a maximum of 0.2 per cent failures in actual production runs.

The majority of food products retain their best flavor and appearance when packaged in tight containers which prevent the transfer of light, air, moisture, grease, and gas. Some products, however, must breathe. To quote Ernest C. Crocker of the Arthur D. Little Company, Inc., Cambridge, Massachusetts:

Instances abound in which some particular type of permeability is more conducive to retention of good flavor, than is complete and general tightness.

An important portion of the flavor of foods resides in the 'aroma' or volatile part, which is not only subject to loss by evaporation, but is sensitive as well to many kinds of chemical reactions, through which it may change its character, or be completely lost. Although loss by volatility is sometimes of outstanding importance and must be prevented, loss by hydrolysis or oxidation is far more important and more serious. Therefore, the membrane of the container must be chosen chiefly for its ability to suppress unfavorable chemical reactions, even if there is not complete tightness against the passage of aroma.

Much work is being done along the lines of incorporating antioxidants in the packaging materials, gas packaging, and electronic sterilizing. A patent was issued to Sidney Musher of New York City in which it was claimed that the oxidative deterioration of cardboard, which leads to off-odors and absorption of those odors into packaged foods, can be prevented by the incorporation of lecithin into the board. The board is treated so as to incorporate 0.01 to 2.0% of lecithin. The sheet is then calendered at a temperature above 180° F. He also suggests the incorporation of sugars or other water-soluble carbohydrates with various phospholipids, phosphates, polycarboxy and hydroxy aliphatic acids, proteins and amino acids, substituted aromatic compounds, and even blackstrap molasses.

Godfrey L. Cabot, Inc., has done work along the lines of incorporating carbon black in boardstock or in the inclusion of small envelopes inserted into the packages to absorb odors which may accompany tight packaging.

It is claimed by others that fresh meats, oysters, and vegetables have been "electronized" and held in airtight containers at room temperature for months with satisfactory results.

The Raytheon Manufacturing Company of Waltham, Massachusetts, has made great progress in another development concerning unique blanching, cooking, and defrosting methods. The "Radarange," a curiosity in 1946, is today an accepted cooking unit in many hotels and restaurants.

Gas packaging for the retardation or prevention of mold growth has been worked on and proved to have very definite possibilities. The best flavored and most easily reconstituted dried fruits are now blanched and dehydrated mechanically, rather than by dependence on the whims of nature. These can now be packaged with a much higher moisture content in thermoplastic dipped cartons or other types of airtight containers which will hold the moisture at a constant high level. Mold growth due either to spores on the food or to contact of the product with the paper or board liner in the presence of air is controlled for a fairly long period of time by an application of germicidal gas to the package just before sealing.

The Product

Basic facts to be considered about the product before decisions can be made concerning the proper packaging material and method are as follows:

1. What state is it in?
   a. Liquid—syrups, oils, vinegars, milk, fruit juices, carbonated beverages, ketchup, liquid eggs.
      How free flowing will it be?
   b. Jellies and semisolids—mayonnaise, jams, fruit jellies, butter, shortening, sauces, luncheon spreads, shucked oysters, precooked items for canning or freezing, such as squash, pumpkin, stews, hash, spaghetti and meat balls.
   c. Powders or free-flowing solids—coffee, flour, bread, doughnut mixes, dried beans, peas, or lentils, cereals, bulk candies, sugar, tea, spices, nuts, potato and corn chips, dessert powders, cocoa. Mixed fruits in juice, blueberries, whole cut corn, peas for canning or freezing, possibly loose, frozen on a belt-type freezer.

 d. Solids in small or measured units—crackers, soup cubes, chocolates and candy bars, gum, cigarettes, doughnuts, olives, prunes, frankfurts, bacon, sausage; fresh vegetables for prepackaging, such as asparagus, beans, corn on the cob, potatoes, onions, tomatoes.

 e. Large solids—molded items such as dried fruits in the form of bricks, spiced meats, that is, luncheon meats, preshaped boiled hams, bread, cakes, cheese, frozen eviscerated turkeys, ducks, chickens.

 f. Irregular or soft solids—fish fillets, whole fish, cut meats for freezing or self-service sales, such as steaks, chops, hamburg, stew beef, liver, beef roasts, lamb legs, hams; bunch vegetables, such as carrots, beets, celery, rhubarb, spinach for self-service retail stores.

2. Must the product be packaged and sealed, or may it be molded and overwrapped? Example: flour vs. butter.

3. Will it require complete impermeability of the film to light, gas, odor, water, water vapor, grease, and oil?

4. What are the volatiles which will affect its quality?

5. What pickup or loss of moisture is permissible and over what period of time?

6. What are the limitations from the point of view of automatic packaging machinery?

7. What are the holding temperatures? Will extremely low or high temperature affect the quality? Must fluctuating conditions be eliminated or avoided?

8. Will acidity or alkalinity of the product enter into the picture? Will this eliminate certain types of wrapping materials because of possible chemical reaction?

9. Does the product require physical-damage protection? Example: fresh eggs.

The Package

The fabricated package must protect the contents with an absolute minimum of breakage from the factory to the consumer.

One extremely important feature of the package that is often forgotten or left to a last-minute rush decision is the problem of getting a proper seal. The adhesive used is a definite and important factor in determining the actual shelf life of the package. It should be, in many cases, completely odor-free and resistant to any migratory portion of the product packaged.

The package must, in most cases, meet many of the following specifications:

1. Moisture resistance (that is, wet strength) or complete water-vapor impermeability.
2. Grease and oil resistance.
3. Gas resistance.
4. Tensile, bursting, tearing, and folding strength.
5. Elongation or shrinkage requirements.
6. It must be the correct handling size and shape to be put on automatic filling and packaging equipment to achieve low packaging labor costs.
7. It must be handled and stored easily by the consumer. It should stand extremes of temperature and sunlight under all possible climatic conditions to which it will be subjected.
8. It must be attractive from a merchandising and printing standpoint for maximum sales appeal. In this connection, will transparency of the film, or an over-all printing job give the best results?
9. It should display easily, and the colors must attract.

Other Important Packaging Factors

1. The feel of the package to the consumer is often a very important sales point.

2. Should the package have a reuse value, a reseal feature, pouring spouts, or other practical advantages? An example of this is the individual cereal package now coming into very prominent use. Many dry cereals packed in large containers, once opened, soon lose crispness and snap.

3. What is the maximum allowable cost of the packaging material? Is it limited by the size of the unit, or by the competition in the same field?

4. Is this size actually the most acceptable to the consumer from a price and use standpoint; that is, is it the correct number of servings, or should there be more than one size of package?

5. Will this unit tie in nicely from a companion display point of view? Examples of excellent work along these lines are packages by Montgomery Ward, Armour, Del Monte, and Kroger.

6. Also make a complete study of the reaction of the consumer, who will be the final judge in the buying of the item. Give him all of the features that he wants in a package.

7. Much of the board stock being produced today contains reclaim. Some of this stock has been previously treated with fungicides, which, if they have not been properly used, are prone to produce off-odors. Improper use of these fungicides, that is, not keeping the stock slightly alkaline, has recently been the cause of serious complaints in certain food industries.

Packaging Fresh Vegetables

The prepackaging of fresh vegetables and salad mixtures started about 1935. Since then, a great deal of work has been done to find improved packaging materials and packaging methods to increase the storage life and salability of the product. This method of merchandising results in somewhat higher costs to the consumer, who benefits in the handling of cleaner merchandise, less waste and bulk. Eventually, it is expected that, with increased volume and new packaging methods, the price differential can be greatly reduced.

During the past few years many West Coast packers have studied the possibilities of prepackaging and shipping via special fast freight or air to the East. This method is still experimental because of the short life of the product after it is removed from the almost perfect storage conditions used during shipping. Ruptured cellular fiber breakdown, due to the mechanical abuse of trimming, washing, and packaging, is slight in the well refrigerated intransit shipping cars, but once a temperature change occurs, as when the package is transferred to the retail store, the broken-surface cell structure quickly deteriorates. Prepackaging in this industry will probably, for some time to come, remain as a limited distribution proposition, with the bulk merchandise being shipped as usual via rail freight to increasing numbers of prepackaging setups throughout the nation, principally in the metropolitan areas. Refrigerated, self-service retail cases are coming into more common use for this class of merchandise because of the increased shelf life obtained and the especial need of refrigeration when plant materials are closely wrapped.[3]

Fresh Fruit Packaging

Under this heading we include the packaging of such items as fresh dates and figs, which, although they cannot be considered fresh in the same sense as a tomato or a pear which must be turned over rapidly once it is placed in a consumer type package, do require the same type of packaging techniques and, in fact, are perhaps the foster parents of the general trend.

The most common method of handling prepackaged apples, pears, tomatoes, etc., is to use a snap-up, glued-end, or automatic lock-end type of carton, or boat, which can be easily handled on automatic equipment, or by hand. The art of making a container of this general type is not new. It has been used in the packaging of crackers and in the bakery industry for many years. Following the setting up of the boat, the merchandise is usually placed in the container by an operator, who also acts as an inspector and a grader. Today, the most commonly used overwraps are Cellophane and acetate film; however, there is a definite possibility in this field for a revolutionary packaging idea, which may mean the use of entirely new materials. Fully transparent rigid containers at three to four times the cost of window cartons, with resultant higher unit cost to the purchaser, have outsold the latter in test runs because the customer buys with the full assurance that imperfections are not hidden.

Such an idea would be to have some type of preservative, either in the form of a gas injected into the package, or a gas emanating from the packaging material itself, which would keep the product in top condition for a long period of time. Dip coatings of the wax emulsion types for citrus fruits are an old story. They have done a partially satisfactory job at a very low cost. One of the latest ideas in that field is the possible use of a vinyl emulsion, having low viscosity and quick-set characteristics at room temperature. Water is the carrying vehicle for the solids; therefore, control over the thickness of the film should be an easy matter. Pliofilm is being handled on automatic equipment in the packaging of five hundred oranges per minute.

Packaging Fresh Meats

Prepackaging of fresh meat cuts is receiving widespread interest due to the possible savings in labor and the greater return on bone and trimmings. It enables the super market operator to give self-service on all counters on all merchandise, and in addition allows a greater amount of the same floor space to be put to work for actual display purposes. There are many problems to overcome as yet in this field. One of the toughest, apparently, is color retention. This may be partially controlled by the use of suitable reducing agents, sodium bisulfite being the most common, but prohibited in some states. It has been shown that beef products require a high rate of oxygen transmission in order to obtain the acceptable and most attractive red color. However, maximum air passage is usually accompanied by porosity of the film with consequent weight loss due to drip of the natural juices. The new transparent films are showing some promise of overcoming these difficulties. Authorities in the Cellophane field say that the discoloration of meat in contact with cellophane can be retarded and shelf life lengthened if the advice of the manufacturer is properly followed. The du Pont Company is recommending the use of MSAT-80 Cellophane for fresh meats. This film has two different surfaces, one being wettable. The wettable side should be placed in contact with the meat. They also suggest chilling the meat at least 24 hours at 32° to 35° F. In other words, the product should be kept at all times at a point where it can be handled efficiently by the cutter, but also where it has the least possible drip tendency. With proper handling, it is claimed that fresh meats will retain good color for as long as 72 hours after packaging. Other Cellophanes having special coatings are also under field test.

Dipping techniques using certain chemicals, such as ascorbic acid, tend to prolong the life of cut-up poultry. A new laminated package, using the combined properties of two transparent films, Cellophane and Pliofilm, is now greatly increasing the life of sliced bacon.

The prepackaging of practically all fresh meats for counter display is definitely, as of today, limited to individual stores. The meat packers, such as Swift, Armour, and Wilson, and the large chain store organizations are quite interested in the possibility of being able to finish the job of prepackaging at the wholesale warehouse, or better yet, at the packing house. This may never happen with prepackaged fresh meat, but a real volume possibility is the packaging and freezing of family size cuts, and it should result in lower cost to the consumer.

Parchment or parchmentized papers have long been used in the packaging of fresh pork products because of their superior water and grease resistance. However, the meat packer is looking for a better film. Consider a box of pork loins which, when wrapped and packaged at the slaughter house, weighs approximately 65 pounds. This might be placed in storage for a few days, then put on freight cars headed for a distant city. Here it is transferred again, either into storage where it is possibly frozen and held for 1 to 4 months due to market conditions, or into distribution warehouses. In the fresh state it may be as much as 14 to 20 days before the product finally reaches the retailer. During this handling, temperature fluctuations have many times entered into the picture, and the product has been constantly losing moisture. When received by the retailer, this package may weigh only 62 or 63 pounds. The fatty portion around the tips of the cut rib bones may have darkened considerably, requiring more trim. The net result is that what left the packer's plant at 65 pounds ends up in the retailer's hands at perhaps 60 pounds, a loss of some 8%. A definite contribution to this field would be a film or sheet to keep the moisture loss and oxidative changes at a minimum. The same film that would do this would also be of interest for the packaging of fresh hams, fresh butts, veal, and possibly for small wholesale cuts of beef, such as loins, hips, or rounds.

Smoked meats, because of the light smoke desired by the trade today, require better protection. Packers place three and four wraps on their top-quality items. One package examined was wrapped as follows:

1. An inner liner of laminated glassine for combined grease resistance and moisture proofness
2. An intermediate cushion wrap of about 0.010 chip stock
3. Heavy-weight printed parchment outer wrap for resistance to scuffing, grease, and water staining, as well as over-all printing attractiveness

A tremendous saving in labor and materials is possible if all the desired characteristics can be incorporated in one sheet.

Packaging Fresh Fish

The field of fresh fish packaging is now receiving some attention in both commercial and college laboratories in an attempt to package prepared fresh fish items properly, so that they can be delivered in the best condition and in a closest to natural state. Again, this trend stems from the idea of a completely self-service store. According to some recent tests, many types of fish can now be fully prepared and prepackaged with satisfactory results. Proper packaging and mechanical refrigeration will apparently eliminate the labor and mess connected with fresh ice packaging for shipping and ice handling in the retail unit. The secret is good quality food, properly packaged, properly handled, and displayed under proper control at the correct temperatures.

Good quality in the raw product is the hardest thing to control in this industry. The fish are caught, gutted on the vessel deck, and then iced in the hold. If the catch is poor, the boat remains out for a long period of time in the hope of a bigger catch and greater financial return. The result is that the earliest-caught fish is subject to a great deal of pressure, contamination from overhead drip, off-odors, and even bilge water. The history of the industry is such that the consumer has been educated to accept an old product. The commonly accepted odor of salt water fish is not the odor of fresh fish at all, but one of decomposition (trimethyl amine). Fresh fish has practically no odor. Lake fish will putrify, but do not give off trimethyl amine.

At the present time, the quality control methods employed by the Eastern Canadian packers are in general superior to those used in the United States. The Canadian boats are usually out one day and back the next, the proximity of the Grand Banks fishing grounds to their ports being a great natural asset.

Some claim the "fresh fish business" is a misnomer and that the only right way to handle most fish products is in the frozen state. It is true that strictly fresh frozen fish, such as that received from Iceland (frozen the day it is caught) is an excellent product. The so-called "fish odor" is not noticeable.

Parchmentized papers, wet-strength krafts, and waxed papers are most commonly used in this field because of their wet-strength characteristics. With reference to Cellophane, only the anchor-coated types should be used. Plain Cellophane will practically dissolve, and non-anchor-coated lacquers will peel off. Some work has been done along the lines of incorporating such items as sodium benzoate as a coating on paper stock for destroying surface bacteria. Ascorbic acid dipping of the fish before freezing has also shown some promise. Some large carton or container manufacturers have experimented with insulated containers for the shipment of fresh cleaned and gutted fish without the necessity of ice packing. The Hinde and Dauch Paper Company has worked with a number of fish packers and research organizations in the development of the Insulpak container. This consists of a corrugated box lined with a Plypak insulation and an inner corrugated box lined with Pliofilm, manufactured by the Goodyear Tire and Rubber Company. Their claim is that the Pliofilm liner, heat-sealed, prevents leakage and odors, permitting shipment in passenger planes, and also that it is inexpensive, light in weight, and a single-use package, easily handled by one man. The most common size tested was of 40 to 60 pound capacity. Test shipments indicated that the fish, if placed in the container at a precooled temperature of 34° F., would arrive at the destination 22 hours later at a temperature of only 44° F.

Other firms have tried a somewhat similar procedure, using dry ice as a temperature-control medium. A third idea is packing fresh ice in a waterproof (rubber or plastic) container inside the carton with or on top of the fish. While this method has never been given extensive commercial trials, it has been noted that the ice will last two to three times as long when held in its own drip. Of course, breakage of the container is always an ever-present possibility and hazard.

Frozen Food Packaging

Of approximately thirty-five billion dollars spent in 1947 for food, less than 1½ per cent went to the frozen food industry. Ice cream as a finished product is not included in this figure. . The average sales throughout the country amounted to only six or seven dollars per family per year. The possibility for growth in this industry has been glamorized and promoted time after time in practically every publication in the country. There are a few who claim that it will eventually entirely replace canning. While the writer is a firm believer in the potential of frozen foods, he also sees it as only one part of the whole food processing and handling picture. Canning is a very economical way to process, and storage difficulties are minimized. Frozen foods can be processed at a somewhat cheaper cost per pound; however, the packaging and packaging techniques must be developed to a much greater degree of perfection. Packaging costs and storage costs of frozen food today are much higher than those required for canning, and in addition the storage life of the food product itself must be improved to reach a minimum of at least 12 months on 90% of the items. The minimum storage life today of any processed food product packed in a metal container is 12 months, and many of them will last 6 to 7 years in edible condition.

To date, very little has been done by the paper, film, and packaging industry with regard to setting up test standards for frozen-food packaging materials. Such research organizations as the Frozen Food Foundation, Inc., Syracuse, New York, are leading the way, but the packaging-materials industry has the fundamental job of proving its own products. During the years 1943 through 1946, the tendency was to provide ever poorer protection of frozen products because of the quick turnover. Great quantities of either poor quality or improper strains were processed on makeshift equipment by men with little or no knowledge of the problems involved. Early in 1947 they found considerable customer resistance to low quality. Millions of pounds of substandard frozen foods were eventually sacrificed at half the original cost to the packer. Many well-equipped, high-quality firms were forced to quit or reorganize in the general break. As a result, the 1947 frozen-food pack was far below the average of the previous 4 years in tonnage, but much more high-grade, top-quality food was packed. Frozen foods have not so far been considered as involving health hazards, such as being carriers of infectious diseases, nor have they been considered as possible sources of food poisoning. Poor handling, however, such as the delay of 1 to 3 hours between the blanching and freezing operations, will often result in a high bacteria count with resultant poor keeping quality and faster breakdown of the product on thawing at the time of use. A properly fast-frozen product, after thawing, will often stand the abuse of an extra 24-hour holding period in edible condition over that which was mishandled.

In ordinary processing methods, the volume food packer must also take into consideration the fact that his product must leave his plant for a storage warehouse via ice-packed cars or trucks and then be transported again from the warehouse to various other localities, perhaps four or five times. Due to temperature fluctuations, each successive handling allows for a change in the size and shape of the crystal formation in the product with consequent further rupture of the cell structure.

In the general nervousness following the slump in the industry, some few packers went even farther than just improving the quality of the food packed. They switched to impermeable all-metal containers. The Dainty-Pak brand was the first to put out a full line of frozen fruits and vegetables in vacuum-packed rectangular tin cans. Drawn aluminum and paper-mounted foil overwraps came into prominence. New plastic films were given much more serious consideration.

At first glance one would say that the impermeability of the film to the passage of water vapor, gas, and odor is the only requirement. If this were true, the metal container would be the best answer. One other big factor, however, is that the

FIGURE 12. *Typical frozen sea food package* (Courtesy of Sylvania
Div. of The American Viscose Co.)

packaging material must adhere closely to the product in order
to reduce to a minimum the moisture loss from the surface of
the product and the free oxygen present. This is a possibility
in metal with practically all fruits and vegetables packaged.
The writer has personally packaged and held irregularly shaped
objects, such as meat cuts, and poultry, in hermetically sealed
tin cans at 0° F. for periods of 3 months to 1 year. At the end
of 3 months definite freezer burn was apparent, and at the
end of 12 months the surface of some products was completely
dehydrated. However, no loss of weight was possible so far
as the completely sealed package was concerned. The moisture
was simply transferred from the product to the inner surface
of the container.

In determining the type of a package to be used for a frozen
food product, the method of freezing must also be taken into
consideration. Some of the more common are as follows:

1. *Still air.* Generally used for storage purposes after quick
   freezing although still a big factor in commercial freezing.
   Convection air currents remove heat from the product to

the air and finally to the expansion coils or plates located on the ceiling or walls of the room. A similar but better arrangement, because of more intimate contact with the product, is the piping of the expansion coils throughout the room for use as storage shelving. The possibility of internal heat generating in the center of a stack is automatically eliminated.

2. *Moving air*. A modification of still air, usually achieved by the installation of fans at various points throughout the room.

3. *Air blast*. A method of controlling the air flow so as to get the greatest possible sweep of air across the surface of the product or the package. Many manufacturers, including Carrier, Frick, and York, manufacture a closet or chamber into which a buggy load of prepackaged goods is placed in front of a high-velocity, high-volume fan, forcing air at temperatures as low as $-65°$ F. across the surface. The Finnegan tunnel has successive stages, each lower in temperature. Many, if not all, of this type also have a precooling chamber, the load usually being carried on a buggy by a continuous conveyor chain set in the floor.

4. *Immersion*. This may be either in a salt brine or a sugar-syrup dip. The sodium chloride brine method is employed to the greatest extent in the fish industry, but it is being replaced rapidly by plate and air-blast methods. The Tennessee Valley Authority developed the sugar-syrup dip for various fruits. Whole strawberries, culled and washed, are carried into the syrup on an endless wire belt for the necessary period of time, then the excess syrup is vibrated, blown, or centrifuged off.

5. *Brine spray*. The method employed here is placing the product into a cabinet and spraying a fine mist of brine over it. Products so frozen must be thoroughly protected. A residual amount of the brine left on the surface of the product may cause rapid deterioration.

6. *Plate froster*. There are many variations of this. How-

ever, the most commonly used is the Birdseye method, which consists of bringing the Freon or "flooded ammonia" cooled plates into intimate contact under pressure with the finished and filled package. This is a fast, clean method of handling.

7. *Belt freezers.* There are two principal types. One called the "double belt" was developed by Clarence Birdseye in the early days of his experimentation, which consisted of two endless metal belts passing through an insulated tunnel between which was carried a packaged or unpackaged product. Cold air or brine acted as the refrigerant. The second belt method, usually employing a belt of the woven stainless-steel wire type, is employed for individual or loose freezing of many items, such as whole strawberries, peas, and lima beans, for either bulk or consumer packaging, as they come off the freezer belt. Air blasts are ordinarily used on the vegetable lines.

8. *Shaker freezer.* This was developed by the Baker Ice Machine Company. The product is fed to the top plate or screen, then passes downward over a series of perforated shaker platforms while cold air is passed through and over the product at high velocity. The York Company also makes a variation of this.

9. *Polyphase freezer.* This was developed at the University of Texas. It might be called a modification of the brine or syrup dip in that either salt or sugar may be employed while the product is carried by a worm drive through the cooling medium. As it comes out at the far end, it is drained, then packaged.

10. A new development which may become a major factor in certain phases of the frozen-food industry is "dehydro" freezing. In this method, the product is slightly dehydrated under vacuum at low temperatures, thus reducing the product weight, but retaining most of the nutritional properties, many of which are destroyed by the common dehydrating processes. It is claimed that berries, when

dehydro frozen, will thaw out much more solidly, than when frozen under the more common methods. This method of freezing may demand vacuum packaging in order to control further physical or chemical change in the product.

Frozen Food Packaging Specifications

The general specifications, therefore, for frozen food packaging materials must include the following considerations, plus other specific recommendations built around the plant or methods of handling.

1. The objective should be a practically perfect water-vapor barrier at 0° F.; that is, it should not pass more than 0.01 gram/100 square inches/24 hours at 0° F. The Frozen Food Foundation, while they would like better protection and constantly strive for it, have set the following standard as being acceptable for the present:

> The package must limit the moisture loss from one pound (1 lb.) of ground round steak to less than 1% during six months (6 mos.) storage at −5° F. to 0° F.

This is approximately 0.035 grams/100 square inches/24 hours.

2. It should be nontoxic and odor free.
3. It must be flexible or able to withstand handling abuse at temperatures as low as −30° F.
4. It must handle easily on fully automatic equipment.
5. Greaseproofness is an added contribution, but it is not of prime importance in the frozen food industry because practically all the fats and oils are solidified until the time of use. Grease resistance at the time of packaging might be sufficient.
6. It should preferably be heat sealing, or some method of closing should be employed which will give completely impermeable and foolproof seams. The package is no better than its weakest point.

7. It should be waterproof and stainproof, so as to work well on wet-food packing lines, that is, fish fillets, broccoli, asparagus.

8. The film should strip easily from the frozen product.

9. It must have good salability and must be able to take and hold a good printing job.

10. The shape and size of the package must give the most efficient use of holding space for storage facilities.

11. Label data must conform to the requirements of the Federal Food, Drug, and Cosmetic Act.

12. In all testing, remember it is the finished package data that really count, not what is obtained in cup tests on flat or creased films.

The industry is interested in a single-unit container which will handle both solid and loose frozen products. It should be possible to manufacture or set it up, fill it, and seal it in the processor's plant. Transparency might be a factor, but frozen foods are an accepted item; therefore, this feature is now not quite so important. Another factor is that a good printing job is better looking than the frozen food itself. The cost of the finished package should be in the vicinity of one cent per pound of packaged product.

The most common package to date is a cold-water-waxed carton using a fairly high grade of board stock and having a regenerated cellulose-film inner liner, along with a printed cold-water-waxed overwrap. In the early days of the industry this was the only proven combination which gave nearly adequate protection. With greater production requirements many faults are now becoming apparent; however, it is still in number one position from a volume-use standpoint.

A composite container consisting of a paper-board body and metal ends is now receiving good acceptance. The paper board is high-grade stock, impregnated and surface-coated with wax, and the metal ends are properly coated to resist rusting. This unit is adapted to be handled in automatic filling and sealing equipment and, because of the metal ends and single-walled structure, it is claimed that 30% faster freezing is achieved over the previously mentioned package. The drawback is that it must be shipped set-up, with the bottom seamed on; therefore, it requires quite considerable storage space.

Light metals, more particularly aluminum, are used in the field. A rectangular container formed from a sheet of preprinted, light-gage aluminum may be shipped in roll form to the packer. Here it will be formed, filled, and sealed on automatic equipment.

Another development in aluminum, still in the experimental stage, is the Tray-Pak. Separate trays and lids are shipped in nested form. Trays may be filled automatically, or by hand, and the top crimped on. Automatic equipment, however, is only in the development stage.

The Dewey and Almy Chemical Company has developed and received wide acceptance of the Cry-o-vac bag, made of a transparent film, in the frozen food industry for the packaging of irregularly shaped objects, such as poultry, meat cuts, and fish. This unit may be pulled over an alligator-type jaw funnel, the product pushed in, then a vacuum drawn, followed immediately by heat sealing of the mouth of the container. Dipping in warm water (185° F.) will shrink the film so as to remove practically all wrinkles and folds. Because of the close adherence of this film to the irregular shape of the product, oxidation, with resultant rancidity, is kept at a minimum.

Pliofilm manufactured by the Goodyear Tire and Rubber Company has been used as an inner liner of a paper container in frozen-food packaging. The film has good water-vapor proofness and in this combination could be heat sealed on all types of bag-sealing machines. The film, in bag form, has also been used in the packaging of irregularly shaped products (poultry, meat, and fish). The package may be vacuumized and heat sealed. Using certain techniques, it can be expanded and later shrunk to conform more closely to the shape of the product.

Polyethylene (Bakelite and du Pont) is an extremely interesting film because of its toughness and flexibility over a very wide temperature range. It is odorless, tasteless, and nontoxic. An excellent weld-type heat seal is possible. This film is now used extensively on poultry, etc.

Vinyl-base synthetic latices, having perhaps a small percentage of other latices, such as Hycar latex, are being utilized in the patented anode dip process. The process is of definite interest in the food packaging field because of the grease resistance, moisture-vapor proofness, transparency, and the fact that the films can apparently be produced without the use of plasticizers in the formulation. With particular reference to frozen foods, they are still in the development stage.

While on the subject of frozen foods, locker plants, that now number approximately ten thousand throughout the United States, should be discussed. Their packaging problems cover the whole range of frozen processed foods. Packaging methods commonly used in this field would not be at all acceptable to the volume food processor; however, these plants are limited to practically no mechanical packaging equipment and a high rate of turnover of labor. With proper control of the flow of merchandise through the locker, the locker operator might do a good job of protecting the consumer's product with only mediocre wrapping materials, but such control is seldom maintained. He naturally must limit himself to a very few types of wrapping materials because of inventory and storage difficulties; therefore, in most locker plants we find heavily waxed paper, laminated or thermoplastic coated stock, Cellophanes, round or nested waxed containers with slipcover tops, bag and box combinations, and small multiwall bags. Tight filling of these containers will often get by, but the more recently marketed films are better because of closer contact of the film with the product and greater water-vapor proofness. All of these must have a surface on which the operator can properly hand-mark or stamp the necessary data. If he runs a good plant, he will have quick-freezing facilities at $-15°$ F., or lower, and his storage equipment will be held at $0°$ F., with a tolerance of $\pm 1°$ in the product temperature, perhaps $3°$ in the air temperature fluctuation. These low temperatures and close tolerances will result in fairly good shelf life of the product. One big item in his favor is that the product, once frozen, will never again be subjected to varying temperature conditions until it is taken home by the consumer.

Dried Food Packaging

Many of the products which might rightfully be considered under this heading have already been fairly well covered from the packaging specification standpoint under the general terms of product and package, that is, cereals, gelatin powders, spices, and similar products.

Dried fruits, however, are a field in themselves, and much work has been done, more particularly on the West Coast, in the development of new methods of processing in order to achieve a much softer and more palatable product. Prunes, peaches, apricots, and figs have for years been sun-dried, and natural humidity conditions determined to see whether or not the products came through in first-grade condition. Properly engineered and controlled blanching methods have been developed and put into commercial use for the processing of such items as apricots and peaches, with the result that the new product is far superior to anything previously on the market. Due to the processing methods employed, plus good packaging techniques and sometimes gas packaging, the moisture content of these products can be kept as high as 25 or 30% without mold contamination. Combinations of paper containers and dip coating have proved fairly satisfactory. A new process for preserving dried figs in metal containers has recently been developed by the University of California Division of Food Technology. The only reason for switching to metal was that a longer storage life with less sugaring was achieved. Since the fig is a moldable product, there is no reason why a paper or combination package of film and paper should not be able to do that job at perhaps far less cost per pound.

Many dehydrated products, such as broccoli and carrots, will retain their nutritional value for much longer periods of time when held at 35° F. or lower. It is quite possible that at some future date dehydrated products of this type, and dried fruits as well, may reach the consumer through the standard cold-storage or frozen-food channels.

Bakery products, such as bread, cakes, doughnuts, cookies, and crackers, might also be considered under the heading of dried foods. In all these items staling must be controlled. Chemical additives are being tested for control in the product itself; however, better overwraps might also help to prolong the shelf life.

Candy Packaging

Production of candy is approximately 225,000,000,000 pounds annually, of which approximately 50% is sold prepackaged or packaged at the point of sale in such forms as wrapped bars, folding or set-up cartons, and transparent bags. Prepackaging, of course, includes glass and metal containers, as well as highly decorated set-up boxes. Light, heat, and extremely cold weather are all enemies of this product; however, sales volume depends to a great extent on the attractiveness of the display and the package. Many new, exotic, or expensive materials might well find their way into the packaging field through this medium. The reflective capacity of foils has been used with effectiveness in the packaging of chocolate bars. Insulation in the form of fancy corrugated strips might be used for summer and winter shipments. Transparent semirigid or rigid containers are bound to find their way into this field. The use of these will, in turn, call for more attractively colored cups and separators. The fact that the dollar volume in the candy field is approximately $1,300,000,000 annually should interest many packaging laboratories in the idea of developing new and better packages for the industry. Also, in many cases, they are not limited to a matter of 1 or 2 cents per pound for packaging materials. The package is often worth far more than the product packaged.

Packaging Dairy Products

The increasing demand for paper packages for dairy products is forcibly illustrated by the all but complete disappearance of the old metal ice cream can in favor of the paper container. The transition from the traditional glass milk bottle to the paper package has not yet been so complete. However, the percentage of paper packages of milk has increased phenomenally in the past decade, and the acceleration was arrested only by the wartime paper shortage. One of the unanswered questions in the dairy industry is how long will it be before paper will completely replace glass as the packaging material for milk.

Dairy foods in general and fluid milk in particular are perhaps more meticulously regulated as to the details of conditions surrounding their production and handling than most, if not any, other food products. The fact that milk is so widely used for feeding infants, as well as persons who are ill, together with the fact that it serves as an excellent biological medium for the growth of microorganisms, justifies the extraordinary requirements for the handling of this important food. It is not surprising, therefore, that when paper packages were suggested for use as containers for milk, the sharp eyes of the milk sanitarian were focused on the sanitary conditions surrounding the manufacture of paper and also the converting plants. A tentative code has been drawn up outlining the types of raw products which may be used in the manufacture of paper board for use in milk containers and also setting forth sanitary standards which must be met in the plants. The code now under consideration of the Advisory Council of the U. S. Public Health Service sets forth sanitary controls and provides for sanitary inspection of the paper mills and converting plants supplying the dairy industry. The investigational work has been carried on largely by the Bacteriology Department of

Syracuse University, Syracuse, New York, under the guidance
of Dr. Ernest Reed.

Approximately 550,000,000 pounds of cheese is processed
annually and packaged in containers ranging from ½ to 5
pounds in size. The most commonly used overwraps are vinyl-
coated foil, pliofilm, and various Cellophanes coated on one
surface with wax and rubber or resin hot-melt compositions.
Low-temperature sealing, good water-vaporing permeability
and ease of peeling from the product are essential requirements.

The average annual production of butter is over 2,000,000,-
000 pounds. Plain and waxed parchmentized papers are the
principal wrapping materials used. Cellophane (MAT) has
replaced these in some cases as a liner for wooden tubs. Foil,
wax-mounted on paper, makes an attractive and excellent protective wrap. Butter has a tendency to accept odors quickly,
so that the problem is to store it by itself, or prevent the pickup
of odors by wrapper protection.

The value of an eye-catching, attractive package must be
stressed. A recent DuPont survey showed that 36 to 39%
of all purchases in chain and unit stores was "impulse" buying.
The package sold the purchaser a product which she had no
intention of buying when entering the store. Also add to this
the fact that the shopper, when buying a staple item, like rice
for instance, will purchase that brand which is most attractively packaged although she may have in mind another brand
on entering the store.

METAL PARTS WRAPPERS

by R. H. Mosher

The packaging of metal parts is difficult to treat extensively
due to the wide variations in methods and materials which
are utilized to do specific packaging jobs. The standardiza-

tion of materials used in this phase of the functional packaging field was practically nonexistent prior to the second World War, but the activities of the armed forces gave a great deal of emphasis to the question and did much toward crystallizing the known data and setting up specifications which are now quite commonly used throughout the industry.

At the present time, there are two main protective packaging techniques used in this field. The first method is the so-called barrier technique which is designed to keep moisture out and the protective fluid or oil inside the package. The second, and a relatively new method, involves packaging the part inside a protective wrapper which has been treated with a volatile corrosion inhibitor which will effectively prevent any rusting or corrosion of the part. Since the two concepts are basically different, each type will be discussed separately. They both have the same basic goal and that is the protection of metallic parts from any corrosion or deterioration regardless of the storage conditions and over an extended period of time.

Barrier Packaging

There are a number of problems to be considered in regard to choosing the proper barrier-type material for any specific packaging job. The metallurgy of the item, the method of application and extent of any protective coatings on the item, and its resistance to mold or fungus attack must all be carefully considered. Certain equipment, such as aircraft engines, which will corrode and rust under moderate temperature and humidity conditions must be protected to a far greater extent than typewriters, which are designed to operate under and resist practically all temperatures and humidity conditions.[4] Similar comparisons can be made for precision items such as ball bearings as compared to packages of automobile tool kits. The size of the item to be packaged as well as its complexity and shape are all important, since it is obviously easy to package individual steel cams or ball bearings as compared to protec-

tively wrapping an automobile carburetor or an air compressor.
The method of shipment, whether domestic or export, and the
expected storage life at the destination are extremely important
in order that the item can be packaged in a container strong
enough and with functional properties sufficient to protect it,
yet so that it will not be overpackaged. The conditions under
which the package must be stored or is likely to meet must be
known since a unit for shipment to Alaska by air with an expected shelf life of 2 years is an entirely different proposition
from the same item destined for shipment to Siam with a
projected shelf life of three months. These and similar data
and knowledge of expected use requirements and conditions
must be known by the packaging engineer, but the interest of
the reader of this book will probably be more concerned with
what types of packaging materials are available and what are
their properties.

The barrier materials produced and used at the present time
fall into several major classifications and each will be discussed
in some detail. Many of them were developed to meet the
Grade A and Grade C specifications of the Joint Army-Navy
Packaging Committees [5] and many more types have been built
to meet specifications set up after the termination of the second
World War, since many of the wartime products were too expensive for normal packaging requirements. The various
packaging materials fall into one of the following classes:

    a. Kraft-paper laminated barriers
    b. Kraft-paper laminated and coated barriers
    c. Foil laminated and/or coated barriers
    d. Film laminated and/or coated barriers
    e. Cloth laminated and/or coated barriers

Each specific type will do certain jobs and each has uses for
which it is uniquely fitted.

The requirements of these barrier materials are, to a great
extent, dependent upon the method of packaging which is
projected. In all cases where metal parts are to be packaged,

it is expected that they will be packaged in one of two conditions.

1. The item will be solvent-cleaned or treated so that there will be no chance that fingerprints or residual acids, salts, or chemicals will be present to act as initiators of corrosion from within the package. It is also assumed that any bare metal surfaces will probably be sprayed or otherwise treated with an anticorrosive and inhibited light oil or fluid.

2. The item will be solvent-cleaned or treated so as to insure freedom from the possibility of corrosion being initiated within the barrier. The parts will then be completely covered with a film of protective heavy oil or grease which will exclude moisture and corrosion sources.

The major requirements of a barrier for individual packaging, assuming that the part is prepared in a satisfactory manner for packaging, is that it will prevent any passage of water or water vapor into the package which could be trapped inside and that there is a protective layer on the inside face which will prevent absorption of grease, oil, or protective fluid by the barrier or passage of the same through the barrier to the outside surface. Where the barrier is to be used as a liner inside a case for multiple packaging or as an overwrap on large units, the requirements for an inner grease-resistant face can often be dispensed with since the major requirement is to resist passage of water or water vapor.

There are three major packaging techniques and each has its best application in a different field.

1. The individual part or unit is packaged in an envelope-type or prefabricated container which has been sealed, except for the opening for insertion of the part, by functional adhesives or a heat-sealing operation. The properly prepared and treated item is then inserted and the opening sealed with a cover or flap using functional adhesives or heat sealing. The resulting package is permanently sealed and the item cannot be removed without destroying the package. The barrier material

must be resistant to the passage of moisture and must not absorb any of the protective coating from the part since this would lower its corrosion resistance. If the grease or oil pene-

FIGURE 13. *Bag-type asphalt-laminated case liner with the outside surface asphalt saturated* (Courtesy of Thilmany Pulp & Paper Co.)

trated to the outside of the barrier, it would be unsightly and might blot out the legendary markings on the surface of the package. This type of packaging is most effective for small unit items. During the second World War, many items were packaged first with a Grade A type wrapper which effectively prevented migration of the grease and then the entire wrapped unit was sealed in a heat-sealing, moistureproof barrier.

2. The individual item or unit mounted on a small frame is protectively treated and then sealed within a water- and water-vaporproof barrier. Since with irregularly shaped parts and large motors, etc., there is a certain amount of air space and there exists a possibility of water vapor being transmitted through the barrier and then condensing out on the metal surface of the unit, this tendency can be reduced by the so-called "conforming wrapper" which reduces the amount of free air space. However, with large units, the total barrier area is so large that over an extended period of time even low-transmission materials would permit the buildup of moisture within the

package. The usual procedure to overcome this difficulty is to package a dehydrating agent of large capacity, such as silica gel, within the sealed barrier, which will absorb any transmitted water vapor. This type of packaging is generally used with large and bulky units which do not readily fit into prefabricated bags or containers. If necessary, the individual parts of the unit may be prepackaged using corrosion preventives and grease-resistant Grade C moldable barriers, or they can be sprayed with an anticorrosive fluid. The major requirement of this type or barrier is water and water-vapor resistance.

3. The individual items or units are protectively treated and prepackaged, if necessary, in greaseproof wrappers. One or more of these items are then overwrapped with a barrier which may be grease-resistant, but must be waterproof. It must, however, possess very little resistance to the transmission of water vapor so that this can circulate freely into and out of the barrier-protected area. The concept here is that liquid water cannot enter the package, and that any water vapor that enters will pass out again whenever there is any change in the over-all equilibrium conditions. The major problem with this kind of packaging is to insure that the individual items are satisfactorily protected since sudden cooling may condense moisture inside the barrier on any exposed metal surfaces and initiate corrosion. This type of packaging is used for large items such as motors, compressors, and vehicles which are awkward and difficult to package in sealed units.

The individual barriers, regardless of the method of packaging, should possess certain characteristics. If designed for heat-sealing, strong, perfect seals must be easily made and this seal should possess the same degree of functional resistance as the flat area of the barrier. Many satisfactory barriers have failed because the heat-sealing operation affected in some detrimental manner the functional qualities of the barrier in or around the seal. If there is a coated face on the inside of the barrier, unless it is designed for self-adherence, it must possess a sufficiently high block point so that when two adjacent faces come together they will not adhere or disturb each other under normal storage conditions. Any functional coatings, laminants, or laminations must age satisfactorily and not lose their characteristics over an extended period of time. Where wax, asphalt, or similar materials are used in the barrier, bleeding tests should show no deterioration or discoloration. In many cases, fungus, insect, mold, and rodent resistance and flame resistance characteristics are desirable and if necessary these should be incorporated into the sheet in such a manner that their effectiveness will not be lost by extended aging or climatic conditions. The most important is that the sheet possesses sufficient physical strength to do the required job and protect the packaged item against abrasion and collision. The interior face of the barrier should be sufficiently abrasion-resistant so that it will not be ruptured even if such items as loose nuts and bolts or other sharp-cornered parts are packaged.

There are several applications where these various sheets may be utilized and these will be briefly described.

1. **Individual Sealed Bags.** The range of materials is very wide and will be discussed at length in the next section of this chapter. Almost any desired combination of requirements can be met by choosing the proper barrier material.

2. **Conforming Wraps.** In this application, the flexibility and moldability of the barrier is extremely important and its resistance to rupture should be high since the packaged unit is often mounted or framed prior to packaging. The range of packaged items goes from individual ball bearings and small motors up to entire machine units and aircraft power units.

3. **Case Liners.** Barrier materials are used here as either a prefabricated bag which encloses the item and which is then packed completely into a rigid container, or the rigid container may be lined with the barrier sheet and the unit or prepackaged items placed inside and the entire package sealed. With this type of application there is often an excessive amount of void space inside the barrier and the desiccant method of packaging becomes a necessity.

FIGURE 14. *High-moisture-content fire clay with asphalt-laminated overwrap inside carton* (Courtesy of Thilmany Pulp & Paper Co.)

4. **Crate and Car Liners.** The major requirements of barrier materials in these applications are water resistance and high physical strength. It is very difficult, if not economically impossible, to completely seal such a unit and the major purpose is over-all protection against the elements and abrasion of the contents.

5. **Bale Covers.** In bale coverings, the barrier may be sealed or may not, depending upon the requirements of the specific job. Strength, abrasion resistance, and water resistance are the major requisites.

6. **Tarpaulins.** In this application, overhead protection of packaged and nonpackaged items is the major problem and resistance to sunlight, water, and physical impact is necessary.

The particular choice of a barrier will depend upon the conditions to which the package will be subjected.

Waterproof Barriers

Waterproof barriers generally should have high physical strength since they are mainly used as outside protective wrappers against weather and physical impact. Such barriers are generally laminated structures composed of kraft paper and asphalt and, in many cases, a reinforcing agent such as cloth, wire, or glass fiber is imbedded in the laminant layer. Some typical barriers are listed in Table II.

TABLE II

Typical Laminated Kraft Barrier Materials

Description of Barrier	Amount of Asphalt in Laminations Pounds/Ream (24x36–500)	Specifications
1. Duplex Kraft (2 plies—1–60 lb. 1–40 lb.)	50 minimum	One ply or both plies asphalt- or wax-impregnated or wet-strength kraft
2. Duplex Kraft (2 plies—1–50 lb. 1–50 lbs.)	50 minimum	Same as 1
3. Duplex Kraft (Creped) (2 plies—30 lb. each)	80 minimum	Reinforced at least 20 strands per foot in two directions
4. Triplex Kraft (3 plies—30 lb. each)	150 minimum	At least one ply creped
5. Duplex Kraft (2 plies—40 lb. each)	50 minimum	Reinforced at least 20 strands per foot in two directions; both plies must be asphalt- or wax-impregnated or wet-strength kraft
6. Duplex Kraft (2 plies—30 lb. each)	40 minimum	Both plies creped 15% maximum stretch in either direction
7. Kraft to Cloth (30 lb. Kraft) (7½ oz. Burlap)	60 minimum	....

Greaseproof and Waterproof Barriers (Ordnance Wraps)

Greaseproof and waterproof barriers of many types were developed and produced in great quantity during the war for the Armed Forces and these materials were required to meet rigid specifications. For ease in differentiation they were colored, the Grade A being red and the Grade C being green.

1. Grade A Ordnance Wraps.[5] The Grade A type barrier material is defined as greaseproof, acid-free, and noncorrosive. The material must be made so that the greaseproof side is red for identification and the pH of the entire sheet as measured by extraction has to be in the range of 6.5 to 7.5. The amount of water-soluble acidity present is limited to less than 0.02% of equivalent sulfur trioxide. The physical strength characteristics are specified according to the type of barrier:

Barrier	Bursting Strength (Pounds)	Tearing Strength (Grams)
Type I	60 (minimum)	125 (minimum)
Type II	40–60	40 (minimum)
Type III	20–40	12 (minimum)

The barrier is required to resist at least 900 seconds by the turpentine greaseproof test and 12 hours plus by the flotation water-resistance test.[5] In all types an aging test involving a week at 140°F. without loss of greaseproofness or more than 15% of the physical strength values is a definite requirement.

There have been a great many different combinations of papers, coatings, laminants, films, and foils used to produce these papers and a few specific types are listed here.

A. Grade A Type I
    a. A 65 lb. neutral kraft with a synthetic resin coating on one face
    b. Two 35 lb. neutral krafts with a synthetic resin laminant and a synthetic resin coating

    c. A 45 lb. neutral kraft with a sheet of Cellophane or cellulose acetate film laminated with synthetic resin laminant

    d. A 45 lb. neutral kraft and a sheet of neutral glassine laminated with synthetic resin

    e. Two 25 lb. neutral glassines laminated with asphalt

B. Grade A Type II

    a. A 40 lb. neutral kraft with a synthetic resin coating on one face

    b. Two 25 lb. neutral krafts with a synthetic resin laminant and a synthetic resin coating

    c. A 25 lb. neutral kraft and a sheet of Cellophane or cellulose acetate film laminated with synthetic resin

    d. A 25 lb. neutral kraft and a sheet of neutral glassine laminated with synthetic resin

    e. Two 20 lb. neutral glassines laminated with asphalt

C. Grade A Type III

    a. A 25 lb. neutral kraft coated one side with synthetic resin

    b. Glassine and parchment—plain and laminated

In all the listed types, the greaseproof barrier must face against the metal part being packaged so as not to absorb any of the protective oil from the part. Where a heat-sealing barrier is required, only a and b in Types I and II, and Type III would be satisfactory. The other types require adhesive seals for fabrication into bags unless an additional heat-sealable coating is laid down on the barrier surface.

2. **Grade C Ordnance Wrap.**[5] Grade C Ordnance barrier materials are based on a heavily waxed sheet which is flexible and moldable. One material was originally patented by the Dearborn Chemical Co.[6, 7] and was developed by them as a covering for underground pipes. Many variations have been available but all had to meet the specifications set up by the Armed Forces.[5] The barrier is specified as being greaseproof, acid-free, noncorrosive, moldable, and self-adhering. The pH value, as measured by water extraction, must be in the range of

6.5 to 7.5 and the water-soluble acid content is required to be not more than 0.02% calculated as sulfur trioxide. The barrier must show 900 seconds resistance to the turpentine greaseproof test and 12 hours plus of water resistance by the flotation method. The physical strength requirements are as follows:

Barrier	Bursting Strength (Points)	Tearing Strength (Grams)
Type I	60 minimum	425
Type II	40–60	175
Type III	20–40	25

There are also spring-back specifications of not more than 40° and where the sheet is crimped, creped, or embossed so as to obtain a minimum 15% stretch, only 50% of the strength characteristics listed in the above table are required. The aging specifications limiting the loss in physical strength to 15% of the original values and allowing no reduction of grease resistance are also valid as with the Grade A barriers.

Some types are listed as being representative of the barriers available. All are based upon the use of microcrystalline wax.

A. Grade C Type I

    a. 44 x 40 thread count cotton scrim cloth laminated to cellulose acetate film using 60 to 100 pounds of wax per ream

    b. Cotton scrim cloth laminated to Cellophane film using 60 to 100 pounds of wax per ream

    c. Creped 60 pound neutral kraft laminated to cellulose acetate or Cellophane film using 60 to 100 pounds of wax per ream

    d. Two sheets of 25 pound neutral kraft, one coated with a synthetic resin lacquer, laminated on either side of a sheet of cellulose acetate or Cellophane film, using 20 to 60 pounds of wax per ream

B. Grade C Type II

    a. Two sheets of 40 pound neutral kraft wax-laminated using 60 to 100 pounds of wax per ream

    b. Two sheets of 50 pound neutral kraft wax-laminated using 60 to 100 pounds of wax per ream

    c. Creped neutral kraft wax-laminated to cellulose acetate or Cellophane film using 60 to 100 pounds of wax per ream

    d. Creped neutral kraft and 40 pound neutral kraft wax-laminated using 60 to 100 pounds of wax per ream

C. Grade C Type III

    a. 40 pounds neutral kraft wax-coated using 20 to 40 pounds of wax per ream

    b. 35 pound creped neutral kraft wax-coated using 20 to 40 pounds of wax per ream.

Since all the above listed Grade C barrier materials are made by hot-melt application technique, the cloth or paper is not only coated on the surface but also impregnated with wax. In some cases the barrier has moisture-vapor resistance. In many cases there are various substances such as polyisobutylene or rubber derivatives added to the wax so as to increase the tack and viscosity and also the adhesive power. These barriers represent only a few of the various types produced, although most of the others are similar to those listed. One distinctly different barrier is produced by multiple coatings of vinyl resin on cloth to yield a flexible, greaseproof barrier material with a high moisture vapor transfer rate.[4]

Greaseproof and/or Water-vapor-proof Barriers

Although the Grade A barrier materials are often fabricated into individual containers for various types of metal parts, the other materials described up to this point are mainly for conforming wraps which are later wax-dipped or merely used as outer waterproof wrappers. The class of barrier materials to be described in this section are those which can be fabricated into envelopes or pouches and will not only retain oil and grease, but will also resist transmission of water vapor into the package. Such barriers must be heat-sealable on their inside face for best results and the bond produced by the heat seal should be as resistant as the flat area of the package. Paper will not give the desired water-vapor transmission rate, therefore a laminated or a synthetic-resin-coated barrier shows the greatest possibilities.

In building a barrier sheet there are a number of components available.

Ply Materials

1. **Paper.** Generally kraft is used since it has high physical strength. Where colors are desirable a bleached white or colored kraft can be used.

2. **Films.** There are several synthetic resin and rubber films available which are suitable for such lamination work.

a. *Polyethylene.* It heat seals, has a low moisture-vapor-transmission rate, and is waterproof. It is grease-resistant, but tends to absorb certain greases and oils.

b. *Pliofilm.* It heat seals and can be compounded to be water- and greaseproof and moisture-vapor-resistant. Its aging qualities leave something to be desired.

c. *Saran.* It heat seals and can be compounded to be water- and greaseproof and moisture-vapor-resistant. Its aging qualities are good.

There are also other films available and several in the development stage, but those listed above are among the most popular for functional lamination work.

3. **Foils.** Lead and aluminum foils are the types most generally used and the volume of aluminum far exceeds that of lead. These materials offer excellent resistance to greases, oils, water and water vapor.

4. **Miscellaneous.** Other common laminating materials are plain and coated cellophane film, cellulose acetate and other cellulose-base films, glassine, and parchment. Scrim cloth is also used to give tear resistance and durability.

Laminants

1. Asphalt. It is water- and grease-resistant. It offers limited water vapor resistance. Its color is poor.
2. Wax. It is water-, grease-, and water-vapor-resistant. Its color is good.
3. Synthetic Resins. They offer a wide range of water, grease, and water-vapor resistance depending upon the specific material and method of application. Their color is good to excellent.

Coatings

Synthetic-resin-base compounds. They are heat-sealable and offer a wide range of functional properties depending upon specific formulation and method of application.

A barrier which possesses a given set of properties and which can be produced for the least cost may be developed by a judicious choice among the above components. The materials listed do not represent the total number and types which are utilized but they do include most of the components which are readily available.

In designing a barrier to meet a given set of specifications and requirements, the first step is to outline the necessary and desirable properties.

1. Must the sheet be resistant or proof to oil, water, or water vapor?
2. Will the part be merely dipped in oil and the excess shaken off, or will the part be submerged in oil?
3. Are aging, light stability, color, and odor important characteristics?
4. Must the barrier be flexible at low temperatures?
5. What are the strength requirements?

When these questions have been answered and tabulated the choice of actual barrier layer can be made. Metal foil, plastic films, cellulose films or glassine, as well as a layer of laminant or coating can each supply certain functional properties, and each to a different degree and probably in a different cost range. Depending upon the choice of the laminated layers and the formulation of the specific laminant and/or coating, the functional, decorative, and physical strength properties of the complete barrier can be adjusted to the performance requirements. The laminant or coating layers do not contribute much toward the strength of the finished barrier, but they can effect the pliability and durability of the material. Many problems regarding the correct laminants may arise since the necessity of adhering layers which possess different surface characteristics such as glassine, paper, films and foils is common. Dimensional balance in the barrier structure is also a possible problem, e.g., where glassine is laminated to Pliofilm, since one layer would not be affected by the exposure to moisture while the other would change dimensions rapidly with change in humidity and thus cause curling and puckering of the sheet. The number of different plies used to build up a barrier material varies from one to six, but in general, the number is limited to three or four because of economics, mechanical difficulties, and other practical factors.

The types of water-vapor-resistant barriers are divided into three classes according to their transmission rates by Joint Army-Navy Specification J.A.N.-P–131.[10] This is not an absolute classification but is one which is quite often used in the field. The samples are creased before testing.

Barrier Classification	Water Vapor Transmission Rate Grams/100 Square Inches/24 Hours
Type I	Up to 0.05, inclusive
Type II	Over 0.05 to 0.15, inclusive
Type III	Over 0.15 to 0.25, inclusive

Some specific barrier materials which are used are as follows:

1. Three-ply glassine, wax-laminated, and coated with a heat sealing coating

2. Two-ply glassine, synthetic-resin-laminated, and coated with a functional heat-sealing compound
3. Two-ply Pliofilm, laminated with a functional synthetic resin compound
4. Two-ply Cellophane M.A.T., laminated with a synthetic resin compound
5. M.A.T. Cellophane and kraft, laminated with synthetic resin or waxy laminant
6. Two-ply kraft, laminated with a functional synthetic resin laminant and coated one side with a functional synthetic resin compound
7. Aluminum foil laminated to Cellophane with a synthetic resin compound
8. Vinyl film and cotton scrim cloth, laminated with a synthetic resin compound to either side of aluminum foil
9. Cellulose acetate film laminated with a synthetic resin compound
10. 50 pound neutral kraft, asphalt-laminated to lead foil. The lead face is coated with a heat-sealing vinyl resin compound
11. Lead or aluminum foil, laminated to scrim cloth and coated with a heavy layer of vinyl resin
12. Saran film
13. Polyethylene film

These various barrier materials will give some idea as to the wide range of materials which are combined to produce sheets which possess the specific properties to do a given job. Paper acts as a carrier and offers a good printing surface. It supplies body to the sheet and a certain amount of strength. The cloth gives tear strength and durability. Films and foils incorporate specific functional properties. The problem is to combine the proper materials using the most suitable laminants and coatings to make the best barrier at the least cost. Care should be exercised when using Cellophane or Cellophane laminations, however, particularly with dehydrated packages, since the desiccant may dry out the Cellophane and cause fracture of the package.

2. *Vapor-Phase Inhibitor Packaging.* The various methods

FIGURE 15. *Uncrated unit item skid mounted and protected with reinforced asphalt paper, ready for shipment* (Courtesy of Thilmany Pulp & Paper Co.)

of packaging metal parts which have been discussed in the previous sections were based upon the fact that a clean and oiled metal surface will show the minimum of rusting or corrosion if moisture is kept from it or that a nonoiled part will be protected if the package is dehydrated. The various barriers, previously discussed were developed so that the clean part, if dipped in protective fluid or covered with oil and grease, will remain in that protected condition and in any case no water and the minimum of water vapor will be allowed to contact its surface. Such barrier materials are expensive and if the barrier is broken or pierced, either by the part or parts inside or because of some outside influence, the water or water vapor can enter the sealed unit and cause corrosion of the contained metal.

For many years, Shell Development Company [8, 9] and others have carried on extensive research and development work on the subject of corrosion and corrosion prevention. In the course of this work, a compound was developed which, when dissolved in water in minute quantities, altered the properties of the water so that it had no corrosive effects on steel or aluminum with which it came into contact. Further study indicated that the material not only was an effective inhibitor against corrosion in water, but that it was slightly volatile and its vapors in the air surrounding a steel object prevented corrosion of the steel. Carrying the work one step farther, it was determined that when a sheet of paper or other carrier was impregnated or coated with the material, steel or aluminum parts wrapped in it remained free from corrosion, even in the presence of high humidities as long as inhibitor was present. No grease, inhibited oil, or protective fluid is required on the parts with the result that they can be packaged easily and when removed from the container they are ready for use. No heat seal or even adhesive seals are necessary on the package, since the part is merely wrapped with the paper and pressure sensitive or gummed tape is used to seal the flaps. Other organizations have also carried on work in this field and several products are commercially available.

Tests indicated that steel parts wrapped in inhibitor-containing paper and placed in a closed humidity chamber for testing along with nonprotected samples for control purposes did not corrode, but considerable protection was also given to the controls. This phenomenon was explained by the fact that sufficient inhibitor vaporized from the protective paper wrappings so that the entire cabinet was inhibited and further tests which were run with the controls and test samples in separate chambers verified this theory. Many other actual performance tests were carried out and in all cases the results were very satisfactory. The only problem appears to be in long-term storage in the presence of very high humidities for the inhibitor is gradually vaporized or is dissolved from the paper so that the parts eventually tend to show signs of corrosion. This period is quite lengthy, however, and is in direct proportion to the quantity of inhibitor present, together with the type of outer barrier used to reduce volatilization of the inhibitor from the package. An inhibitor concentration of 1 gram per square foot has been found to be satisfactory for general packaging requirements using the more economical cellulose or wax-treated cellulose outer barriers or cartons. For extreme service requirements papers containing more inhibitor may be recommended. The inhibitor contributes only antirust properties to the paper and imparts no added physical or moistureproof characteristics. The desired physical and handling properties of the treated paper are, therefore, chiefly dependent on the type of base sheet selected.

The paper treated with the inhibitor offers the greatest promise in the packaging of metal parts. The paper can be used as a liner or insert in packages now in use as case liners, in envelopes, or as wrapping paper. It is recommended as the best practice that:

1. The paper containing vapor-phase inhibitor is so located in the package that the incoming air must pass through it on its way into the package so that it is forced to pick up enough inhibitor to render the moisture harmless, or,

2. The paper containing vapor-phase inhibitor is distributed uniformly throughout the wrap in such a way that the surface to be protected is within a foot of the source of the inhibitor.

It is not necessary to have a hermetically sealed package in order to adequately retain the inhibitor. Experience has shown [8] that a wrapper containing the inhibitor reduces any tendency for an unclean or fingermarked metal part to corrode. The degree to which this extra protection can be achieved depends upon the corrosiveness of the fingerprints and the severity of subsequent atmosphere conditions. Toxicity studies have been made on the inhibitor and the results show no evidence of skin toxicity. Ingestion tests also indicated that the average dosage required to kill 60 per cent of an experimental group of animals was comparable to the amount of a standard preservative (sodium nitrite) used in canned meats.

The inhibitor is a stable, crystalline, organic compound which very slowly sublimes or vaporizes. See Table III.

It works by passivating the surface of ferrous metal by forming an invisibly thin protective film which resists the corrosive action of water and water vapor. This protective film lasts and is effective just as long as the inhibitor is present in the atmosphere around the metal. Even when water vapor condenses on the metal surfaces in a very humid atmosphere, corrosion is prevented because the inhibitor in the air immediately dissolves in the condensed water film and only a trace is necessary to make the water noncorrosive to steel. The inhibitor is not detectibly consumed by this action, because it does not react with or remove water vapor or oxygen but functions as a corrosion inhibitor in the presence of these agents. It does not affect the pH since it is a neutral compound.

The inhibitor-treated paper should open a new era in metal parts packaging. Proper packaging with the inhibitor can be expected to keep articles on dealers' shelves entirely free from rust even in very hot and humid climates over extended periods of time. The same packages will be protected against corrosion during shipment through widely varying weather conditions. Plant storage of steel stock and equipment often presents corrosion problems which the inhibitor-treated paper will rapidly alleviate. In some cases where manufacturers suffer from corrosion of articles between manufacturing steps in their plants, this can be eliminated by use of the inhibitor-treated paper as linings in the transfer boxes.

Under very severe conditions of humidity and temperature the vapor-phase inhibitor may have a deleterious effect on bare magnesium and its use is, therefore, not recommended where this occurs as a critical surface. This may also be observed in much less degree in the case of bare cadmium or zinc; in these cases the effect, if any, is only superficial.

TABLE III

Vapor Pressure of VPI 260* at Various Temperatures [8] **

°F.	Vapor Pressure, mm. Hg
30	0.000007
40	0.00001
50	0.00002
60	0.00005
70	0.0001
80	0.0002
90	0.0004
100	0.0007
110	0.001
120	0.002
130	0.003
140	0.007
150	0.012
160	0.020
170	0.042
180	0.059
190	0.089
200	0.16

* (Vapor pressure of VPI 220 at 70°F. is 0.004(5) mm. of Hg.)
** Data Courtesy Shell Development Company.

Duration of Inhibitor Protection

The rate of loss of inhibitor from a given package will be a function of a number of factors including 1. ambient temperature, 2. nature of the external barrier, and 3. rate of circulation of air. For the ordinary, paper-wrapped packages at usual temperatures, the limiting factor in service life will be the vaporization rate of the inhibitor. In the case of vapor-tight barrier wrapped packages, no substantial loss of the inhibitor will occur by vaporization and the protection will continue for long periods.

There is one factor which must be considered in storing packages at high temperatures, however, and this is the conversion of the V.P.I. inhibitor into a secondary form which is less active than the original compound. The conversion is independent of the inhibition of corrosion and the secondary product also has rust inhibiting properties, although less effective than the original. In a sealed package, the net result is that with complete conversion of the inhibitor the unit is left without adequate vapor-phase protection if only the normal amount was present. Laboratory tests have indicated[8] that at 150°F. the inhibitor is completely converted in a 10 month period. The rate of conversion falls off rapidly with lower temperatures and at 120°F. the expected life of the same amount is 6 years, while at 100°F. the life is 20 years. Therefore, except in case of prolonged exposure at temperatures above 150°F., vaporization is the only significant factor with which to be concerned.

REFERENCES

1. Anonymous. "Properties of Flexible Packaging Materials." *Modern Packaging Encyclopedia*. Packaging Catalogue Corp., New York (1946–1947), p. 630.
2. F. S. Leinbach. "Heat Sealing Principles." *Modern Packaging Encyclopedia*. Packaging Catalogue Corp., New York (1946–1947), p. 558.
3. C. W. Hauck and J. J. Crawford. "Reporting Results of Experimental Shipment of Pre-packaged Vegetables." *Packaging Parade,* **16**, No. 181:36–45 (1948).
4. W. L. Hardy. "Barriers and Liners." *Modern Packaging Encyclopedia*. Packaging Catalogue Corp., New York (1948), p. 231.
5. Joint Army Navy Specifications J.A.N.–B–121, U. S. Government Printing Office (1947).
6. A. H. Reynolds. "Material for Wrapping Pipes and for Covering Metallic Surfaces." U. S. Patent 2,311,572 (1943).
7. R. A. Shoan. "Material for Wrapping Pipes and for Covering Metallic Surfaces." U. S. Patent, 2,311,573 (1943).
8. Anonymous. "Vapor Phase Inhibitors of Corrosion." V.P.I.—Report No. S–9908. Shell Development Co., Emeryville, Calif.
9. Anonymous. V.P.I.—Shell Development Corp., Emeryville, Calif.
10. Joint Army-Navy Specifications J.A.N.–P–131. U. S. Government Printing Office (1945).
11. *Food Industries.* McGraw-Hill Book Company, Inc., New York.
12. *Western Canner and Packer.* Miller Freeman Publications of California, San Francisco.
13. *Modern Packaging.* Modern Packaging Corporation, New York.
14. *The Glass Packer.* Ogden Publishing Company, New York.

15. *Quick-Frozen Foods*. E. W. Williams Publications, Inc., New York.
16. *Food Technology*. Institute of Food Technologists, Champaign, Ill.
17. *The U. S. Egg and Poultry Magazine*. Institute of American Poultry Industries, Chicago, Ill.
18. *Food Research*. Garrard Press, Champaign, Ill.
19. *Chain Store Age*. Lebhar-Friedman Publications, Inc., Orange, Conn.
20. *Packaging Abstracts*. Allied Trades Research Association, London, England.
21. *Food Processing Preview*. Putnam Publishing Company, New York.
22. *Packaging Parade*. Haywood Publishing Company, Chicago, Ill.
23. *Drug Trade News*. Topics Publishing Company, New York.
24. *Paper Trade Journal*. Lockwood Trade Journal Company, Inc., East Stroudsburg, Penn.
25. *The Food Packer*. Vance Publishing Corporation, Chicago, Ill.
26. *The Modern Packaging Encyclopedia*. Packaging Catalog Corporation, New York.
27. *Paper Year Book*. Davidson Publishing Company, Chicago, Ill.
28. *Refrigeration Applications*. American Society of Refrigerating Engineers, New York.
29. *A.S.T.M. Standards*. American Society for Testing Materials, Philadelphia, Penn.
30. *The Canned Food Reference Manual. 2nd Ed.*, American Can Company, New York, 1943.
31. S. C. Prescott and B. E. Proctor. *Food Technology*. McGraw-Hill Book Company, Inc., New York, 1937.
32. Donald K. Tressler and Clifford F. Evers. *The Freezing Preservation of Foods*. Avi Publishing Company, New York, 1943.
33. Harold W. von Loesecke. *Outlines of Food Technology*. Reinhold Publishing Company, New York, 1942.
34. Ernest C. Crocker. *Flavor*. McGraw-Hill Book Company, Inc., New York, 1945.
35. A. L. Winton and K. B. Winton. *The Structure and Composition of Foods*. John Wiley and Sons, Inc., New York, 1937 (four vols.).
36. W. V. Cruess. *Commercial Fruit and Vegetable Products, 2nd Ed.*, McGraw-Hill Book Company, Inc., 1938.
37. Saul Blumethal. *Food Products*. Chemical Publishing Company, Inc., New York, 1947.
38. Ben Nash. *Developing Marketable Products and Their Packaging*. McGraw-Hill Book Company, Inc., New York.
39. A. W. Bitting. *Appetizing or the Art of Canning*. The Trade Pressroom, San Francisco, 1937.

Chapter V

HIGH-GLOSS SPECIALTY PAPERS

by R. H. Mosher

SOME of the earliest decorative and fancy papers were the high-finish, glossy papers which were used for wrapping and label work. This type of sheet was first produced by the flint-glazing process and this later led to the development of friction-glazing and the brushed enamels. These processes were all based upon the technique of coating a base paper with a plain or colored pigmented or dyed coating compound which could be burnished or polished in a later operation so as to produce a smooth glossy surface. The formulation of the coating is very important as the final surface effect is directly dependent upon it. The formulae always have been closely protected secrets and even today each mill carefully controls and guards its own formulations. The mechanical finishing operations all involve a surface polishing technique for burnishing the coated surface, which contains a certain amount of lubricating and gloss producing agents, until the desired finish is obtained. This burnishing operation involves three basic principles with the three different types of paper.

1. *Flint-Glazed Paper*. A polished stone is drawn back and forth across the surface of the coated paper. This action burnishes the surface and produces the flint-glazed paper.

2. *Friction-Glazed Paper*. The coated paper is passed through a friction glazing calender. These calenders consist

of two or three rolls; a metal and a paper roll or a paper and two metal rolls. The rolls are driven at differential speeds with the metal rolls operating at about one and a half to four times the peripheral speed of the paper rolls. The coated face contacts the metal or polishing roll and the differential speed produces slip and a burnishing effect.

3. *Brush-Enameled Paper.* The coated paper is passed through brushing machines where the coated surface is polished by a series of rotating brushes of varying degrees of stiffness. Then it is supercalendered and a satiny glazed surface produced.

These processes are all relatively slow and correspondingly expensive. Therefore, work has been done on the development of coated papers which can be mechanically treated at relatively high speeds, after coating, to produce a glazed surface. The original offerings were mainly in the field of white papers, but recently colored sheets have also been introduced. At the present time, there are certain limitations to the types of pigments which can be used as the sheet must stand extensive calendering and in some cases buffing or brushing in order to develop the required surface finish. The speed at which the paper can be produced is a real improvement over the prior methods, but two operations, a coating and a finishing stage, are still required.

The other major development in the glossy paper field has resulted in the production of a high-finish paper in one operation. This process has been carried out in several different ways, but all are based upon the same principle. The basic technique involves laying down a film of pigment and adhesive in the normal manner and then pressing this wet, or partially dried film, while still in a plastic stage, against a polished mirror-finished surface and completing the drying in this position. The resulting coated paper, when stripped from the polished surface, retains a mirror image of the casting surface. The polished surface may take the form of a rotary drum drier, an endless metal belt, or a precast impervious film or coated paper. Although the rate of production has been generally rather slow on most of the equipment developed to date, the process has shown a great deal of promise. The separate coating and smoothing operations are reduced to a single combined coating and glazing process and the width of the sheet is only limited by the coating and glazing facilities which can be built.

Each method of production and the various problems involved will be discussed in detail.

FLINT-GLAZED PAPERS

by R. S. Blount

The flint-glazing process of finishing coated paper so as to produce a sheet with a high-gloss surface finish is one of the oldest known methods of the paper converting industry. The technique originated in Europe about the middle of the 19th century and the major portion of the development work was done in Germany and Belgium. One of the major drawbacks of the process is the low-volume output and limited width of the equipment, but no other method has ever been devised which completely replaces this type of finish. Flint papers are for this reason still being produced and sold in limited volume today, even though other methods have been developed which produce high-gloss papers faster and at a lower unit cost.

Mechanical Equipment

The principle involved in producing this type of finish is one of "ironing" the sheet by means of a polished stone which passes to and fro across the web, with a slight overlapping. It is the surface friction of this smooth stone passing over the surface under pressure which produces the so-called "flint finish" on the coated paper.

The average flinting machine is a small unit, about 4 feet square, which consists of a flat bed on which is placed a board made of hard wood or, more recently, of very hard fiber. The remainder of the unit consists of a unwind and a rewind stand which are set up so that an extremely fine control of web tension can be maintained. The precoated paper is passed over the top of the board at a very slow rate, approximately 7 feet per minute.

The stone is mounted in an iron clamp and this, in turn, is attached to a long pole which is usually centered on the ceiling of the room. By means of a cam-driven rocker arm, the stone is forced back and forth across the sheet under pressure. The matter of unwind and rewind is extremely important and requires delicate adjustment since the stone operates on the sheet at right angles to the direction of web travel and any wrinkles or bulges can easily result in cuts and tears or other imperfections. The coating must be properly formulated and lubricated if the machine is to be run efficiently.

FIGURE 16. *Flint-glazing machines* (Courtesy of Kupfer Bros. Paper Co.)

The pressure with which the stone is forced down upon the paper surface as it is moved back and forth must be varied with the color and the coating formulation in order to obtain the best results. As a general rule, the darker colors are somewhat more difficult to process than are the tints, black being the most difficult.

This is the basic nature of this type of finishing, but many details are involved, both in the selection and cutting of the proper finishing stone and the formulation and application of the coating. Everything else being equal, however, the selection of the stone is the most important problem in producing the right quality of finish.

The average mill which carries on flinting operations has a large number of individual machines since each unit can only produce approximately 3 to 5 reams per day and multiple operations are required in order to obtain any reasonable volume. The resulting operations are similar to those in a textile factory where a large number of individual looms are required to keep their over-all production up to a reasonable figure. This requirement necessitates a large amount of floor space so that, measured by modern methods of streamlined production, the flinting technique is rather primitive and definitely dated.

Base Paper Requirements

The base papers best suited to the flint glazing process are those which have a uniform, well-closed formation so that they present a smooth surface to the coating. The sheet must not be too porous and must be sufficiently sized so that the absorption of the coating is reduced to a minimum. Many types and weights of base stock are used including ground wood as well as the stronger and higher-priced fibers. In general, the appearance of the coated sheet is dependent upon the formation of the base paper.

Practically any good method of coating paper can be used to make the coated stock for the flinting process. Brush, spray, or air-knife techniques have all been used and it is simply a matter of getting uniform coverage of the proper coating so as to obtain good results on the flinting unit. The matter of formulation is extremely complicated and depends entirely upon the properties desired. Casein is the most common adhesive and all the formulae contain certain amounts of lubricants, generally finely divided talc and/or various waxes. Approximately 6 to 8 parts of talc and/or $1\frac{1}{2}$ to $2\frac{1}{2}$ parts of carnauba wax, beeswax, or other polishing wax is needed to do the job. The deeply colored sheets are obtained by the use of pigments, either pulp or lake colors, and pastel colors are generally achieved with either pigments or pigment-dyestuff combinations. These pigments must be soft and rub out readily in the flinting process.

Applications

Flint-glazed papers possess certain characteristics which make them very attractive to both printers and box makers and this probably accounts for the fact that the method is still in existence. When this method of finishing is used, the bulk of the paper is retained to a much greater degree than when a similar finish is obtained by the use of the heavy pressures exerted by calender rolls. This, in turn, retains many of the desirable characteristics in the sheet which are necessary for fabricating boxes, labels, box coverings, and cover papers. The sheet will lie flat and can be worked easily without curling.

Another advantage of this method of finishing is the lack of a crushed effect which is likely to appear after a friction calendering operation, since in flinting there is a more delicate application of pressure. This allows for the retention of a superior color, particularly in the case of whites and pastel tints, and permits a color match made on the coating machine to be carried through into the final product without change of shade due to subsequent processing. This is an important feature and one appreciated in the box and fancy paper trade. However, the sheet, particularly in the deep colors, often shows a characteristic mottled appearance.

The question of how much longer it will be economical to produce this type of coated paper is impossible to answer at the present time. It goes without saying, however, that this laborious process will be superceded or replaced by other developments. Due to present costs and the necessity of meeting severe competition in the realm of all types and kinds of high-gloss papers, the production of such papers by direct machine operations in connection with the coating unit and by relatively high-speed calendering action will in all probability gradually replace the flinting business. They are making definite inroads today in all phases except the deeper colors and small runs of special shades.

FRICTION-GLAZED PAPERS

The development of the various glazing or friction-finishing processes parallels in many respects the history of the coated-paper industry. In the early days, paper was handcoated in the sheet form and at that time both sheet flint glazing and sheet friction glazing were in use as finishing techniques. It was not until about 1830 that the first continuous friction-glazing calendering operation was reported, and there has been a steady volume of glazed paper produced by this process since that date.

When friction-glazed papers were first studied on an experimental basis, it was found that the heavy metal and hard paper rolls which were originally utilized tended to produce wrinkles and hard spots in the papers. Experiments proved that a softer backing roll, preferably composed of a combination of woolen and cotton fibers, did a very satisfactory job and most of the early units contained such rolls. In the early work on these papers, the wax was applied to the surface after the coating operation had been completed, either by wash coating or by dusting it on the sheet in a dry form ahead of the frictioning roll. In later years, the wax was incorporated into the coating color and the entire coating applied on the coating machine.

The friction calender itself usually consists of two, three, or four rolls, but the three-roll calender is the most popular.

In this type of unit, the polishing or frictioning roll is mounted at the top of the stack and is driven directly from the power source. The bottom roll is, in turn, geared to the top roll so that a speed differential of one and a half to four times less than that of the top roll is maintained. This roll is made of cast iron and used to both drive and support the paper roll. The paper or backing roll, which usually has a diameter about three times that of the polishing roll and is made of cloth or a paper containing woolen fibers, is not directly driven but obtains its motion by contact with the bottom roll. In some of the early two-roll setups, the paper roll was directly geared to the polishing roll, but such units are no longer in use in this country, although some may still be used in Europe. A special heavy steel core was used in this case to support the paper roll. The production rate varies from 200 to 500 feet per minute depending upon the quality and finish desired.

FIGURE 17. *Friction-glazing calender* (Courtesy of Kupfer Bros. Paper Co.)

The polishing or friction roll is normally made of cast and chilled iron, as highly polished steel and chrome-plated rolls have been found to be relatively unsatisfactory. It has been felt by some authorities that the minutely porous surface of the chilled iron is essential for the production of a high glossy finish. This roll is usually cored so that cooling water or steam can be circulated through it as desired. Pressure can be applied to the roll journals by either mechanical or hydraulic means. Many calenders are fitted with steam jets as the humidifying of the sheet is often found to be beneficial in the frictioning operation.

A great deal of work has been done in studying the relationships between the roll pressure and the frictioning ratio so as to attain the best conditions for glazing a sheet. Most of this work has been done by the mills themselves and very little of published data is available. It has been the general experience, however, that good glazed paper cannot be obtained without the use of pressure, but that the minimum pressure consistent with satisfactory glazing results should be utilized. In general, the lower the applied pressure the higher the required friction ratio to obtain equivalent gloss. The lower pressure results in less curl in the sheet and a more uniform appearance, however, due to less crushing of the structure of the base paper.

Different colors and papers have also been found to require variations in machine conditions to obtain the best glazing results. Metal papers, such as the so-called "argentine silvers" usually require the highest pressures and friction ratios, while deep shades and dark colored papers require less severe conditions. The whites and light, bright colors require the least severe conditions to obtain a satisfactory product. In mills where a wide variety of frictioning conditions had to be met, it was necessary to use machines whose frictioning ratio could be readily adjusted, and in the early days these conditions were met by the use of belt drives and pulleys of different sizes. The present procedure involves the use of chain drives or direct drive gears and the trend is away from varying the machine conditions other than pressure, in order to obtain the desired finished product. Modern practice involves the use of machines with fixed gear ratios and varying the coating color formulation so as to obtain any desired differences.

Practically any desired color shade can be readily produced by this process, and both light-weight papers and boards have been glazed. In general, however, the extensive working of the sheet between the paper and metal rolls causes curling and where higher roll pressures are used, the sheet structure may be crushed to the extent that any nonuniformity of density and formation may be unduly emphasized.

Although at the present time the introduction of the cast coated papers and high-gloss calendered papers has cut into the volume of friction glazed papers to some extent, but they are still produced in fairly large quantities. Their particular field of application is in the deep shades and special shades since that type of sheet is more difficult to produce economically on the larger and higher-speed units.

Base Stock Requirements

The base stock for the production of friction-glazed papers must possess first of all a very smooth surface. This is usually obtained by the presence of soda pulp or ground wood in the sheet since it should also be a fairly bulky stock so as to react well in the friction-calendering operation. The sheet should possess a uniform density and formation and should be sized sufficiently to hold up the coating color, since nonuniform penetration of the coating will produce mottled paper after glazing. For most of the applications wherein these papers are used, the physical strength requirements, other than fold, are not too important. The sheet must possess sufficient physical strength to handle satisfactorily on the coating machine and during the glazing operation and beyond this, these properties are not of exceptional importance.

Coating Formulation and Technology

The major requirements of a coating color for use in friction glazing work are as follows:

1. **Fine pigment particle size.** This is usually obtained by ball milling the coating color, wherever possible, since the finer and more uniform the particle size of the pigments, the higher the gloss which can be obtained from the final glazed surface.

2. **High-finishing pigments.** The pigments used in friction calendering formulations are usually relatively soft, finely dispersed types in those cases where colored pigments are needed. The high-finishing clays, satin white, high-finishing calcium carbonates, and titanium pigments are used where white pigments are desired.

3. **Adhesives.** The adhesives used should possess high brightness and high bonding strength, since the minimum amount of adhesive is used in the formulation (7 to 12%) so as to allow glazing of the pigments.

4. **Lubricants.** High-finishing waxes, such as beeswax or carnauba wax, are included in the formulation to assist with the polishing operation. Talc is also used to serve the same purpose. About 2 to 5% of talc based upon the dry pigment and between 5 and 9% of wax on the same basis are commonly used.

In general, the binder ratio is held to a low value so that the pigments are polished and the highest gloss and brightness obtained.

In order to illustrate some of the customary formulations used in friction finishing work the following type formulae are given. In all cases the concentration of the wax dispersions is 12.5% and the concentration of the casein solutions is 18%.

1. *White Friction Finish*

English Clay Slurry (60% solids)	170 lb.
Talc	3 lb.
Red Dyestuff (10% solution)	2 qt.
Casein Solution	8 gal.
Beeswax Dispersion	5.5 gal.

2. *White Glazed Finish*

High-Finishing Domestic Clay	200 lb.
Titanium Pigment	32 lb.
Carbonate Pigment	150 lb.
Water	45 gal.
Quadrafos*	1 lb.
Talc	12 lb.
Beeswax Dispersion	9.5 gal.
Casein Solution	32 gal.

3. *Black Friction Finish*

Black Special Frictioning Pulp (53% solids)	240 lb.
Talc	6.5 lb.
Nigrosine Dye (5% solution)	9 oz.
Water	14 gal.
Carnauba Wax Dispersion	8 gal.
Casein Solution	10 gal.

These are fairly typical base formulae. To these formulations must be added the various surface active agents, plasticizers, preservatives, and other additives which are necessary to make for optimum operating conditions on the coating machine.

Applications

Friction-glazed papers are used in large quantities in the fancy box and packaging field for producing attractive and eye-catching sales units. They are also used in display work and for specialty cover papers. In both of these last applications they are often laminated to one or both sides of a news

---

* Sodium tetraphosphate; surface-active agent.

middle so as to give a certain amount of rigidity to the final structure.

These papers can be readily embossed and printed in order to decorate the surface beyond the glazed finish itself. They can also be hot-stamped or hot-embossed for use in the fancy-box trade.

BRUSH-ENAMEL PAPERS

by F. C. Heywood

During the earlier periods when the flat bed stone lithographic process was popular, surface-coated papers were a prime necessity, especially for color work. Ordinary lithographic plate paper was generally used for much of the work, but where a fine job in multicolor was required, the regular plate finish was not high enough to do a satisfactory job and produce the best result. Brush-enamel papers were developed which had a higher gloss and finish and these papers were produced and used extensively in the second half of the 19th century and early part of the 20th century.

Like the lithographic process itself, the new development came from Germany. The art of paper coating had been developed there to a high degree, and the brush-polishing process which was first used for single sheets and later on full webs by the Germans soon was brought to this country. The production of these papers, which involved coating the sheet with a compound which could be burnished to a high polish and then calendering, was carried out by a few of the high-grade mills and further developed by them.

Base Paper

The base paper used was a good sulfite-soda sheet. Its formation was uniform and well closed up and the sheet was well sized to hold the coating. The surface was also smooth and level so as to take the exceptionally smooth and uniform coating.

Coating Materials

The English china clay used as the base of lithographic plate paper was replaced in brush enamels by higher and higher percentages of satin white, a synthetic pigment made by the reaction of alum and lime. English china clay and the aluminum hydroxide acted as a good finishing agent. As the commercial production of satin white became more standardized under better manufacturing control, the coating superintendent was able to use higher percentages of it in his coating formulae. At the time when the manufacture of brush-enamel paper was at its height, during the first decade of the 20th century, some coaters were using practically all satin white and no china clay, with perhaps an additional portion of blanc fixe ($BaSO_4$) to give body to the coating.

This was a pigment formulation difficult to use, especially after casein had displaced animal glue as the sizing agent. It was a tempermental composition to handle and as practically no coating plant of those days had what would be called a chemical staff, its use was mostly a matter of trial and error. Fortunate was the coating superintendent who could run day after day, batch after batch, a high-percent satin white formula without getting into trouble, as the mix often thickened up with a false body which could not be thinned by any reasonable amount of extra water.

The satin white itself, while giving good lustre, was light and weak and rather hard and brittle so that some additional filler was necessary to give the richest, evenest surface. Less blanc fixe than china clay was required to do this so that a higher percentage of satin white could be used. Since both satin white and blanc fixe were considerably more costly than china clay, however, the formulae had to be governed by the economic factors. If cost was not important, a very good formula for a high-finish, smooth surface was 80% satin white and 20% blanc fixe.

It took somewhat more sizing to bind this mix than to bind

100% clay plate finish formulae. A lubricant had to be used in the formulation to give the best results in the brushing process. A very finely divided talc powder to the extent of 5% of the weight of filler along with 1 to 2% wax emulsion and saponified castor oil were added. The talc dusted off during the brushing process while the wax and oil helped as a lubricant as well as a plasticizer for the hard, brittle satin white.

There are a number of problems facing the brush finisher in connection with his choice of coating pigments. The pigment particles must not be too hard and sharp or excessive brush wear results. On the other hand, if they are too soft or insufficiently bound, excessive dust is produced resulting in dusty paper and reduced finish. The amount of adhesive must be adjusted to permit a high supercalendering after the brushing and yet the adhesive must be sufficiently hard to bind the pigments during the brushing operation. Lubricants such as mineral oil emulsions or hydrogenated fish oils are sometimes used to reduce dusting and increase brush life although this is not a general practice.

The moisture content of the sheet being brushed should be high enough to prevent the formation of excessive static. Steam is sometimes blown on the brushes to help in this respect.

Coating Techniques

The coating process is the same as for other types of surface coating. At the time brush enamels were at their fullest demand, brush-coating technique was the usual coating method but there is no reason why the air doctor, roll, or spray coating techniques should not be satisfactory.

The high satin white content of these coatings slows up the drying considerably, so that additional drying capacity is necessary or slower production results as compared with ordinary lithographic plate paper.

Brushing and Finishing Operations

The only mechanical equipment needed in addition to the regular coating and finishing equipment of a coating plant is the brush machine. The first brush machines in use were on the cylinder or drum principle. Later developments of the brush machine were for flat bed or arch-back machines of considerable length where more brushes could be used and higher speed obtained with satisfactory burnishing.

FIGURE 18. *Angle view of brushing machine* (Courtesy of John Waldron Corp.)

A machine having a drum of some 48 to 60 inches diameter was set up with some six or eight cylinder brushes around its periphery so that with an unwind stand and a reel, a very work-able brush machine was obtained. The coated paper is fed around the drum and on the reel. The drum travels with the paper. The brushes are adjustable so that the pressure they exert on the paper passing under them can be varied. This pressure is only sufficient to make the tips of the brushes just whip the paper surface. The brushes are then driven at high speed in counter direction to the flow of the paper. The brush speed may range from 2000 feet per minute peripheral speed to nearly 7000 feet per minute on some modern installations. The paper can be run through such a brush machine at 200 to 500 feet per minute and receive a very satisfactory burnishing. One man and helper can take care of several machines at such speeds.

The brushes are usually graded from a fairly stiff hair bristle for the first one contacting the paper to a soft badger hair for the last. In the past, bristle brushes have been used. The bristle material was usually imported pig or similar bristle. Today, Nylon is tending to replace the natural bristle. It wears longer and if the ends of the bristles are rounded it seems to impart a burnishing action which improves the finish. For different types of pigment, brushes of different face densities and length of bristle are used.

The final finishing is done by supercalendering the same as when handling litho-plate paper. It is a combination of the satin white in the coating, the burnishing by the brush machine, and the supercalendering that produces the glossy lustre of the brush-enamel paper.

With the development of the rotary offset lithographic process, a radical change occurred in printing paper requirements. The offset process required no coated surface to produce its best results. In fact, a surface-coated paper was not desirable in order to give the soft tones of the offset and it was a detriment in obtaining the speeds at which the offset presses were designed to run.

Therefore, as the stone bed lithographic presses passed into history, the demand for lithographic plates and brush enamels rapidly diminished. Only a limited amount of this paper is now produced, and mainly for other purposes. It would not be surprising, if, in another generation, its production became one of the forgotten arts.

CAST-COATED PAPERS

The basic objective with cast-coated papers is to produce a paper possessing a high-gloss finish for use as a printing paper and as a converting base stock. The process generally involves applying a fluid coating to the paper and then solidifying this coating while it is in contact with a polished, nonadhering surface, so that the finished coated surface is a mirror reproduction of the surface upon which it dried.

The weight of coating applied may range from 1.5 pounds per 1,000 square feet to 7 pounds per 1,000 square feet, and the major problem with the heavier coating loads in this process is the reduced rate of drying. In many cases the paper first receives a base coating on a paper machine or off-the-machine coating unit and then the final cast coating is applied. With this type of multiple-coating operation the base coat may be colored using color pigments or soluble dyestuffs or an over-all colored printing or coating job can be done before applying the cast coating.

The coated surface must harden in contact with the casting surface. It is advisable that the coating and the surface are of such a nature that the paper will stick to the solid surface of its own accord until set, and then break loose spontaneously. The moisture content of the coating at the point where the sheet is stripped from the casting surface is quite critical and must be controlled within narrow limits for successful operation.

Base Paper

The base paper for use in cast coating may be of any desirable basis weight or fiber composition. The physical strength will depend upon the end use of the coated product. Its surface should be as smooth as possible with no surface fuzz and in general practice the sheet is often machine calendered and even supercalendered before cast coating. It should be sized sufficiently to hold up the coating and should not curl when the base coating is applied. A commonly used base stock is a soda-sulfite sheet which is well sized with rosin. The surface characteristics have a great deal to do with the amount of coating required to produce a smooth glossy coated finish; the smoother the surface, the less coating is required to produce a satisfactory finished sheet.

Coating Equipment

The coating may be laid down directly on the base stock, or on a precoated or printed sheet. The application mechanism may be of the brush, roll, air knife, gravure roll, spray, or other suitable type which will apply a uniform and smooth coating to the surface of the paper.[3,5,7,9,12,14] The sheet may be partially dried before it reaches the glazing unit, or the drying may all take place on the casting surface. In some processes the surface of the partially dried coating is rewet just before it is applied to the polished surface.[4,13]

Casting Equipment and Technology

The actual cast-finishing equipment may consist of a large polished metal cylinder of the Yankee drier type, of an endless metal or rubber belt, or of the surface of a highly finished impervious sheet. If a metal drum or endless belt is used, the surface must be ground smooth, polished, and then plated with chromium, nickel, Monel, or other metal.[3,6,7] This surface is finally polished until flawless. A hard rubber casting belt or apron has also been used. Where an impervious web served as the casting surface, Cellophane, coated paper, cellulose acetate film, or metal foil has been suggested.[12] The method of drying may be internal, as in the metal drum or a heated metal belt, and/or external using heated air or radiant heat directed to the outer surface of the sheet.[3,4,5,10,13,14]

There are three basic methods of handling the casting process. 1. The sheet may be coated, and while the coating film is still wet, or only partially dried, the coated face is pressed against the casting surface. 2. The sheet may be coated, completely or partially dried, and then the surface rewet just before it is pressed against the casting surface. 3. The coating film is cast on a belt or drum, and the paper is pressed against the wet film and dried *in situ*. The coating and paper are then stripped off together.

The different techniques are all based upon the fact that the surface of a fluid coating will conform to a surface to which it is applied and assume the appearance of that surface if the coating is dried or set and loses its flow properties. The coated paper may be caused to adhere to the casting surface (a) by the use of a rubber pressure roll, which should be preferably driven,[3,4] and then held in contact with the polished face by other rolls; (b) by an endless rubber or felt blanket; or (c) merely in the case of a Yankee type drier, by the curvature of the drum and the tension in the paper web. One of the major problems is to prevent any slippage or movement of the coated surface in relation to the casting surface since this will tend to reduce the surface gloss and mar the coating. The problems of wrinkling or tearing of the paper at the pressure roll or on the casting surface, particularly in the lighter weight papers, requires careful control of web tension, roll alignment, uniformity of press-roll pressure, and slippage of the contact pressure belt.[3,4,13,14] By driving all rolls and controlling the uniformity of pressure, however, most of the difficulties may be overcome.

Once the wet or rewet coating film has been brought up to the casting surface to receive the glossy finish, there are several problems which may appear. Webs coated by the usual methods may carry a slight bead of wet coating on either edge,

and this may tend to build up a ridge on the casting surface
and pressure rolls. Attempts to eliminate this by edge doctors
or by leaving a small band of paper at the edges uncoated has
not generally been successful due to the tendency of the paper
to stick to the casting surface where the coating feathers out
at the edge.[4] It has also been found that when the wet coated
sheet passes under the pressure roll and makes contact with
the casting surface, small amounts of air may be entrapped
and carried between the coating and the casting surface. This
entrapped air holds the coating away from the surface in spots,
which forms defects in the coated surface or in the coating itself. Much work has been done to reduce or eliminate these
effects, and according to Warner,[4] by rewetting or recoating
the surface of a partially dried sheet and then forcing the
coated surface against the casting face while at least a portion
of the coating is in a fluid state, the trouble can be avoided.
According to this author,[4] a coating composition of high viscosity containing up to 50% of entrapped air bubbles by volume
can be cast-coated in this manner without forming any defects
in the paper. It has also been claimed that any backward flowing coating also serves to remove any particles of dirt or foreign matter which would otherwise pass through and mar the
cast surface of the finished paper.

Assuming satisfactory coating application to the sheet, proper
sheet application to the casting surface, and elimination of
wrinkles and entrapped matter, the final problem is proper
separation of the coated sheet from the casting surface with no
marring or disturbance of the glossy surface. The adherence
of a given coating to the casting surface depends on the type
of metal in the final plating or the chemical composition of the
surface, the presence of lubricant in the coating, the moisture
content of the coating, and the uniformity, smoothness, and
other characteristics of the casting surface.

In many cases where a single coated sheet has been produced
by the cast process, sometimes certain microscopic and larger
defects have appeared. These are varyingly described and are

attributed to unequal absorption of the vehicle into the paper, unequal drying and shrinkage of the coating material, or swelling of the fibers by the water and subsequent shrinkage.[7,9] Most of these problems were solved by a multiple coating procedure, where the different layers may be of the same or of different composition. In many cases the total load may be no more than is customarily applied in a single coating operation. The usual sheet is composed of two layers, as this has been generally found to produce satisfactory results. The base coating may be a paper-machine coated job, or made by a subsequent coating operation and may be air dried, calendered, supercalendered, or cast coated. If desirable, the base coat can be colored or printed. The cast coating is laid down directly on the precoated sheet and a smooth, defect-free surface can be obtained. Several theories have been advanced as to the improvement resulting from this precoating technique and it is believed that the absorbing power of the base coat is more even and uniform and a smooth surface film is obtained. The base coat protects the fibers from swelling when they are wetted and so eliminates defects caused by such wetting.[9] According to Montgomery and Bradner,[7,9] 2 pounds of top coating per 1,000 square feet will produce a perfectly satisfactory cast-coated surface.

There has been one major problem from a printing standpoint which has appeared when working with this type of high-gloss coated paper. Relatively poor printing results were originally obtained when using high-gloss inks and varnishes.[8,11] Most of the other high-gloss pigmented coatings are dense and hard due to the calendering or surface working during the glazing process. The cast coatings, however, usually have a relatively low density and are fairly porous since they owe their gloss to a polished surface and not to surface densification and glazing. These coatings when made by standard formulations are quite absorbent to printer's ink and the ink or varnish film tends to dry and set with a smooth velvety appearance, but little gloss. There are two major approaches in solving this problem, the first by increasing the adhesive to pigment ratio and the second by hardening the coating.

1. **Increasing the Adhesive to Pigment Ratio.** In making supercalendered high-gloss papers, only enough adhesive is ordinarily used to make the sheet resistant to picking in the printing press, since with the usual calendering pressures, any excess of adhesive will reduce the gloss and smoothness which can be obtained in this process.[8,11] With cast coatings this is not true since the use of excess adhesive not only increases printing ink hold-up, but it also enhances the gloss and improves the smoothness.

The adhesive to pigment ratio can be adjusted to meet any requirements. Where a single coating is desirable, the adhesive ratio can be held to a minimum in order to maintain opacity and coverage. With multiple coating operations the adhesive ratio can be increased and some titanium oxide pigment added to the formulation to produce opacity and still retain low ink absorbency. Where a colored base coating is used, the top cast coating may be made relatively transparent by using a high adhesive to pigment ratio and by choosing pigments whose refractive indices are close to those of the adhesive (clay and casein). In such cases as much as 50% of adhesive can be used to produce the desired results.[8,11]

2. **Hardening the Coating.** Another technique for reducing penetration of the ink or varnish is to waterproof or fix the adhesive, since by proper treatment, a normal amount of adhesive will produce results equivalent to a high adhesive to pigment ratio which has not been so treated. The usual waterproofing agent is formaldehyde, but other aldehydes and hexamethylene tetramine have also been suggested.[8,11] The waterproofing treatment can be carried out in several ways: (A) The fixing or waterproofing agent can be incorporated directly into the coating mixture, (B) the sheet can be passed through a vapor chamber containing the desired fixing agent before it is made to adhere to the casting surface, and (c) the waterproofing treatment can take place at the rewet roll or in

a treating tank prior to pressing the wet coated face to the polished casting surface.

Coating Formulation

Practically all of the common adhesives used in other printing papers have been evaluated for use in the cast coating process. Casein, starch, soya protein, glue, and other binders have been studied, but casein is the usual adhesive. High-finishing clays, calcium carbonate, blanc fixe, and titanium oxides are the usual pigments. The pigments used in this process must be in an extremely finely dispersed form and extensive milling has been found generally to be a necessity.

Applications

This type of glossy coated paper is used as a converting base for printing and embossing for the fancy, decorative, display, and wrapping paper fields. In the graphic arts industry, now that satisfactory gloss inks have been developed for its printing, it has been extremely popular. In general, the colors available have been rather limited, and this has somewhat retarded its use in the specialty paper field, but all indications are that a wider range of colors will be soon available.

CALENDERED HIGH-GLOSS PAPERS

When it became desirable to manufacture high-gloss papers more economically and in greater widths than could be handled by flint and friction glazing techniques, supercalendering and various other smoothing processes were developed. The supercalendered papers today represent the largest volume of medium high finished product, and various modifications of supercalendered papers are extensively utilized in the high-finish field. A wide range of colors can be produced, and an increasing volume of such paper is used both in the field of graphic arts and as base papers for further specialty converting operations.

Base Paper

The base paper for use in this process requires certain minimum physical strength since it must undergo at least one and possibly more coating operations and a severe polishing operation. A smooth, well-sized, and dense sheet, free from fuzz is desirable since the smoother the base paper, the smoother and glossier will be the surface after burnishing. If the sheet is well sized and has a relatively dense structure, the coating pigment and adhesive will remain on the surface of the sheet and less of these substances will be required to produce a given effect.

Coating Equipment

Brush, roll, air knife, spray, or other types of equipment are all satisfactory for applying the base coating. The major requirement is to lay down a smooth coating which contains no surface markings and has no fibers protruding from the surface. The weight of coating laid down on the sheet varies with the end use, but heavier loads of coating generally produce glossier papers.[1] The usual loads of coating vary from 10 to 20 pounds (25 x 38-500). This is equivalent to 5.5 to 11 pounds (20 x 26-500). Festoon or straight-through tunnel driers, a slatted wheel, or drum driers can be used to remove the water and dry out the sheet. The coated paper is then wound on a reel and taken to the supercalenders or other burnishing equipment.

Polishing Equipment and Technology

The machine generally used to polish and burnish the coated sheets to develop the glossy effect is the supercalender. Such units can be built to handle great widths of paper and the polishing effect on a given sheet can be varied to some extent by controlling the hardness of the cloth or paper rolls.[1] In general, cloth-filled rolls are used on coated paper. A buffing technique has also been used subsequent to calendering to increase the finish.[21] Another technique has been suggested which is also suitable for handling great-width paper economically. In this method, the coated web is passed over a resilient moving bed, and heated elastic blades effect the glazing action.[2] The resilient bed may be an endless rubber-covered roll. The elastic blades are made of a material which will not mark or blacken the coated surface, i.e., steel, and are designed so that they can be heated to a controlled and uniform temperature.[2] The use of modified friction-type calenders has also been suggested as has the use of a brush or buffing machine subsequent to the super-calendering operation.

The desired properties in the finished sheet are 1. good, uniform ink absorption and printability, 2. good brightness, 3. uniform color, and 4. high gloss. The first properties are mainly dependent upon the adhesive to pigment ratio which should be such that the pigment is firmly bonded so that it does not pick off during the converting operation or on the printing press. The amount of adhesive should generally be kept as low as possible, however, since in a calendering operation, everything else being equal, the smoother and glossier sheet is generally obtained with the least amount of adhesive present.[8,11] The uniformity of the base paper and the uniformity of the coating, all else being equal, are important since if either is not uniform, the calendering operation will produce nonuniform density and surface appearance which will result in nonuniform ink absorbency. The brightness of the final product is dependent upon the allowable pressure in the calender, the amount of moisture in the sheet, the coating formulation, the base stock, and the type of pigment used. The color match depends upon the pigments and dyestuffs used, as well as the color and brightness of the body stock. The gloss is dependent upon the specific pigments used, the adhesive to pigment ratio, the type of drive and rolls in the calender, the effect of the calendering action on the coating, the moisture content of the coating, and the pressure in the calender stack. Where the smoothing bar type equipment is used,[2] the brightness and gloss are dependent upon the pigment used, the adhesive to pigment ratio, the presence of lubricants such as talc and polishing waxes in the coating formulation, the temperature of the bar, and the pressure applied to the sheet.

Supercalender Finish. Supercalender stacks are probably the oldest and most commonly used apparatus for polishing paper surfaces at high speeds. In general the finish obtained is not as high as with the other methods discussed but the cost is usually somewhat lower. Supercalendering is also the basis or preliminary process for some of the other methods. This is particularly true of the brush-finishing and buff-finishing techniques.

FIGURE 19. *Supercalender stack used in the fancy-paper industry* (Courtesy of Marvellum Company)

The fundamental aim in calendering coated paper is to obtain the maximum gloss with the minimum development of color and reduction of opacity. The compacting of the mineral and fiber contained in a sheet of paper tends to reduce the opacity and the light refraction. This causes a calender "black-ening" which is often referred to as dinginess or calender burning. The finest calendered paper is the sheet which has arrived at the optimum point between the calender blackening and high finish.

In general the factors that result in high finish are as follows:

1. Softness of mineral pigments
2. Fineness of the particle size of the mineral pigment
3. Low adhesive ratio (slack-sized coating)
4. Moisture content of the paper
5. Weight on the calender roll
6. Hardness of the cloth- or paper-filled calender roll
7. Temperature of the calender rolls

In virtually all cases, all the factors which tend to increase finish also tend to increase dinginess, so that this same list could be repeated under the heading "Factors Which Tend to Increase Dinginess of Calendered Paper."

In general, it has been found that a moderately hard pigment, such as calcium carbonate, will stand more drastic calendering treatment without blackening and thus give a better finish than most soft materials such as clays, satin white, and talcs. On the other hand, the very hard pigments such as the silicates, barytes, etc., are very resistant to calender action and will result in low finishes within the practical limits of usual calender pressures.[1]

It is possible to obtain pigments which are too fine for practical calender processing. Carbonate precipitates have been produced which are so fine—less than 0.2 micron—that they give a very poor color and actually yield lower finishes than carbonate particles of about 0.75 micron size. In general, clay particles in the range of 1 micron and carbonate particles in a range of 0.75 micron seem to give about the most satisfactory surfaces for supercalendering treatment. Probably 95% of the supercalendered paper produced today is coated with one or a combination of these two materials.

The smaller the amount of the adhesive used to bind the pigments to the paper, the higher the resulting calender finish. Obviously, this adhesive-pigment ratio cannot be reduced too far for then the pigment is not sufficiently bound to stand the pick of the printing press or to resist flaking or crumbling on folding. If the paper is to be used for offset printing, the coating must be more tightly bound than if it is to be used for letterpress or gravure printing and accordingly the finish must be lower than that of the paper used in the latter two processes. The nature of the adhesive has an effect on the finish, but if high-quality adhesives, such as casein, are used, the amount present in the paper and/or the degree of adhesion of the coating to the paper has much more effect on the finish than the normal variations between various types of adhesives. Of course, some adhesives such as certain grades of starch are recognized as being consistent producers of poor finish.

The moisture content of the paper should be kept as high as possible without excessive blackening. The actual amount of moisture varies with the nature of the pigment and adhesive. With calcium carbonate a moisture content as high as 7 to 8% is sometimes permissible. With some of the softest clays 4% moisture may be the maximum. The presence of satin white usually requires a lower moisture content in order to be able to calender without blackening.

The greater the weight per lineal inch on the calender roll, the higher the finish and the more blackening. Some carbonates and many of the barytes and silicates will stand all the pressure that is practical to exert in a calender stack without blackening. Too great pressure per lineal inch will result in short life of the fiber rolls.

Increasing the hardness of the fiber roll has an effect which is almost identical to increasing the weight per lineal inch of the stack. The harder roll is deformed less by the steel roll, and consequently, the nip area is reduced. This reduction in nip area results in greater pressure per square inch in the same way as the increase in the weighting of the stack. The disadvantage of hard calender rolls is that, in general, they are less resilient than the soft rolls and consequently, they "mark" or dent more readily than the soft rolls. However, the hard rolls can stand more weight per lineal inch of nip without excessive heating than can the softer rolls.

A higher finish is obtained from hot calender rolls than from cold ones. However, practically no increase in finish is seen at temperatures above 200° F. Some calender rolls are equipped for heating with steam although generally enough frictional heat is developed in the operation of the stack so that additional heating is unnecessary. Excessive heat materially shortens the life of the fiber calender rolls.

Where a carbonate-base paper with a normal amount of adhesive (10 to 20 parts) receives a severe supercalendering with steam, a good gloss can be attained. When the adhesive is increased to 40 to 50 parts, however, the gloss produced by the supercalender drops off sharply. If this high adhesive content sheet containing a small amount of wax is calendered on a modified friction-type unit with a low friction ratio (1:1.5 or 1:2) a sheet with fairly high gloss can be obtained, particularly if the moisture content in the coating is sufficiently high during the calendering operation. With such a formulation, it has also been found possible to polish the coated surface without crushing the entire sheet.

A specific example of the conditions required to produce a satisfactory finish using the supercalender on a carbonate and casein base sheet has been given by Clarke as follows: [1]

Moisture Content of Sheet	7%
Number of Rolls on Calender	9
Linear Nip Pressure on Paper	
Top of Stock	2,000 lb.
Bottom of Stock	2,600 lb.
Roll Density (Shore-D)	93
Roll Type	Paper-filled

Buffed Finish. There has long been a need for a sheet which would have the high finish and scuff and abrasion resistance of a flint paper without the disadvantages of slow production and high cost and the general difficulties usually associated with flint papers. To obtain such a product, in a recent development, the metal-polishing operation known as buffing has been adapted to paper manufacturing.[21] The previously coated and supercalendered web passes over a number of backing rolls. Above each backing roll is a rapidly rotating cloth-polishing or buffing roll. The buff is made up either of cloth discs or preferably of spirally convoluted cloth strips cut in such a manner that a continuous bias edge contacts the paper. An abrasive consisting primarily of stearic acid and silicate is applied almost continuously to the buff.

According to Clark [21] other abrasives suitable for use in the process include: very finely divided oxides of aluminum, chromium, iron, silicon and similar oxides; silicon carbide; and naturally occurring siliceous matter such as diatomaceous earth or tripoli. Generally speaking, in polishing paper of white or light color, it is preferred to use an abrasive which is also light in color to avoid danger of discoloring the paper surface by particles of abrasive which might be retained in microscopic crevices of the paper surface.

The buffs are usually about 18 inches in diameter and are rotated by a direct drive to a 1750 rpm motor giving a peripheral speed in the neighborhood of 10,000 feet per minute. Because of the considerable stress applied by the buff, holdback rolls are necessary between the buffing units. Paper speeds of 500 feet per minute are possible depending upon the nummer of buffs in the machine. The polishing roll may rotate in a direction the same as, or opposite to, the direction of paper travel, as desired; obviously, in the former case the rotative speed must be somewhat higher than in the latter case if an equivalent differential between paper travel and roll speed is to be maintained. The paper may be repassed under the polishing roll as many times as desired, or it may be passed in succession

into contact with a plurality of polishing rolls. If it is desired
to polish both sides of the paper, the polishing equipment may
easily be arranged so that one or more of the polishing rolls
contact each side of the web as the latter makes one passage
through the apparatus. The pressure of the soft resilient polishing surface against the paper surface to be polished is difficult
to define numerically. The polishing surface preferably contacts the paper so lightly as to allow considerable slippage while
bringing the finely divided abrasive into engagement with the
paper surface.[21]

The effect of this treatment is to increase the gloss of a
paper but is confined entirely to the surface of the sheet. The
surface is closed up and densified so that its resistance to
penetration by spirit or oil varnish, lacquer or similar agents is
remarkably increased, but the underlying portions and bulk
of the sheet are affected little if at all by the polishing treatment.

Examples of the degree to which the gloss of various papers
can be increased by polishing in the manner described are given
in Table IV. All gloss figures were obtained by use of a
Bausch & Lomb glossmeter.[21]

TABLE IV

The Effect of Surface Polishing on the Gloss of Coated Papers

Paper Sample	Gloss before Treatment	Gloss after Treatment
1. High-grade, Varnishable, Supercalendered, Un-coated Paper	45	70–75
2. High-grade, Glossy, Supercalendered, Mineral-coated Printing Paper	63	97
3. Yellow, Supercalendered, Mineral-coated Box Liner	58	92
4. Friction-calendered, White, Coated Box Liner	65	80
5. Cast-coated Paper	83	100
6. High-grade, Flint-glazed, White, Coated Paper	95	99

Formulation

Calcium carbonate seems to be the most popular pigment for
use in these coatings since it is a bright pigment and will take

a high gloss in the polishing operation. Where high-finishing clays are also used in the formulation they harden up the coating and add weight to the sheet. In some cases satin white has also been used with both clay and calcium carbonate. An enamel finish, for example, can be made by using 33 parts of satin white, 33 parts of calcium carbonate, and 33 parts of high-finishing clay.[20] According to Hughes and Roderick,[18] a small percentage of added satin white, clay, or titanium dioxide will actually increase the gloss of the sheet over that obtained with plain calcium carbonate.

Certain high-finishing carbonate pigments, although they develop a high finish, do not retain satisfactory opacity and covering power, although this is generally a result of the average particle size, or particle shape. The addition of titanium dioxide will help to overcome this deficiency, without loss of brightness or gloss. Flint-glazed papers are often made with 75 to 100% carbonate, whereas in friction glazed formulae the usual ratio with clay is 50 to 50. The carbonate will not replace any of the talc or waxes which are used to produce slip and act as lubricants in the polishing operation.[20] When satin white is used in the coating, it assists in waterproofing the sheet without additional treatment and it polishes to a high gloss on supercalendering or friction calendering. This pigment needs much more adhesive than is normally required for satisfactory bonding, as much as 35 to 50 parts with casein and 70 to 75 parts with starch and this is an additional deterrent to its use.[19]

A wide range of coating weights can be used and 10 to 25 pounds (25 x 38-500) have been successfully handled. Casein is the usual adhesive although starch, soya protein, and polyvinyl alcohol have been claimed to be satisfactory.[1] According to Roderick and Hughes,[17] starches do not produce as much gloss as soya protein, while casein is the best adhesive for this purpose. At least 10 to 20 parts of binder per 100 parts of pigment are generally required. The coating may be colored or tinted with dyestuffs or pigments. In general, where any substantial amount of color is required in the sheet, it is obtained by using special high-finishing pigments or dyestuffs, since most pigment colors do not produce the required gloss when the sheet is polished.

Where heavy-weight coatings are desired, multiple coating may be necessary. Sheets of the highest gloss can often be produced by such multiple-coating methods, since the surface coating in this case is laid down the most uniformly and on the smoothest base.

It is sometimes desirable to produce a coated paper which has water and wet-abrasion resistance and a minimum of ink penetration. Such a coating can be produced by treating or fixing the adhesive used in the coating formulation. In some cases, urea-formaldehyde or melamine-formaldehyde resins are used for this purpose. The waterproofing treatment may be carried out by adding the fixing agent to the coating mixture, by passing the wet or partially dried sheet through a vapor chamber, or by passing the coated sheet through a dip tank containing the fixing solution or spraying the surface as it passes through the drier. The treatment waterproofs the adhesive, which is important in papers for the converting industry, and hardens the coating and improves ink holdup which is important in the printing paper field.

Applications of High-Gloss Papers

The glossy papers produced by these processes are in great demand as printing-base papers for both the converting and the graphic arts industries. The white, ivory, buff, and other delicate tints are used as printing-base papers and the colored sheets are converted and applied as box and fancy papers, greeting cards, and decorative and display papers, as well as for many other such uses. They are sold both in rolls and sheet form. The sheet makes an excellent gloss ink base and is also used in the varnishing field.

For many years, there has been a very pronounced trend towards more attractive packaging and labeling of retail products. A primary cause of this trend is the "super market" type of retailing. The consumer is faced with a number of competitive brands of the same product, all placed on the same shelf and therefore the attractiveness of the package plays a major part in his selection. To make a package attractive, certain fundamental properties are required in packaging or labeling paper. One of the most important of these properties in certain applications is a glossy, high-finish surface. This surface can be obtained by a number of methods. Some of these processes not only improve the appearance of the package, but also add functional properties such as scuff resistance, etc.

Because of the tremendous demand for high-finish papers, a vigorous effort has been made by the paper-manufacturing industry to improve the finish, reduce the cost, and increase the volume of this type of paper. The conventional methods have been slightly advanced, but what is more important, several new and improved methods have been developed or are in the process of development.

A box-cover or label paper is a functional product. It has a job to do. It is not enough that it looks well and prints well; it must also produce a practical and satisfactory package. Some general requirements for an ideal box cover and label paper are as follows.

1. *Abrasion resistant surface*
   The paper must stand rough handling without scuffing or "color marking."
2. *Flexibility*
   It must have a flake-free, leathery fold that will bend around the contours of the package and double over on itself without cracking.
3. *Glossy, nonabsorptive surface*
   It must not pick up dirt readily and must resist all types of greasy finger marking. It should permit ready cleansing by wiping with a dry cloth.
4. *Printability*
   It must be capable of good reproduction when the standard inks and printing processes are applied.

5. *Appearance*

The appearance must be attractive, the finish very glossy or attractively dull as desired, the colors rich and deep, and the whites bright and brilliant.

6. *Handling*

It must handle satisfactorily for both hand and machine box-cover work.

7. *Cost and production*

The cost must be competitive with that of other packaging products and the method of production capable of high-speed, quantity manufacture.

These requirements will be taken one by one and examined from the standpoint of the various high-finish papers.

1. Abrasion Resistance. Supercalendered paper is only moderately resistant to abrasion. Brush-finished paper is slightly better in this respect and friction-calendered paper is considerably better. Cast-coated paper with its soft uncalendered surface often causes trouble. It scuffs and "color marks" very easily. By far the best papers in respect to abrasion resistance are flint glazed and the buffed paper. Their hard, slippery surface will stand a great deal of abuse.

2. Flexibility. Flexibility is generally a function of bulk and apparent density. All the papers that are compacted through a calendering or glazing operation are better than those which are not so compacted. The cast-coated papers are usually the poorest folders. The supercalendered and brushed sheets are somewhat better. The friction-calendered, flint-glazed, and buffed papers are the best.

3. Glossy, Nonabsorptive Surface. The nonabsorptive surface is necessary to prevent soiling of packages. Unfortunately, a nonabsorptive surface is not a readily printable surface and so absorptivity and printability are more or less opposed to each other. Cast coated papers which have a porous, ink-receptive surface are also receptive to soiling and finger marking. Supercalendered paper is a little better. The surface is partially closed by the calendering operation. Brushed papers are quite a bit better. The brushing operation greatly reduces the absorbency of the surface. Friction-glazed, flint-glazed and buffed papers are quite resistant to soiling. They can be readily cleansed of finger marks and most normal soil by wiping with a dry cloth.

It should be kept in mind that while the initial appearance of the package is important, its appearance after normal storage and handling life on a shelf is even more so. The customer chooses a package by its appearance at the time he sees it on the shelf—not by its original appearance when first manufactured.

4. **Printability.** To produce an attractive package, a packaging or label paper must be capable of good reproduction by standard printing processes. The cast coated papers probably stand well above the other types in printability. Their flat absorptive surface is ideal for ink reception. Their initial serious disadvantage, i.e., that gloss inks do not give good results on them, has been partially overcome by recent ink developments. Supercalendered papers have good printability and will generally print gloss inks satisfactorily. Brush papers are a little less receptive to ink than the supercalendered ones. Friction-glazed, buffed, and flint-glazed papers are relatively poor printing papers. The hard, closed, waxy surface will not absorb ink very readily. The lubricating wax which is necessary in the glazing or burnishing processes penetrates the coating so that it is not very ink-receptive.

5. **Appearance.** The highest finish is obtained by buffing, flint glazing, and cast coating methods. One disadvantage of the cast-coated sheet is that it is difficult to manufacture in rich, dark colors due to the lack of deepening action in cast coating, which is present in the other processes. However, pastels and medium shades are obtained with considerably less mottle than by the other methods. Calendered and buffed paper does not have as good depth as the flints and frictioned sheets.

6. **Handling.** Friction and flint papers have a general reputation for difficult handling. Most of the other types are easy to handle. It is generally conceded in the box cover and

labeling industry that the cast-coated papers have better pasting properties due to their less smooth back.

7. Production and Cost. The supercalendered, brushed, friction-calendered, cast-coated, and buffed papers are all large-scale production items. The flint papers are very definitely limited by the slow speed of the flinting operation. Thus the high finished flints are only partially competitive with the other grades. Obviously, the supercalendered papers are the cheapest due to their high-speed production. The brushed, buffed, and friction papers are somewhat higher in cost; the former due to the additional brushing or buffing operation and the latter due to the lower productivity of the friction stacks. The cast-coated papers are simpler to make, since they require fewer manufacturing operations. However, the initial machine installation is very expensive and the production rates are low due to the necessity of drying in contact with a single dryer.

REFERENCES

1. J. W. Clark. *U. S. Patent 2,395,992.* Mineral-Coated Printing Paper (1946).
2. A. R. Trist. *U. S. Patent 2,404,606.* Method and Machine for Burnishing the Surface of Paper (1946).
3. D. B. Bradner. *U. S. Patent 1,719,166.* Process of Calendering Mineral-Coated Paper and Product (1929).
4. E. Warner. *U. S. Patent 2,331,922.* Method for Coating Paper (1943).
5. W. J. Montgomery. *U. S. Patent 2,331,922.* Process of Coating Paper (1943).
6. W. J. Montgomery and D. B. Bradner. *U. S. Patent 2,245,045.* Coated Paper (1941).
7. Id. *U. S. Patent 2,214,566.* Coated Paper and Method of Making the Same (1940).
8. Id. *U. S. Patent 2,214,564.* Coated Paper and Method of Making the Same (1940).
9. Id. *U. S. Patent 2,214,565.* Coated Paper and Method of Making the Same (1940).
10. Id. *U. S. Patent 2,029,273.* Process of Coating Paper (1936).
11. E. G. Bennett. *U. S. Patent 2,369,427.* Paper Coating Composition and Method of Making (1945).
12. F. Kabel and G. F. Whiting. *U. S. Patent 2,267,470.* Method and Means for Coating Paper (1941).
13. W. F. Grupe. *U. S. Patent 2,428,113.* Machine for Coating Paper (1947).

14. Id. *U. S. Patent 2,304,818*. Art of Coating Paper (1942).
15. Edwin Sutermeister. *The Chemistry of Pulp and Papermaking, 3rd Edition*. John Wiley & Sons, Inc., New York (1941) p. 368.
16. A. E. Hughes and H. F. Roderick. "A Study of How Calcium Carbonate, Clay, and Casein Coating Mixtures Affects Certain Sheet Characteristics." *Paper Trade J*. **109,** No. 11 74–79 (1939).
17. H. F. Roderick and A. E. Hughes. "An Evaluation of Calcium Carbonate Coating Colors Formulated with Various Adhesives." *Paper Trade J*. **110,** No. 8:104–108 (1940).
18. A. E. Hughes and H. F. Roderick. "Paper Coating Pigments." *Paper Trade J., ***110,** No. 26:83–86 (1940).
19. Anon. Satin White T.A.P.P.I. Special Report No. 351 Technical Association of the Pulp and Paper Industry, New York, 1944.
20. Anon. Calcium Carbonate T.A.P.P.I. Special Report No. 346 Technical Association of the Pulp and Paper Industry, New York, 1944.
21. J. W. Clark. *U. S. Patent 2,349,704*. Paper with Improved Surface (1944).

Chapter VI

MISCELLANEOUS DECORATIVE PAPERS

by R. H. Mosher

THERE are several types of decorative papers which are produced by the specialty converting industry but do not fit into any of the other larger groups of classification. Such papers are used in one or more specific applications and are manufactured by a special technique or using a type of material which is not common to the rest of the industry, therefore, they will be discussed separately.

Such papers are:

Metallic coated papers
Luminescent coated and printed papers
Mica-coated papers
Dull-coated papers
Decalcomanias or transfers
Flock-coated or velour papers
Marbled papers

METALLIC COATED PAPERS

Some of the most popular fancy papers, which have been on the market for many years, are the metallic coated papers. Such sheets, produced on a wide range of basis weight papers, and with gold, copper, silver, or colored metallic surfaces, are utilized in many ways in the box and fancy paper field; for match covers, menu and brochure covers, greeting cards, tags, labels, announcements, booklet covers, display papers, and many other applications.[1,2]

There are three types of such papers:

1. The standard metallic coated papers are made by dispersing a gold, copper, aluminum, or other colored metallic pigment in an adhesive vehicle and coating this on a sheet of paper. The pigment is firmly bonded to the sheet surface and the resulting product gleams in a brilliant and truly metallic manner.

2. Another type of metallic paper is made by coating the paper with a tin, lead, cadmium, antimony, or other metal oxide dispersed in a suitable binder and friction calendering the resulting sheet. This operation burnishes the relatively dull coating so that the resulting sheet has an appearance in many ways similar to a metal foil paper. The sheet may be colored to represent gold or copper by incorporating dyestuffs into the coating or by staining the finished sheet. In many cases the product is coated with a clear lacquer to enhance the gloss and protect the surface from tarnishing.

3. The third type of metallic paper is prepared by a dusting technique. The paper is first coated with an adhesive layer, which is then dusted with the gold powder. The excess powder is removed, and the sheet calendered to produce the desired effect.

Such papers can be used as base papers for printing or can be laminated to the surface of other papers or boards for decorative applications. Some of the aluminum-coated papers have been used as structural insulation due to their ability to reflect heat and light waves and prevent the loss or gain of heat through a wall by radiation.

The Technology of Metallic Coatings and Coated Paper

1. **Pigment Coated Metallic Papers.** The general technique for producing metallic coated papers involves the disper-

sion of the metallic powder in a suitable vehicle and the application of this coating compound to the paper surface. Any desirable base paper can be used, and it may be precoated if necessary. In any case, the paper must possess uniform formation, density, and surface finish and should be fairly highly sized to prevent penetration of the coating adhesive into the base paper. The base coating may be plain or pigmented, and can be formulated from casein, glue, starch, or synthetic or natural resins.

The metallic coating may contain bronze powders (gold or copper), aluminum powder (silver), or the various specially colored metallic powders. These metallic powders vary in particle size, particle shape, degree of polishing, and density and the specific requirements depend upon the adhesive and vehicle formulation used and the method of application. Some powders are highly *polished* and contain a high percentage of stearic acid, olive oil, oleic acid or other polishing medium and others are low in polishing agent. The reason for incorporating a polishing agent is to produce "leafing" of the metallic particles in the vehicle after it is laid down on the paper. To produce a high metallic lustre, the flakes must go to the surface of the film and so orient themselves that a continuous film of metal is obtained. When "leafing" metallic powders are applied to the sheet in a vehicle which permits this phenomenon to take place, the flakes are carried to the surface and form the desired film. Leafing is a surface-tension phenomenon, and the higher the surface tension the more rapid and complete is the leafing.[3] The coverage of these coatings depends directly upon the particle size (i.e., the finer the particle size the better the coverage), smoothness, and hiding power. The metallic brilliance of the resulting coating depends, however, inversely on the particle size, i.e., the larger the individual particles, the greater the metallic brilliance.

The adhesive and vehicle used produce varying effects, and these are selected according to the type of metallic powder used. With vehicles dispersed in water, such as casein, glue, starch, soya protein, or natural or synthetic resin or rubber, relatively coarse golds are used which contain some polishing agent or agents which produce water miscibility.[3] These coatings can be applied to uncoated base papers using brush, roll, spray, or air-blade coaters. Synthetic-resin- or rubber-base vehicles, the so-called plastic coatings, which require the use of solvent or hot melt application techniques, generally use finer, highly polished metallics and these are laid down on precoated base papers. Roll, gravure-roll, or knife coaters are generally used as the application equipment. The type of adhesive has much to do with the final properties of the coated sheet. Water-base metallic coatings are generally more brilliant, require heavier loads for coverage, and do not possess much film flexibility. The plastic-coated metallic papers generally show less brilliance and brightness, but they are more flexible, require less of a coating load to obtain coverage, and show a smoothness and luster which is not obtainable by other means. The water-base coatings tend to tarnish faster than do the plastic types.

The finished coated paper is usually calendered and/or embossed to bring out the full brightness and luster of the metallic surface. In some cases the coating is brushed to obtain special effects.

2. **Synthetic or Frictioned Metallics (Argentine).** The so-called "silver paper" is made with a metal oxide base coating (Argentine) which was originally produced from a mixture of zinc and antimony oxide powder. In later developed formulations also tin oxide, cadmium oxide, lead oxide, and other waste or by-product metallic oxides were used. These compounds are mixed with starch, casein, glue, or synthetic or natural resin adhesives and coated on the paper in a manner common to other pigmented coatings using water as the carrier. Brush, roll, spray, air-blade or other special application equipment are all satisfactory for the job. Almost any type of coating base stock can be used, but the sheet should have uniform density, formation, and sizing, and as smooth a surface as possible is desirable. The coating is applied in a thin layer to the paper surface and

it is possible to obtain a well-covered, readily frictionable surface without the use of excessive amounts of polishing waxes.[1, 2] If casein is used as a binder no further addition of frictioning agents is necessary, but if starch, glue, or resins are used, some polishing wax in the formulation is generally recommended for best results. The coated paper can be dried in the conventional manner and then friction-calendered to produce the desired smooth silvery metallic finish. Synthetic golds and colored metallics can be produced by the addition of dye-stuffs to the coating mixture or the finished frictioned sheet can be stained in a final operation.

A typical formulation is as follows: [1]

	Parts
Metal Oxide	100
Casein	16
Polishing Wax	10

It has been found desirable to coat two layers of the metallic film on a pigment-coated base stock. A pyroxylin top coating is suggested to improve the over-all appearance and properties of the sheet.[1]

3. **Dusted Metallic Papers.** Dusted metallic paper can be produced in a wide range of basis weights since the finished sheet only requires calendering or embossing to be ready for use. Almost any type of base paper can be used. The equipment required is rather unique, however, although very similar in design to that used for producing flocked or velour and abrasive papers. A roll coater is generally used to apply the adhesive to the sheet, and this is followed by a duster, excess powder removing attachment, and rewind unit. The finished sheet is then calendered and/or embossed to set the metallic film and produce the desired smooth and brilliant surface. This operation also tends to adhere the powder firmly to the adhesive layer. The finished sheet may be lacquer coated to protect the metallic surface from tarnishing.

The adhesive used to make the metallic pigment adhere to

the paper may be shellac or another natural resin, a synthetic resin, a rubber, or a protein such as casein, zein or corn protein, or soya protein. The formulation may be solvent, heat, or pressure sensitive. The solvent and pressure sensitive coatings must be coated, then dusted, brushed, and the excess coating mixture and any solvent removed before the paper can be rolled up. The heat-sensitive coatings can be laid down on the paper, dried, and cooled. Then the sheet can be wound up in one operation, and then dusted in a secondary operation if desirable. Such a system is described by one author as follows: The paper is coated with shellac dissolved in denatured alcohol using a roll coating unit, then passed over a steam drum and dried, and finally wound up. This sheet is then dusted with bronze powder in a second machine, following which the paper passes over a heated surface which softens the shellac so that the bronze adheres firmly to it. Two rapidly rotating rollers covered with flannel rub the bronze firmly into position and dust the residue cleanly from the paper surface. A suction box is disposed above these rollers and this with an air exhauster unit collects the freely flying bronze for reuse. The excess bronze still on the paper is then rinsed off with water and the wet paper passes over a drying drum which dries off the water and, by softening the shellac layer, again causes a more complete adherence of the metallic powder.[2] The sheet can then be calendered, friction calendered, or glazed and a thin lacquer coating can be applied.[2] Such papers probably show the most metallic properties since there is no binder on the surface to dull the metallic finish.

LUMINESCENT COATED AND PRINTED PAPERS

Luminescent pigments can be fluorescent or phosphorescent. Fluorescent pigments emit visible light only while they are exposed to an exciting light source, which is usually of the ultraviolet or "black-light" type. Phosphorescent pigments also emit visible light when exposed to ultraviolet rays, but their main advantage is their ability to continue to emit visible light after the exciting source has been removed. With phosphorescent pigments, daylight or visible light can also be used as an exciting medium.

The fluorescent pigments possess daylight colors of varying shades of yellow, blue, gray, cerise, blue green, and white. When excited by "black light," they exhibit colors ranging from orange red to yellow, green, blue, and blue-white. The pigments are fairly coarse and can be formulated for use in coatings or in inks.

The phosphorescent pigments can be divided into two main classes; those with a short afterglow period (30 minutes to 2 hours), and those with a longer period of afterglow (6 to 12 hours). The first, or short afterglow type are very coarse in texture, and efforts to reduce the particle size generally result in a degradation of the light properties. These pigments can be obtained in green, orange-yellow, blue-green, and blue in both the daylight and the excited state. They can be used in the formulation of coatings and printing inks. The longer-afterglow types are also quite coarse and diminution of particle size will cause degradation in properties. They are both very susceptible to moisture and cannot be used in a water system. Their use is limited to coatings and inks in which organic solvents are the basic carriers.

The fluorescent pigments are usually based upon zinc sulfide or zinc and cadmium sulfides. The phosphorescent pigments are formulated from calcium and strontium sulfides. In general practice, small amounts of other metals such as copper, bismuth, silver, or manganese are mixed with the pure soluble compounds since none of them alone would have a brilliant luminescence. This activating metal will cause the pigment to glow colorfully.[4] Both the phosphorescent and the fluorescent pigments can be modified in their daylight form by the addition of small amounts of dyestuffs or suitable pigments without materially affecting the luminescent color or brightness. Fluorescent pigments can be used in casein, starch, or water-dispersed resin systems. Varnishes or lacquers are also satisfactory vehicles for more resistant films.

FIGURE 20. *Uses of fluorescence in printing and coating murals, wallpaper, and drapes* (Courtesy of New Jersey Zinc Co.)

The intensity and length of afterglow of phosphorescent pigments depend upon several factors which include (1) type of pigment, (2) medium in which it is incorporated, (3) intensity of exciting light, (4) the length of time the pigment is exposed to the light, and (5) the temperature. The amount of activation required to obtain maximum afterglow depends upon the type of pigment. In general, a pigment which has a long afterglow requires more time of exposure than does a pigment which has a short afterglow.

There are also a large number of dyestuffs which can be used in similar applications although those commercially available at the present time are limited to fluorescent types which require excitation before they show any visible radiation. These materials are available in a wide range of daylight colors and solubilities and a correspondingly wide range of fluorescent colors. They find a limited use in both coatings and printing inks.

The coatings and printing effects obtained with these materials open up many interesting applications. Treated paper can be used in safety papers, decalcomanias, match cover stocks, greeting cards, gift wraps, synthetic leathers, adhesive and marking tapes, and religious item mountings. The printed applications include special wallpapers, paper drapes, shelf papers, gift wrappings, lampshades, and display and advertising papers.

MICA-COATED PAPERS

Mica-coated or satin papers are a special type of fancy and decorative sheet whose surface glistens and sparkles with thousands of tiny reflections of light. The sheet is produced in a wide range of colors and may be printed or embossed at will. The most popular colors are the pastel and light shades and they are used in the fancy box and packaging field, for labels, and for various other decorative applications. The sparkling effect is obtained by suspending finely ground mica flakes in the coating mix and these orient themselves in the coating when it is laid down on the paper so that their reflecting surfaces are parallel to the surface of the sheet with the result that they act as countless tiny mirrors which reflect the light. Mica is usually the only pigment used in these formulations as it is not desirable to cover the brilliance in any way. No colored pigments or pulp colors are generally used in the coating to obtain colors for a similar reason, but dyestuffs are commonly used to attain the desired shade.

Base Paper and Coating Equipment

The base paper for mica coatings is similar in basis weight and structure to that used for dull coats or other box papers. Its basis weight ranges from 38 to 65 pounds (25 x 38–500) and the sheet should be well sized and of uniform formation and density. It should have a smooth surface finish. The coating can be applied by brush, roll, spray, or air-blade coating equipment and all produce a satisfactory sheet. The only major problem is to keep the mica flakes suspended in the coating mixture prior to application to the paper and to obtain a good, uniform coating on the paper where the flakes are oriented in a plane parallel to the paper surface. Generally light coating loads (2 to 4 pounds 20 x 26–500) are used.

The coated sheet is usually given a calender finish after coating and is often embossed before shipment.

Coating Formulation

A typical mica coating formula is as follows:

	Parts
Mica Flakes	55
Casein (Dry)	14
Dyestuffs	To obtain desired color
Suspending Agent ..	50

It is also necessary to include in the formulation dispersing agents for the casein, antifoam compounds, leveling agents, plasticizers, and possibly some polishing wax, such as carnauba. As a suspending agent a gum, starch, water-soluble resin, or other compound is used which will assist in maintaining a good dispersion of the mica prior to coating. Waterproofing agents can be incorporated if this is desirable.

There is sometimes a demand for certain special coating effects and in these cases, mica flakes may be incorporated into pigment coatings, but this is not a regular practice since the effect of mica is very much reduced by the presence of the pigment.

DULL, SUEDE, OR MATTE COATED PAPERS

Dull, suede, or matte coated papers are used widely in the fancy, box, and decorative paper fields because of their diffusely reflecting, dull, satiny surface. Although they do not possess the striking appearance of the highly glossy papers, they do exhibit a soft, rich effect which is widely utilized. They are made in a wide range of colors and can be made lightfast, and water and wet-rub resistant. The papers print well, although they tend to absorb more ink, in general, than do the glossy coated papers. The commonly used white pigments include the carbonates, clays, and blanc fixe. Pulp colors and dry pigments are both utilized to produce the desired colored shades. The sheet is generally given a light calender treatment to smooth the coated surface but not enough to produce any gloss or finish. Casein is the adhesive generally used, although some of the new synthetic resins have shown definite promise. Color and brightness are extremely important, particularly in the light and pastel shades, and any dark color contributed by the adhesive tends to reduce both brightness and purity of shade. The major problem with this type of coated paper is to obtain smoothness without gloss.

Base Paper and Coating Equipment

The base paper generally used is a soda-sulfite sheet, ranging in basis weight from 38 to 65 pounds (25 x 38–500). The paper should be well sized and show a uniform density and formation with the surface uniform but not too highly finished, since a slight "tooth" will assist in producing the desired dull effect.

The paper is generally coated on brush, air-blade, or spray equipment and all produce an equally good sheet. The main requirement is uniform color distribution on the paper so as to produce uniformity of shade and coverage on the backing sheet.

Coating Formulation

A few standard formulations for four shades of colored dull-coats are listed below. The color pigments are listed on a dry basis, but both dry pigments and pulp colors are commonly used. The amount of adhesive used in generally about 16 to 20% based on the adhesive-pigment formulation. Other agents added to the formula, besides those required to solubilize the casein, are wetting agents, dispersing agents, leveling agents, anti-foaming compounds, and such compounds as wax dispersions which produce smooth flow out and aid in printing ink holdup. Waterproofing agents may also be included if desirable.

Dull Coat Formulae

White	Parts	Yellow	Parts	Blue	Parts	Maroon	Parts
Casein	225	Casein	100	Casein	264	Casein	81
Special Coating Clay	365	Special Coating Clay	283	Special Coating Clay	113	Maroon	257
English Clay	554	Lemon Yellow	134	Blue Pigment No. 1	849	Red	6
		Chrome Yellow	53	Blue Pigment No. 2	108	Grey	29
				Violet Pigment	30	Chrome Yellow	1

The coating loads applied with these formulations range from 3 to 7 pounds (20 x 26–500).

There have been suggested other formulae for producing dull-surfaced coatings, particularly for printing paper. These formulae usually included some dulling agent. Bradner [6] suggests the addition of uncooked dry starch to the coating mix, about 25% based on the solids, and this mix is applied in the usual manner and the coated paper calendered. The sheet is passed over a moistening roll and then dried. According to Bradner's disclosure the water is absorbed by the starch grains which swell slightly and produce a surface which tends to diffuse the reflected light. In a second disclosure,[7] he suggests the use of pulverized cellulose fiber which is claimed to produce a similar effect. Sutermeister states,[8] that a fine dull-surfaced paper can be produced by applying a thin wash coat to a pre-coated and calendered paper. This technique is claimed to produce a peculiar velvety surface which prints readily, but which is easily abraded and marred.

DECALCOMANIA OR TRANSFER PAPERS

The development and utilization of decalcomanias or transfers is an interesting story which dates back to the beginning of the 18th century. In 1826, an Austrian named Rothmüller patented a method of obtaining lithographic transfers, in black and in colors, which could be transferred to the surfaces of tin, wood, waxed cloth, and other difficult surfaces. The early technique was based on a lithographic impression on a sheet of paper which had been surfaced with a water-soluble coating, with the order of the printing of the colors for the final effect being reversed. A final coating of white pigment gave the illustration its background. This print was then pressed upon an object which had been previously varnished with copal resin, the paper back was moistened and removed and the picture it supported remained fixed on the new surface.[9]

The technique spread from one European country to another, but Germany was the center of the industry, particularly for the decoration of china and toys. The technique became so popular in the late 19th century that it earned its name, "decalcomania," which is coined from a Greek root "decal," meaning off the paper and "mania," meaning craze. Hand decorations with elaborate styling were costly and took a long time. In contrast, the decals, or transfers, offered the advantage of ease of application and flexibility of use and economy. The early volume in this country consisted mainly of stock designs, and these later developed into special designs and name plates, and today decals are used to decorate ceramics, wood, ivory, glass, plastics, and trademark designs, window signs, trucks and mobile equipment. The sizes run from a fraction of a square inch, on the state tax seal on cigarette packages, to the thousands of square inches, for trucks and giant air transport planes. In general, they are used to decorate or print anything which cannot be run through a printing press.[9]

The actual manufacture of decalcomanias in the United States was begun by Herman Pfeil at 1020 Arch Street, Philadelphia in the early 1890's. The volume grew steadily and the domestic items gradually replaced the imported products. About 1912, the manufacture of ceramic decalcomanias was started. This portion of the industry was an instantaneous success and the volume increased very rapidly.[9]

The present-day decalcomania is the result of a highly specialized process. In consists of one or more layers of ink which form a design or pictorial representation which is built up on a special paper or cloth backing. The "decal" is actually an image of printing ink, lacquer, or synthetic enamel forming a homogeneous film which slips or slides off the moistened paper surface. The paper is a special coated type which allows the built up film or print to be transferred to the object to which it is to be applied. The printing or building up of the various films of pigments is generally produced by the lithographic process, but letterpress, gravure, offset, and silk-screen techniques are also commonly used for special purposes. Some decalcomanias have consisted of as many as 25 to 30 single impressions, although most of them are limited to 3 to 8 individual colors. The pigments used depend upon the requirements, and range from cheap prints, on toys and cheap pottery, to the heat- and light-stable types, used on good fused ceramics and weather-resistant vehicle decorations. A film of plastic lacquer is often laid down first, the printing done on top of this film, and a final film of lacquer laid down on the surface. These films are protective in nature and the final decal is a sandwich structure which can be conveniently handled.

There are two main classes of decals, classified according to their method of application. The direct-transfer types are those which are applied to the desired surface, either by moistening a gummed layer on the inside face and attaching the decal to the object, or by applying varnish or shellac to the surface and pasting the face on the object in this manner. In either case the paper back is then sponged with warm water until the paper or cloth backing is released, leaving the print adhering to the object. The "slide off" transfer type decal is first floated on water, which separates the print from the paper backing, and the print is then applied to the desired surface, either by self-adherence, or by the use of additional adhesive. The decal print is immersed in water for about 15 seconds and then allowed to stand until the print can be slid off. Too long immersion washes away too much of the soluble adhesive which is depended upon for the adhesion of the decal to the object.

A further differentiation in these two classes can be made according to whether the print is applied face up or face down. The order of application of the various color prints depends upon which variety is desired and calls for a skillful handling of the colors, as well as a thorough knowledge of the principles of the art work involved. Where the face-down type is used, such as on the back of a window where the print is viewed through the glass, the base or background coat is printed first, followed by the various colored designs which make up the over-all design. Where the face-up type is desired, which is applied to an opaque background, the various portions of the design which blend to make the final effect are printed in order and the opaque background is printed the last. A special type is the two sided window decal which can be viewed from either side of the window. One side to be viewed is printed first, each color in the correct order and finally several impressions of opaque background. The design is then repeated in reverse

FIGURE 21. *Offset printing decals* (Courtesy of Palm, Fechteler & Co.)

order so that it can be viewed from the opposide side. As a rule, an adhesive is applied over the final print so that the decal can be used as a "slide off" or a direct transfer on to the glass.

The register problem in printing decalcomanias is an acute one and air-conditioned pressrooms are generally needed. It is a painstaking, intricate process which requires care and ingenuity to obtain perfect register of brilliant colors. The designs may vary from simple lettering to multicolor pictorial representations while the shapes vary from simple squares and circles to complicated irregular contours.[9]

Base-Paper Requirements

The base sheet for use as a backing for the decal may be one of two types. It may be a single sheet to which all coatings and printings are applied, or it may be thin tissue paper which is laminated to a heavier paper or cloth to eliminate curl and dimensional change and to facilitate the printing and registering operations. In each case, the paper is an absorbent, rather open, unsized sheet, possessing uniform color, formulation, and surface properties and preferably a high wet strength. The basis weights range from 50 to 90 pounds (25 x 38–500). The backing sheet is generally relatively unsized and in some cases may be a waterleaf sheet [10] to facilitate the penetration of water for releasing the decal from the transfer paper.

Transfer Paper Preparation and Technology

The preparation of the coated transfer paper ready for further coating and printing of the actual decal is that portion of the process which falls in the field of the specialty paper industry. Further treatment and the actual production of the finished decalcomania is beyond its scope and will not be covered in any detail.

The first coating laid down on the transfer paper is the coating on the decal side of the sheet and this must be water-soluble and ink receptive. This coating acts as a base for the actual printing operations but must dissolve when treated with warm water so as to release the finished decal. The coating is applied to the felt side of the sheet to reduce curl, and must be very smooth and uniform and contain no ridges. Brush, roll, or air-blade coating equipment is generally used to produce the desired results. The coating may be composed of starch and gum arabic; albumen, glycerin, and starch; egg albumen; starch and dextrose; or it may be any other suitable water-soluble coatings.[9, 10, 11, 12, 13] A fairly heavy coating load is applied since it must produce a smooth printing surface and yet separate the two layers smoothly when it is dissolved out. It is sometimes desirable to lay down a coat of clear or pigmented lacquer over this coating at the converting plant so as to make a better printing base, but this is optional and depends upon the requirements of the customer. It is general practice to calender the finished coated paper to produce the required over-all smoothness for further printing operations.

This type of sheet will be very sensitive to atmospheric conditions, particularly humidity, and may curl badly if not stored in moistureproof wrappers and handled in air-conditioned rooms. This curling, of course, not only makes the sheets hard to handle, but also makes registration in the printing press practically impossible to attain. Stewart,[10] suggests that the finished transfer paper is coated on the reverse surface with a film of gelatin. This tends to exclude atmospheric moisture and seal in the moisture already present. The coating may be prepared from 10 parts of gelatin and 90 parts of a mixture of water and methyl alcohol in a ratio of 3 to 2. Other water-miscible solvents, such as ethyl alcohol, acetone, and tertiary butyl alcohol, may also be used. The coating is applied on a roll applicator and the bath temperature should be maintained at 115°F. to obtain the desired solubility and solution viscosity.[10] This coating is claimed to balance the stresses in the sheet and prevent water absorption, both of which lead to curl. It dissolves off readily in warm water when the decal is applied to the desired surface.

A technique for preventing curl in the transfer paper and to eliminate registration problems in printing is disclosed by Marksberry.[12] The approach is entirely different from the usual processes for decalcomania preparation and involves printing the desired decal on a waxed or other nonadherent surface, coating the finished print with a water-soluble adhesive, and then causing the transfer paper to adhere to this coating. The printing is thus carried out on a dimensionally stable surface, and the transfer paper only acts as a carrier.[12]

FLOCK-COATED OR VELOUR PAPERS

Flocked, or velour papers are specialty coated sheets which simulate the appearance and feel of a pile finish. The actual surface effect may range from plush, velvet, mohair or fur, to a felt or suede. There are innumerable types, lengths and colors of flock available and the basic varieties are cotton, rayon, wool, silk, and other animal fibers. Cotton flock may be described as having practically no nap. It is not fibrous and produces a dull finish similar to suede. Wool flock is somewhat rough and fibrous and is never used where a soft finish is required. It is often used as a durable rug or carpet material. Rayon flock is probably the most widely used type because the length of the fibers can be closely controlled, and can be made to simulate plush, velvet, or velour. The material is available in a number of standard fiber lengths, generally 1/32 inch, 1/16 inch, 1/10 inch and in some cases 1/4 inch. The longer fibers produce softer-textured finishes, but they are much more difficult to cause to adhere satisfactorily to the surface. A wide range of colors is available from the natural shades of gray and tan of the animal fibers and white in cotton and rayon to a full range from red, yellow, green, blue to black and brown in the various dyed materials. The colors can be made washproof and drycleaningproof, as well as completely fast to fading.[15, 17]

Flock coatings become a part of the sheet to which they are applied and their durability depends upon the type of flock, the method of application, and the type of sheet surface upon which they are coated. By printing the adhesive on the base stock in designs rather than as an over-all coating, velour prints can be made.

Flock-Coating Technology

Backing Sheet. A flock coating can be laid down on any weight or type of plain, saturated, or treated base paper, film, foil, or cloth. It is purely a surface coating and may cover all of the surface or portions, as desired. If an over-all coating is required, the adhesive is uniformly coated over all the surface, while if only portions must be covered, the adhesive is printed on those areas which are to receive the flock. The other areas will not be affected. The backing material should be sufficiently sized or dense to hold up the adhesive and this is the only major requirement. The sheet should possess sufficient strength to meet its use requirements. In general, sufficient flock is used so that the background is completely covered, but to obtain the brightest effects with light-colored flocks, a white backing is advisable.

Flocking Adhesive. The flocking adhesive is one of the most important components of the finished flocked paper. It must be flexible so that it will not crack off when the paper is bent or flexed, it must bond the flock to the paper so that it will not fall out or abrade off, it must be water-resistant so that the flock will not be removed in damp weather, it must age satisfactorily without loss in the properties, and must size the paper and hold up on the surface to bond the sheet and flock together. The adhesive can be used clear, or dyed or pigmented. If it is colored to match the flock, it can increase the depth of shade and uniformity and tend to cover up a poor or defective base sheet. If colored in a contrasting shade, it can be used to produce interesting two-color effects.[15]

Because of the almost dust-like lightness of most flock materials, "stickiness" is a prime characteristic of a good flocking adhesive. A wide range of materials are on the market, and they are formulated depending upon the type of application equipment that is available. Roll, knife, gravure roll, and spray unit application equipment have all been used successfully, since the major requirement is that a uniform film is applied to the base sheet.

The adhesives used fall into three major classes:

    1. Water-soluble adhesives
    2. Synthetic resin and rubber solvent base adhesives
    3. Synthetic resin and rubber dispersion type adhesives

Each has special characteristics and merits, and each is used for particular jobs.

1. Water-Soluble Adhesives. Water-soluble adhesives formulated from glue, starch, or casein can be very satisfactorily used on most sheets, but the finished product does not offer much in regard to waterproofness unless the product is specially treated. There are recent developments in this field, however, which offer much promise, particularly in water-soluble resins which are later insolubilized by heat or catalysts. These films tend to be brittle, unless plasticized, and this should also be taken into consideration in their use.

2. Solvent Adhesives. Solvent adhesives formulated to serve as flock adhesives are available both clear and in a wide range of color. Since they dry rapidly, speed is necessary in applying the flock so that the flock fibers will contact the adhesive-coated surface while it is still wet. Such films, when properly formulated, provide excellent adhesion of the flock to practically any type of surface; cheap or expensive solvents can be used where desirable; the film can be formulated to be flexible and water-resistant; and if the surface to be coated is porous, the adhesive can be compounded so that when coated with a knife applicator the loss of adhesive by absorption is relatively negligible. Many base resins have been used in formulating such adhesives, but the most popular types seem to be the rubbers or other inexpensive elastomers, since they are soluble in cheap solvents, and do an excellent job in causing the flock to adhere to the surface. Surface skimming is a problem with some of these adhesives and the material should be carefully evaluated from this standpoint, since if the surface skins and a film forms, the flock cannot be piled on, even though the complete film of adhesive has not thoroughly dried.

3. **Water-Dispersion Adhesives.** A good deal of work has been done in the last few years on the evaluation of latices for use as flocking adhesives, and although there has not been much commercial application, the experimental results have been promising. The use of solvents is completely eliminated, skinning does not usually occur, and excellent adhesion can be obtained to most types of surfaces. New developments are forthcoming in this field and many development groups are experimenting with this type of compound.

Flocking Technique and Equipment. The equipment used to apply the flocking adhesive and flock is fairly simple and it is basically a coating and dusting machine. A major problem is the possibility of dusting excess fine flock into the various rooms of the plant and if possible the flocking department should be segregated so that contamination of the rest of the plant is eliminated. Unless the flocking equipment is of an exceptionally foolproof design, it is usually desirable to arrange some type of dust removal system whereby all the air in the flocking department is sucked out through a cyclone collector or a water spray or screening system so that fresh air is continuously being drawn into the plant and any flock laden air is cleaned and discharged to the outside. The flock can be reclaimed for reuse.

The flock-coating operation is divided into two parts, both of which take place in different portions of the same machine. The first step involves coating or printing the flocking adhesive on the paper, film, or foil. The second involves the actual piling of the flock into the adhesive and then drying out the solvent or water, thus setting the adhesive. The adhesive can be laid down on the surface by a roll, reverse roll, knife, gravure roll, or spray technique, depending upon the type and formulation of the adhesive and the surface to which it is being applied. The amount of adhesive laid down varies with the flock type used and the porosity and smoothness of the surface to which it is applied. Two general rules can be given as follows: (1) As the length of the fiber flock is increased, so must the thickness of the adhesive film be increased, and (2) on applying ordinary flock fibers (1/32 to 1/10 inches), as the thickness of the adhesive film is increased, so will the thickness of the resulting flock mat be increased.[15]

The adhesive-coated paper is then passed into the flocking chamber. This is usually an enclosed chamber, preferably run under a slight vacuum so that excess flock is carried out and into a separate collection chamber where it is recovered for reuse. The flock is generally held in a hopper which continuously feeds it on the adhesive-coated surface by means of a vibrating screen or a special nozzle, the main purpose of which is to distribute the flock fibers uniformly over the surface area. The flock should be distributed while the surface is still wet since then the ends of the fibers sink deeply into it and become permanently anchored when the adhesive dries. If the adhesive is allowed to partially dry and become tacky, the fibers only get a surface hold.

At the same time that the flock fibers are falling on the wet surface, agitating and orienting means will pile the fibers deeply and uniformly into the adhesive. This is usually accomplished by vibration and/or electrostatic orientation. With the vibration technique, the coated surface is agitated by a series of beaters whose vibrating bars strike a flexible screen surface which is positioned just under the moving adhesive-coated web. As the bars rotate at high speed, the screen surface is set into motion which creates static and causes the flock fibers to bounce 1 inch to 2 inches above the screen. An electrostatic unit sets up an electrical field which causes an orientation of the fibers and improves their packing. Air jets have also been suggested to improve the flocking operation.[16] The basic purpose of the operation is to have all the individual fibers adhered at one end and piled into the adhesive, as well as to have sufficient flock present on the sheet for coverage. The vibration method of flocking usually produces excellent results as it packs the fibers tightly into the adhesive—as many as 200,000 per square inch.[15]

The flock-coated sheet can then be passed through a drying chamber where the adhesive film is dried and set. Hot air, steam coils, or infrared heating units have been used satisfactorily. The sheet may be then passed under a vacuum nozzle and/or a rotating brush which removes nonadhered flock and brushes up the surface. The finished sheet can then be rewound into rolls, slit, or sheeted as desired, or printed in further converting operations.

Applications

There are many applications of flock coated paper. Box and fancy packaging papers, specialties, display papers, as well as cover stocks are all being produced. This paper is also used in curtains and drape stock; greeting cards; menu, book, brochure, and memo covers; drawer, cabinet, and box liners; lamp bottoms; gasket stocks; floor covering in automobile rear decks; interior walls and for countless other purposes.

MARBLED PAPERS

by R. S. Bracewell

The process of marbling paper is an old and specialized art which was developed in the early 17th century and probably existed at a much earlier date.[18] It was first practiced as a hand process for producing certain designs by making patterns in floating colors on a mucilaginous liquid or ground, and then transferring these to a sheet of paper or the smoothly cut edges of a book by a dipping technique.

The early hand-marbling processes were based upon the use of a ground mucilage prepared from gum tragacanth, Irish or carrogeen moss, or another hydrophyllic colloid. In a typical formula [18] 1 pound of gum tragacanth was soaked in 2 gallons of water for a week, and as it slowly dissolved, additional water was added until the desired consistency was obtained. The final mucilage was strained through a fine cloth sieve to insure the elimination of any lumps or dissolved matter. The colors, which consisted only of pigments, were prepared for use by grinding them with a beeswax composition in the proportion of 1 ounce of wax preparation to 1 pound of color pigment. The beeswax composition was prepared by melting together 2 pounds of beeswax with 1/4 pound of soap and adding sufficient water to make a frothy mass of curds which can be crumbled between the fingers [18] and which could be ground with the color without sticking to the milling stone. For preparing the marbling composition, the compounded pigments were mixed and thinned with water and ox gall. In some cases, in the preparation of special patterns, olive oil, linseed oil, turpentine, kerosene, or a solution of alum was utilized.[18] This color was dropped or spattered on the surface of the ground mucilage or substrate. The wax acted to bind the pigment to the paper and permitted a later glazing operation. The purpose of the ox gall, alum, and various oils was to vary the surface tension of the mucilage and permit the formation of the patterns.

The heavy mucilaginous consistency of the ground gum and the wax mixed with the pigments resulted in a tendency of the colors to float on the surface. The colors desired were spattered or dropped on the surface of the ground and the pattern of swirls, ribbons, or spots was developed by means of a comb or other instrument. The sheet of paper was then rolled across the surface and the pattern transferred to it. The marbled sheets were then hung up to dry on drying frames. This process was slow and laborious and the art was a closely guarded secret and protected and passed down by the apprenticeship system. Much of the marbled paper was later sized or flint glazed in order to produce a desirable glossy surface.

The development of this art from a sheet to a web-processing operation was carried out by the Marvellum Company. It was determined by careful experimentation that pigment colors and metallic pigments could be floated on the surface of a water bath and transferred to a continuously moving sheet of paper and thus handled in a web form. The early experiments with oil as a binder and various oily thinners to cause spreading were carried out by George Sensenay. The designs could be made with combs or other forming tools and patterns of different character from the older type of marbling were produced. This field was explored both by changes in formulation and by different machine application techniques.

Base-Sheet Requirements

The requirements of the paper for continuous marbling are a minimum absorption of water previous to its being blown off the surface by a slotted air nozzle and sufficient sizing so that the oil binder is not absorbed and does not leave the pigment or the metallic setting on the surface without proper bond to the paper. The surface of the paper has to be smooth enough that the pattern retains its details and at the same time has enough tooth for handling to prevent offset and smearing. Pigment-coated papers are not suitable for this marbling. Mica-coated papers are used quite successfully.

Marbling Technology

Spot Marbling. This process was first carried out by combs and other forming devices. In order to produce marble patterns it was necessary to work on the surface of water that was comparatively free from flow. This was a simple matter when done by hand in a pan of water, subsequently rolling the sheet along the surface and picking up the pattern. The problem was to produce the same results with a continuous web.

A circular machine or "Merry-Go-Round" was built which could handle paper up to 30 inches wide at a speed of approximately 50 feet per minute. The circular pan with a wooden fabricated base, 36 inches wide, was mounted on a circular monorail track, approximately 25 feet in diameter. A gear rack on the bottom outside of the pan base facilitated the drive of the pan containing water of about 1 inch depth. When the drive was started, there was of course a tendency for the water to lag, but this soon became a constant and a negligible factor.

Opposite the pan drive, a set of contact rolls was located to bring the web of paper down to the surface of the water and pick up the pattern. After blowing off the excess water by a jet or air emitted from a slotted pipe, the paper was carried over drum dryers. The half of the machine on the approach to the contact rolls was in general used for successively applying the colors and forming the pattern. The half of the machine following the contact rolls was used for clearing the water surface, if necessary, before the applications of the colors.

Four color stands were set up which straddled the moving tank. At first, special cylindrical brushes were used to spatter the color on the water. These consisted of a wooden roll on which were spaced, in approximately a 2 inch cross section pattern, little tufts of bristles mounted on a wire stem about 4 inches long and hinged on a staple on the roll. As this special brush slowly revolved, the tufts fell down and drew across the surface of a color roll picking up its charge of color. As the brush left the color roll it swung on the hinge on which a stop was arranged. This was just enough to throw the color from the tufts on the surface of the water in drops sufficiently large to form the desired pattern. These special brushes did an excellent job but their main drawback was their cleaning and the wash up. The brushes were later replaced by slow-spinning disks which did satisfactory work. These allowed the color roll to be cut down to a 2 inch face from 30 inches and thus simplified the wash up and allowed great economy in color.

As previously stated, stationary or moving combs were used for variation of patterns. Also by varying the oil-vehicle formulation different effects could be obtained. For instance, a varnish of high gum content produced a characteristic pattern under the action of the comb, whereas a formulation based on nonblushing lacquers produced a different effect.

This machine was later widened to marble 36 inch webs. This was about the limit for the diameter of machine since the difference in the circumference of the outside and the inside of the pan caused some distortion of the pattern on the web.

Grain Marbling. In contrast to the spot marbling which was carried out on a moving though nonflowing water bath, grain marbling was produced on a water surface flowing down a stationary inclined tank. This tank was straddled by a single stand handling four colors which were led down pipes to an inclined baffle board which made contact with the surface of the water on the entire width of the tank. These four pipes were in the form of a pendulum which swung back and forth across the tank depositing a blend of the colors on the baffle board. This blend of colors filmed out on the water, was formed into a pattern and then picked up by the web and handled just as on the other machine.

A so-called rippled effect was produced on this machine by setting a dam with an apron across the tank just ahead of the contact rolls. As the water carrying the colors on the surface flowed down the apron a ripple was formed and by making contact at this position, rippled patterns were obtained on the web.

Applications

Marbled papers were used as box papers, envelope linings, gift wraps, cover paper, photomounts, and calendar mounts, etc. In the box papers, envelope liners and gift wraps much use was made of gold and aluminum as well as of the brilliant colored metallics. In the cover paper and photomount field, marbling was done in colors with perhaps just a vein of metallic pigment running through the design. Grain marbling was suitable for this purpose and was perhaps more popular than spot marbling.

Marbling was also used in laminating base papers for panels, table tops, etc. Later this was replaced by printing which was a cheaper process but unusual effects were still obtained by marbling.

Marbling was developed for top coating rubber and similar films, but later marbled effects were achieved by blending colored plastics in the film casting or coating operation.

Filled cloth which was marbled for book binding was handled quite successfully. Some attempts at marbling silk and cotton were made and very attractive samples were produced but the trade did not take hold of these developments. A method of marbling vat colors on cotton was developed in which the vats were marbled on the cloth in pigment form and the dye subsequently developed on the fibers. A method was also developed in connection with one of the large textile concerns wherein a water soluble dye was marbled directly on fabric but neither of these became of commercial importance.

There has been some indication that a demand would develop for the return of the spot marbling in the fancy paper field but with the modern treatment of fancy papers it has been possible to offer items that have satisfied all the tastes and at the same time which could be made more economically than by the marbling process. The wood grain has remained popular and will probably continue since it has an interesting natural appearance.

REFERENCES

1. P. F. Denner. U. S. Patent 2,069,648. Paper and Method of Making (1937).
2. August Weichelt. *Buntpapier-Fabrikation.* Verlag der Papier-Zeitung Carl Hofmann, Berlin, 1923, p. 212–221.
3. Anon. *Bronze Powders.* Metals Disintegrating Co., Elizabeth, N. J. (1941).
4. Anon. "Black Light and Color Magic." *Architectural Eng.* 115–119 September (1946).
5. Anon. *101 Useful Luminescent Applications.* New Jersey Zinc Sales Company, New York (1947).
6. D. B. Bradner. U. S. Patent 2,006,208. Dull Finish Coated Paper (1935).
7. D. B. Bradner. U. S. Patent 2,006,209. Dull Finish Coated Paper (1935).
8. Edwin Sutermeister. *Chemistry of Pulp and Paper Making.* John Wiley & Sons, Inc., New York (1941), p. 369.

9. Anon. "Decals." *Modern Lithography* **16,** No. 3:32–34, 101 (1948).
10. J. W. Stewart. U. S. Patent 2,425,653. Decalcomania Paper (1947).
11. H. F. Sheetz, Jr. U. S. Patent 2,419,918. Decalcomania (1947).
12. R. D. Marksberry. U. S. Patent 2,426,462. Decalcomania Manufacture (1947).
13. Anon. *The Dictionary of Paper.* American Pulp and Paper Association. George Banta Publishing Company, Menasha, Wisconsin (1940), p. 126.
14. C. A. Dickhaut. "Decalcomania Paper." *The Manufacture of Pulp and Paper. Vol. V.* Joint Textbook Committee of the Paper Industry of the United States and Canada. McGraw-Hill Book Co., Inc. New York (1939), p. 78–79.
15. D. J. Bostrom. "Flock Finishing in a Custom Shop." *Ind. Finishing* 1–8 (March 1947).
16. Andre Burnett. U. S. Patent 1,883,535. Process for Producing on Paper or Fabric a Suede-like Finish or Waterproof Property (1932).
17. Anon. *Surface Coating with Flock.* Rayon Processing Company of R. I., Inc. (1945).
18. C. W. Woolnough. The Whole Art of Marbling. George Bell and Sons, London (1881).
19. August Weichelt. *Buntpapier-Fabrikation.* Verlag der Papier-Zeitung, Carl Hofmann, Berlin, p. 252–306, 1923.

Chapter VII

MISCELLANEOUS FUNCTIONAL PAPERS

by R. H. Mosher

THERE are decorative papers which do not fit into the over-all pattern of discussion, and also there are functional papers which cannot be directly classified into any other group. Such papers are produced because of some functional property which is separate from any decorative value which the sheet may possess. For example, a fancy boxpaper may be attractive to look at, but it may also possess antitarnish properties:

Such papers are:
1. Coated Chart Papers
2. Safety and Anticounterfeit Papers
3. Magnetic Recording Paper or Tape
4. Antitarnish Papers
5. Electrically Conducting Papers
6. Mold, Bacteria, Insect and Rodent Resistant and Preventative Papers
7. Flame-Retardant Papers
8. Plasticized Papers
9. Photosensitive Papers

These sheets are often produced merely for their functional characteristics, yet many of these characteristics can be incorporated into regular decorative papers.

Coated Chart Papers

Coated chart papers are made for use with recording instruments where a metal stylus acts as the recording head. The coated surface shows a permanent black marking wherever a metal surface is drawn across it. Such a paper, in a recording instrument, will show a continuous or intermittent record without the need for an inking pen or pencil. When it is desirable to make an additional notation or marking on the chart paper, this can be made with a regular pen or pencil, or merely by using the edge of a coin, a key, or other blunt-edged metallic object.

The pigment in the coating used on such papers is generally a baryte or blanc fixe, or some combination of the two. Clay or other extender may be used but it is seldom applied. Casein is the usual adhesive. A relatively high coating load, about 10–12 pounds (20 x 26–500) is applied to the paper, since a light touch of a stylus must definitely mark the surface.

The coating can be applied by a brush, roll, air knife, or spray coater and the only problem is the possible settling of the heavy pigment. Good agitation will overcome this trouble. The coating dries readily and the finished sheet should be given a light calender finish to smooth the surface, but not sufficient to give it any polish.

A type formula for coating such papers is as follows:

> Blanc Fixe Pulp (66% Solids) 500 lb.
> Casein 57.5 lb.
> Water 37.5 gal.

Sufficient cutting agent for the casein, eveners, foam killers, etc. are also added to make satisfactory mix.

SAFETY AND ANTICOUNTERFEIT PAPERS

Safety papers are special papers which have been treated so as to make visible any attempts to alter the writing or printing on them. They can be produced by the addition of certain chemicals in the beater when the paper is being made, by a surface treatment or coating, or by printing and/or embossing an over-all design on the surface with sensitive inks. Methods of introducing the compounds in the beater are of no significance to the converting industry, but coating and printing techniques will be discussed. Anticounterfeit papers are papers which have been made or treated so that their identity can be verified by some easy visual or chemical means so as to prevent counterfeiting.

Safety Papers

The principle upon which all safety papers are based is their peculiar ability to exhibit telltale reactions when they are altered or tampered with. Some inks or coatings change color when acids, alkalis, or bleaching agents are used; some blur and diffuse the coating or printing over the area in contact with the agent used; and some show bleeding of a water- or oil-soluble dyestuff when any attempts are made to remove or alter a stamp or seal. The basic feature is similar whether an over-all clear or colored coating or an over-all printed design is used, therefore, both types will be discussed without specific differentiation.

By using an ink or coating the color of which is a function of the acid concentration or pH, any employment of acid bleaching agents or alkaline compounds can be detected from a variation in the shade of the design or surface. Inks can be made acid-sensitive by the addition of zinc chloride or hexamethyl and pentamethyl monoethyl-*p*-rosaniline, the diazo dye from tetrazotized *o*-toluidine, sodium naphthionate, sodium hydroxide, and monosodium phosphate.[1] Compounds which contain metallic salts of fatty acids will change tint when treated with a detergent. Aniline hydrochloride will discolor by the decomposition of the hydrochloride when a bleach comes into contact with the paper.[1] Many common dyestuffs change color with change in pH.

Colorless or slightly colored manganous compounds which are changed to colored manganic compounds by oxidation have been suggested as wash coatings. Dioxy- and trioxy-benzoic acids and their derivatives will give color reactions with even weak oxidizing agents and these are almost impossible to reverse or bleach out by the use of the most powerful reducing agents. The use of a colorless pyrogallol wash coating which turns brown on the application of an oxidizing bleaching agent has been suggested. A paper containing polyoxybenzoic acid does not react with acids, but does provide an almost complete protection against partial chemical falsification or erasure by color change.[2] A special preparation is disclosed by Baush and Schroth[2] which is sensitive to oxidizing agents and the resulting stain cannot be eliminated by reducing agents. The sheet is treated with a wash coating of ferric salts, such as ferric acetate, and then a suitable ferrocyanide which is acid soluble, such as lead ferrocyanide. The final solution used is a mixture of equal parts of pyrogallol carboxylic acid and pentagalloyl glucose brought to a pH of 3.0 to 3.5 by the addition of alkali.[2]

The same authors also disclose the use of another class of reducible inorganic salts which are resistant to decomposition by light and which form differently colored substances upon decomposition by oxidizing agents. The salts used are selected from a group consisting of manganous tellurite, barium tellurite, and alkali selenite.[3]

To guard against the sending of secret messages by war prisoners who might be writing with invisible or sympathetic inks, papers have been produced which immediately develop writing with invisible inks into visible characters without the application of heat or chemical reagents.[36] The sensitive coated paper which was first utilized in these experiments consisted essentially of a paper base, coated with clay, containing a mechanically incorporated dyestuff, which reacted when moistened or when written upon with an acid invisible ink, to produce a green color.

This paper did not react, however, with alkaline invisible

inks to produce distinctly visible writing. Therefore, a second ingredient was incorporated into the paper coating of which reacted with alkaline sympathetic or invisible ink to produce a red coloration. The paper manufactured on this plan immediately showed up the writing with acid or neutral invisible inks in green color and with alkaline invisible inks the writing appeared in red. In this way, all markings on the paper were visible to the censors, or other authorities.

In evaluating the permanence of these developing colors, surveillance tests have shown that they will last for months and surely a sufficient length of time to be clearly detected by censors. The advantage of this device lies in the fact that a prisoner of war may be permitted to write freely upon this specially prepared so-called "Sensicoat" paper with any kind of visible ink but cannot use any invisible writing inks since all of them, acid, neutral or alkaline or even plain water itself, will develop color when brought into contact with the paper.

The paper, as originally developed, was a 56-pound coated sheet, basis 17 x 22 inches per 1,000 sheets, with the color sensitizer incorporated into the coating. Its high cost and heavy weight were factors influencing the development of a lighter, uncoated, and much less expensive paper.

The requirements for such a paper were severe. It was to be an uncoated stock, very sensitive to writing with all types of solutions which could be used as sympathetic inks, as unreactive as possible to humidity and ordinary handling, but nevertheless capable of being manufactured at a substantially lower cost than the first paper used for this purpose. Intensive research revealed ways of meeting these requirements.

A series of laboratory and plant experiments were made, ending in a completely satisfactory paper which could be made in one plant from start to finish, including the grinding of the special dye in the sensitizing formula. The new paper was called "Anilith" to differentiate it from the original "Sensicoat."

The above examples are representative of the type of safety

papers which are made to resist alteration of printing or writing of checks, legal documents, stamps, and other security papers and to show up attempts to use invisible inks. Another type of such papers is used in the preparation of government codes, military orders, and other documents which must be preserved in secrecy and/or which must be destroyed in an emergency so as to prevent their falling into the hands of the enemy. Some such papers are made so that they will burn leaving practically no ash, but in many cases this is not a sufficiently fast and reliable procedure for destruction, telltale smoke may be given off, and unless the ash is completely decomposed, it may be possible to reconstruct the contents using recently developed scientific detection techniques. According to Foote and Guertin [4] a paper can be coated with a special composition which can be destroyed by merely submerging or dipping the sheet in water. The paper and coating are so constructed that the water permeates almost instantly and causes a chemical reaction by which gas is developed in large volume and in the form of bubbles which loosen the coating from the paper. At the same time, the bubbles in the material of the coating destroy it. Any matter printed or written on the coating is obliterated and destroyed to such an extent that nothing remains which will give any information about what appeared on its surface before destruction. A waterleaf sheet is recommended, and this may be surface-sized with starch or not, as required. A suggested coating for the printing side of the paper is as follows:

	Parts
Methyl Cellulose	6.5
Calcium Carbonate	0.78
Water	Sufficient to make a coatable composition

This coating can be applied by a normal coating procedure and will be decomposed at a high hydrogen ion concentration. Small amounts of plasticizer may be added if desirable to pro-

duce additional flexibility, but are not necessary to good results. Instead of methyl cellulose, such binders as gum arabic,
dextrine, or glue may be used.

When this coating has been completed, a second coating is
laid down on the back side of the sheet. This coating is applied
at as high a viscosity as possible to prevent its penetration into
the sheet and is composed of methyl cellulose or another binder
and an acid such as tartaric, citric, maleic, or lactic. Plasticizers
may also be used. The acid is dissolved in an anhydrous solvent
such as anhydrous alcohol so that a reaction will not occur during the coating operation.[4]

Anticounterfeit Papers

According to Kantrowitz [36] there were several interesting
developments in the field of anticounterfeit papers which were
used extensively during World War II. Papers which had
been previously made as identifiable types, specifically for cur-
rency or bank note paper, had been based on the use of short
red and blue silk fibers which were incorporated into the sheet
when it was manufactured on the paper machine.

These silk fibers are visible to the naked eye since they differ
from the cellulosic fibers from which the paper is fabricated.
Identifiable paper was also proposed in which the mark of
identification comprised fibers which fluoresce under ultraviolet
light.

In the printing of war ration book I for sugar rationing and
book II for food rationing, precaution was taken to discourage
the counterfeiting of stamps by incorporating into the paper
structure fluorescent cellulosic fibers invisible in ordinary light
but visible under the influence of ultraviolet light.

In connection with the printing of subsequent war ration
books, the technical division of the Government Printing Office engaged in research to develop identifiable paper which
would distinguish genuine from counterfeit ration coupons by
means other than the use of fluorescent fibers.

It was found that ferric chloride-treated fibers incorporated into the structure of the paper to the extent of 0.5% would remain colorless and invisible in the sheet until treated with certain reagents, such as potassium ferrocyanide and ortho-phosphoric acid. They then become visible and individually identifiable by acquiring a distinctive and permanent blue color.

These fibers presented several advantages which are not obtainable with silk or fluorescent fibers. One such advantage of employing chemically treated rather than silk fibers is that they are invisible within the paper structure and do not reveal their presence to counterfeiters. Another advantage is that they are basically identical in composition with the untreated fibers of the entire sheet of paper.

As compared with fluorescent fibers, paper containing chemically treated fibers can be used in the field without necessitating expensive ultraviolet light equipment for tests. Another advantage of chemically treated fibers is that, unlike fluorescent fibers, they do not lose their effectiveness upon exposure to sunlight, bleaching agents, acids, alkalies, water, oil, or gasoline and, therefore, remain in the paper structure as a permanent means of identification.

As a result of the passage of the Soldier Ballot Bill by Congress, it became necessary to supply the soldiers with forms which could be readily and positively identified as genuine. The identifying characteristics of this paper were to be such as could be incorporated very quickly and with existing paper-making equipment. They were to be able to withstand the action of salt water, heat and high humidity, and to require no complicated tests to reveal their presence.

Several samples were submitted to Army and Navy officials and upon their approval there was included in the paper a safety feature which consisted of printing, on both sides of the ballot, a design using an ink invisible under daylight or artificial light but which fluoresced brightly when stimulated by ultraviolet radiations. The fluorescing design was composed of the phrase, "Official Federal War Ballot," horizontally repeated and separated by a star between each repetition.

The work of the Government Printing Office as outlined by Kantrowitz [36] shows how far the development of such specialized papers can be carried when specific problems must be solved.

The anticounterfeit papers can be made by the use of such identifiable printing or coating techniques but they are also produced by laminating together a number of plies of colored paper so that when a document or ticket is torn in half, the arrangement of the colored layers identifies its authenticity.

MAGNETIC RECORDING PAPER OR TAPE

An interesting recent development is a metallic-coated paper which serves to supplement or replace wire as a medium for recording sound. Such paper is coated with a magnetically reactive metal powder and this film of powder acts in the same manner as the wire in becoming activated in a magnetic field and recording and reproducing sound effects.

FIGURE 22. *Details of recording and erasing heads on playback instrument which utilizes paper tape* (Courtesy of Amplifier Corp. of America)

In the process of sound recording by this technique, the sound waves are picked up by a microphone and are converted into corresponding electrical energy. This is amplified electronically and fed into a special magnetic tape recording head which converts electrical energy into corresponding magnetic fields of varying intensity. Magnetic tape moving at a constant speed is brought into direct contact with or very close to the recording head. Magnetic patterns are formed upon the tape which correspond in wave length, intensity, and polarity, to the acoustic pattern of the original sound waves. When the tape is played back, the magnetic tape is passed at a constant speed and in direct contact or very close to the magnetic tape pickup head. The magnetic flux on the tape passes through the pickup head and creates electrical impulses which are subsequently amplified and fed to a loud speaker which converts the electrical energy back into sound waves corresponding to the original sounds picked up on the microphone.[5] An alternate playback system passes a constant-intensity magnetic field or bias voltage through the tape which is altered by the flux present in the tape itself, and this variation creates the necessary impulse for amplification of the original sound.

There are several advantages of paper tapes as compared to wire. The tape hangs limp, and will not coil, knot, and break like wire. It can be easily edited and spliced with pressure-sensitive tape. The tape can be made in any widths suitable for the machine and a number of different sound tracks can be run in parallel. At the present time there is a very favorable cost differential, but if the cost of the wire can be reduced, this advantage may be eliminated.

The actual medium upon which the magnetic modulations are impressed is a layer of finely powdered crystalline magnetic particles uniformly coated on a paper base. Magnetite and purified iron oxide as well as a number of special alloys have been used. High physical strength and the minimum possible caliper or thickness are essential in the paper base. The density of the sheet must be absolutely uniform and the surface must be as smooth as possible to obtain the best results. Some of the paper now in use is about 1.5 mils in thickness and an even thinner medium is desirable. The metallic coating must be bound firmly to the paper surface and the film must be flexible and absolutely uniform. Synthetic resin adhesives are generally used to bind the pigment to the paper surface. The denser the coating, the better fidelity in the recording. The magnetic coated layer is being run 0.5 mils in thickness by one producer at the present time, and the thickness of the coating has been found to be quite important in regard to the effectiveness of the response.[5] A recent investigation in magnetic tape design also closely relates the high-frequency response of the tape to its thickness. The thinner the tape, the better its high-frequency response. The residual magnetism retained by the tape (all other factors remaining constant) is also a function of the thickness. The thicker the tape, the more magnetism it retains, and this causes overtones and noise during the playback. The present tape made at 2 mils over-all thickness seems to be a reasonable compromise between tape strength, effectiveness of response, and undesirable magnetic phenomena.

The recorded wave length of a given frequency is a direct function of the speed. The slower the tape speed, the shorter the wave length. As very short wave lengths correspond to very short bar magnets, and as extremely short magnets exhibit a marked self-demagnetization property, it is desirable to run the tape at sufficient speed so that half the recorded wave length is not much smaller than the recording head gap, and is at least ten times larger than the average magnetic particle size. With proper design, a magnetic recorder utilizing a tape speed of $7\frac{1}{2}$ inches per second can record and reproduce a 9,000 cycle tone. Magnetic wire requires a lineal speed of 24 inches per second to reproduce a 5,000 cycle tone.[5]

The same magnetic tape may be used and reused many times since the magnetic patterns impressed upon the tape may be readily erased electronically without affecting the tape in any way. The tape merely need be demagnetized and it is ready for a new sound track to be imposed upon it. Such a demagnetizing process consists in subjecting the tape to an intense supersonic magnetic field of gradually diminishing intensity so that as any given previously magnetized particle leaves the demagnetizing field, it resumes its original unoriented state. In wire recording another problem may arise due to the fact that an uninsulated wire is wound in direct contact with other magnetized wires. As a result, magnetic cross interaction may take place and a cross transfer of signals may occur. This phenomenon is virtually eliminated when paper tape is used, since the paper tape backing acts as an insulating layer between two magnetic layers in the spool.[6]

One type of tape now on the market is described as follows: [7]

Composition . . . . Metallic powder coated on paper tape
Tape Dimensions . . . . Width . . . . ¼ inch
                                   Thickness . . . . 0.002 inch
                                   Coating . . . . . . 0.0005 inch (thickness)
Break Load . . . . 6 pounds
Dimensional Stability . . . . Excellent

The machine designed to operate on this tape has the same head for the recording and playback circuits. It has a gap of 0.0005 inches and the tape runs across the top of the gap and not through it. In recording, a bias signal of 18 to 20 kilocycles is applied to 130 turns of the winding and the audio signal to the remaining 30 turns. For the playback, the signal is picked up from the 130 turn winding. This tape is claimed to operate satisfactorily for recording up to 6,000 cycles per second with a speed of 8 inches per second. Further development may permit a wider frequency range for fidelity or a lower tape speed for economy.[7]

ANTITARNISH PAPERS

The antitarnish papers in general use are usually based upon 10 to 16 pound tissue where the sheet is to be used directly for the wrapping of individual pieces of silver or metal parts. Anti-tarnish requirements are also important for special coated and printed papers which are to be used in box coverings, decorative panels, napkins, labels, household wrapping papers, and other applications where the paper may come into direct contact with polished metal surfaces. Silver antitarnish paper is white and usually made from an all rag or a rag and sulfite fiber base. Other antitarnish metal wrappings are produced from 100% kraft and are brown in color. Any pulp used in the production of such papers must be washed sufficiently to reduce the sulfur content to less than 0.005%, and the paper must be dense and free from pinholes.[17]

According to Rowe and Kress,[8] there are two major lines of thought as to what constitutes a good antitarnish paper. One group of investigators has claimed that the tarnishing is caused by the paper itself. In the case of silver, tarnishing is caused by sulfur compounds in the paper, while in the case of steel and aluminum the trouble results from the presence of free acids. Paper for wrapping silverware should be free from sulfur, sulfides, and dyestuffs containing sulfur. Some authors also felt that the paper should not only be free from harmful substances, but should be dense enough to prevent the passage of tarnishing gases.[8]

There has been much dispute as to the nature and origin of substances causing the tarnishing of metals wrapped in paper. It has been stated that wrapping paper should be free from acids, chlorine, and sulfur compounds. One author claims that very few papers, when used, are completely free from tarnishing ingredients.[9] It has even been stated that it is dangerous to guarantee sulfur, chlorine, or acid free papers as they may not remain free of these substances all throughout storage and transit.

A second group of investigators believes that tarnishing is due to conditions outside of the paper and that hydrogen sulfide and other sulfuric gases are the main trouble-producing factors with silver, while carbon dioxide and oxygen are conducive to tarnishing of steel and aluminum. This school of thought maintains that a dense and impermeable paper which is waxed or coated or a sheet which contains chemicals which are capable of adsorbing these gases before they reach the metal is the best solution to the problem. Most authorities today agree that the major source of trouble, particularly with silver, is the presence of sulfides, and the paper must not only be free from them, but some method of barring them from the metal surface is required.

Much work has been done on various coatings and impregnants which can be used in the manufacture of antitarnish paper. The use of a mixture of light and heavy oils for impregnating has been suggested.[11] A treatment with a soluble salt such as zinc acetate is claimed to be very satisfactory.[10] Other suggested salt treatments involve the use of lead acetate, cadmium acetate, copper acetate, copper sulfate, nickel acetate, and copper oxide.[8, 12, 13] In all these cases the principle of protection involves a preferential absorption of the hydrogen sulfide gas by the salts rather than by the silver piece contained in the salt-impregnated wrap. Such treatments have been found to be quite satisfactory and probably represent the best available protection at the present time.

Other suggested protective methods have involved such soluble salts as those listed above together with waxing,[14, 15] the use of copper sulfate and copper oxide added in the beater,[8, 13] and the treatment of the paper with alkaline earth bicarbonates.[15]

ELECTRICALLY CONDUCTING PAPERS

Papers which will allow the passage of electric currents and which simultaneously record the passage of these currents have a number of applications, such as, the facsimile recorder, electronic tuning devices, and the Marconi depth sounder recorder. Others are represented by the various conducting and antistatic treated sheets. In most of the first type papers, signals of varying strength are recorded on paper by means of a moving stylus. The current flows from the stylus through the paper and to a metal plate which supports the paper. These fall into two categories, those in which the stylus takes part in the reaction, and those where an inert stylus is used. In these papers, the current must produce a sharply defined stain along the path of the stylus, the stain should develop instantaneously, show an increase in intensity as the voltage is increased, and should not fade.[20] The principal objection to many of such papers is the instability of the trace and the impossibility of storing them for long periods without drying them out, and this must be followed by rewetting before use. The question of mold growth is important in this respect, and must be considered, particularly in the tropics and during the summer season.

The second classification includes those sheets which can be surface plated or receive a metallic deposit from solution by electrolytic means and nonconducting papers or films which behave unsatisfactorily because of the buildup of surface static. The conductivity of plating or conducting papers depends, to a great extent, upon the voltage used and this may be a limiting factor on the system. The antistatic treatment varies with the conditions under which the system will operate, i.e., the humidity and presence of conducting bodies.

1. **Conducting and Recorder Papers.** Such papers have been made by several methods including treatment with various salt solutions and the use of starch iodide,[3] as well as coating and saturating with carbon black, acetylene black, or graphite. Coatings and treatments with aluminum, copper, and other metal powders and mixtures of the metallic powders and glycol stearates[18] have also been utilized. The pigments may also be beater dispersed.

Examples of salts used to saturate recording papers are benzidine and sodium bromide; pyrogallol, monosodium phosphate, and sodium nitrate; *p*-anisidine and sodium bromide; and *o*-toluidine and sodium bromide.[20] Such papers when tested with an irridium stylus passing over the paper at 0.2 foot per

second or 0.5 foot per second, resting on a metal plate with
an applied voltage of 0 to 7.5 volts gave satisfactory discoloration. The efficiency and stability of such papers varied widely
and their usefulness depends upon the specific application.

Carbon-containing conducting papers can be made by beater
dispersion of the conducting medium, or by coating or saturating the sheet with the compound. Acetylene black and graphite
are the best for this application. The conductivity of paper containing such blacks depends greatly on the resistance built up
between the particles, and the binder, if any, should be carefully
chosen. Metallic stearates are often used. The conductance of
a beater-dispersed or saturated sheet depends to a great extent
upon the amount of conducting material present, and a choice
must often be made between strength in the sheet and the desired conductance. Such papers are generally black in color and
this is a disadvantage because the paper cannot be used for
recording.

The metallic-base powders are often used to produce conducting papers but their electrical conductivity is often found
to be impaired by the presence of oxide films on the particles,
which act as insulators.[18] The addition of stearic acid esters of
diethylene glycol, monohydric alcohols, simple polyhydric alcohols, sugars, hydroxy carboxylic acids, aldehydes, and ketones
are all recommended.[20] These substances produce a film readily
and possess a low melting point which simplifies the calendering
operation. Where color is desired so that the sheet can be used
in recording or for facsimile, lead thiosulfate, lead thiocyanate,
or mercuric sulfide may be added when the metallic portion is
coated on or combined with the sheet.[18]

In some cases it is desirable to combine a conducting paper
and a recording surface, especially for fine-definition facsimile
work. This is particularly true where fine half-tone pictures,
charts, and diagrams must be reproduced. The body of the
blank may be made conducting by impregnation with such salts
as sodium, potassium, and aluminum iodides, sulfocyanides,
bromides, chlorides, nitrates and sulfates.[19] The recommended

carriers are diethylene, triethylene, propylene, butylene, or polyethylene glycols. As a coating on the surface which will take the marking, the water-insoluble sulfur-bearing compounds of metals are suggested. These compounds comprise thio-oxalates, thiolates or mercaptides, thioacetates or thioglycolates, and thiocarbamides of metals such as copper, silver, mercury, and lead.[19] Such compounds are white, and turn black where the current passes through due to reduction or conversion of the compound. The sulfides produced are insoluble and permanent in color.

FIGURE 23. *Facsimile broadcast receiving-unit installed in standard radio* (Courtesy of Radio Inventions, Inc.)

The base paper used with such facsimile recording units varies with the desired results from a cheap ground-wood containing sheet to a multiple-coated, smooth-surfaced paper for accurate reproduction. One recommended paper was a 60% sulfite—40% bleached kraft sheet of high wet strength. The sheet was treated with *p*-chloro-*m*-cresol, 0.05%; trichloro-phenol, 0.05%; or sodium fluoride, 0.5% as a fungicidal agent. After treatment, saturation, and/or coating, the paper was calendered to make a smooth recording surface.

2. **Conducting and Antistatic Papers.** The antistatic problem refers to the accumulation of electrostatic charges on the surface of nonconductors such as sheets or rolls of some plastic films and coated papers. The usual procedure involves coating the surface with an extremely thin layer of a conducting medium such as a polyhydric alcohol, sugar, metallic stearate, or metallic salt film. Such films are extremely effective and do an excellent job of bleeding off any electro static charges before they become troublesome.

MOLD, BACTERIA, INSECT, AND RODENT RESISTANT AND PREVENTATIVE PAPERS

Packaging papers of all types, but particularly food packaging papers, are susceptible to attack by molds or fungi, bacteria, and insects, and even to some extent by rodents. Each of these types of attack are rather specific, both from the standpoint of the result if unchecked and the method of protection. These papers will be discussed from the standpoint of the package, since that is where the property is of importance.

1. **Mold and Bacteria Resistance.** The mold- and bacteria-resistant papers are designed to resist the growth of mold on the packaging medium and the mold preventative papers are mold resistant and in addition act to inhibit any growth on the material contained within the package. The growth of molds generally produces an objectionable discoloration and blotchiness on the surface of the package and/or product which often gives off objectionable musty odors. Fungi may also produce considerable quantities of organic acids which may react with

either the coating or saturant in the packaging medium or with the product itself. It has also been noted that the presence of molds or fungi will bring about an unusual concentration of moisture at the infected area.[21] The growth of molds and fungi may occur on the coating or saturant or it may occur on the base paper or film itself. Protective compounds may be incorporated into the paper, the saturant or the coating and all have been used.

2. **Insect Resistance.** The insect repellency can also be divided into two parts:[21] the repelling of insects from the exterior of the package and the erection of a barrier which they cannot penetrate, and [22] the prevention of the growth and development of insects from eggs as well as active or dormant insects enclosed in the package. Many packaging materials have been evaluated over a period of time in package form but no material has yet been found which is completely resistant to penetration.[25] Many are highly resistant, however, and are only penetrated after subjection to extremely severe conditions. It has been determined that insects will generally only attack packages which contain foods which are attractive to them. Their activity is almost wholly regulated by temperature and they are killed if the temperature is reduced to 30 to 40°F. for extended periods or if the temperature is raised to 120°F. for 1 hour or more.[25] Their optimum growth seems to be in the range of 70 to 95°F. and their life cycle is usually about 4 to 6 weeks. It is their ability to multiply which accounts for the serious damage they can inflict once they are inside of a package. The problem of keeping them from inside is as much a sanitation problem in the packaging operation, with a thorough sterilization of the contents, as it is a protection of the package from outside infestation.

Many tests have been run in order to determine what compounds are most effective in repelling insect attacks and dinitrophenol derivatives and D.D.T. have shown the most promise. At least 5% D.D.T. is recommended for use in coatings, and care must be exercised when using wax or hot-melt coatings since its effectiveness is diminished when it is held at high temperatures. The best over-all recommendations for this type of protective packaging are as follows:

1. See that all materials to be packaged are fumigated or otherwise sterilized before packaging.
2. Use a streamlined package, as free of folds and creases as possible, and completely sealed in every respect.
3. Incorporate D.D.T. to the extent of 5% in the coating whenever possible.

Almost any package which is properly made and sealed will protect the contents for a long period of time if both contents and package are sterilized and treated.[25]

Low temperature (below 65°F.) and low humidity are very important in preventing external attack of the package. High humidity and 70° to 95°F. temperatures present optimum conditions for insect penetration. There are also a number of physical conditions of the package which will influence penetration. A smooth over-all surface of the package with no crevices and the minimum of seams, will make it difficult for an insect to obtain footing and a point of attack. The thicker the packaging medium and particularly the coating, the more difficult it will be to infest, since small insects cannot bore into a thick coating and it is correspondingly more difficult for the larger ones to penetrate. Surface hardness is important for obvious reasons. An abrasive layer makes insect penetration extremely difficult. A wax double dip has been very successful as an insect barrier.[25]

3. **Rodent Resistance.** The question of rodent resistance is an unsolved problem at the present time. There is not a single flexible barrier which is effective against rodents and no chemical is available commercially which is satisfactory as a rodent repellent or a rodenticide.[23] There are some proprietary rodenticides, such as 1080 and Antu (α-naphthyl thiourea) which are quite powerful, but generally they cannot be used in packaging materials since they are also very toxic to man and domestic animals.

Technology of Fungicidal Wrapping Materials

Packaging materials may consist of foil, films, and/or plain or treated papers. Foil will not support the growth of molds unless coated or the surface contaminated in some manner. Films vary in their resistance to fungus growth and the cellulose acetate, cellulose acetate butyrate, ethyl cellulose, polyethylene, Saran, polyvinyl chloride and polyvinyl chloride-acetate copolymers, and Pliofilm all appear to be fungus resistant. Polyvinyl acetate shows some resistance, but cellulose nitrate supports moderate growth. In many cases such growths may be due to the plasticizers if they are not resistant in themselves.[24] Scrim cloth does not offer any mold resistance, nor does MSYT and PT type of Cellophane. MST and MSAT both exhibit good resistance.

As a paper base, sulfite and kraft are both used and kraft seems to possess more inherent resistance than does the sulfite. Glassine and parchment both support growth, although the parchment exhibits more resistance. It is possible to sterilize the packaging paper before use, and sterile conditions should exist in the packaging plant. Since the air is full of spores or bacteria which are constantly being deposited, however, even

FIGURE 24. *Effect of using fungicides in casein-coated paper in preventing mold growth* (Courtesy of Dow Chemical Co.)

sterile packages quickly become contaminated under normal storage and use. The safest procedure is to incorporate a fungicidal agent into the barrier material.

Many agents have been used, but care must be exercised so that the compound used will not present toxicological problems to the user and handler of the package. Calcium propionate is a satisfactory fungicide in that it is odorless, tasteless and non-toxic.[24] Sodium propionate and propionic acid are not toxic, and are efficient but they are not permanent and are limited in their use to materials with a short shelf life.[23] Biphenyl and o-phenyl phenol are good fungicides and also prevent growth within the package. o-Hydroxybiphenyl and chlorobenzoic acid are also suitable for the same reasons. Benzaldehyde, 2-chloropyridine, ethyl mercuric chloride, and o-chlorophenol all exhibit interesting properties, but have not been cleared completely for use in food wrappings.[24] Pentachlorophenol is only slightly volatile, but is only used to protect the outer wrapper as it is toxic. Phenyl mercuric compounds are excellent fungicides but are also toxic and cause skin irritation. Salicylanilide is an effective fungicide which is nonvolatile, colorless, odorless, and reported to be nontoxic.[24] A special moldproofing agent is made by adsorbing silver on collodial carbon. This is incorporated into plastic coatings.[26] The coatings are dark in color, but are nontoxic, odorless, and tasteless.

Some fungicides perform well in some coatings and yet fail in others. Chlorinated phenols are among the best agents used in casein coatings, yet they often fail badly in other than protein-base coatings.[21] Various mercurial-base compounds have been investigated and found to be very satisfactory in protective coatings, but can only be used in small amounts due to their toxicity and are mainly limited to outer protection on packages. Mercury oxide, mercury chloride (calomel), mercury bichloride (corrosive sublimate), as well as organic salts of mercury such as mercury naphthenate, pyridyl mercury stearate, phenyl mercury naphthenate, and phenyl mercury oleate, all have shown definite promise.[21] These are very effective against fungi, but also have some bactericidal action. Certain investigators claim that long-chain mercurial compounds are

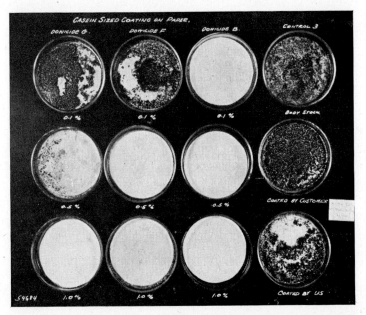

FIGURE 25. *Effect of varying the fungicide concentration of various agents in casein-coated paper on the fungistatic properties of the sheet* (Courtesy of Dow Chemical Co.)

safe for use with most foods, even when they contain large amounts of water since their solubility in water is so negligible.[23] These compounds can be used coated on the inside of the barrier in amounts of 1/1000 to 1/5000 concentration and do a perfectly satisfactory job as a fungicide and still be perfectly safe in respect to toxicity.[23] Solvent-type coatings using pentachlorophenol and salicylanilide produced fair fungus resistance while a plain paraphenyl-phenol-formaldehyde varnish offered very good resistance to fungi.[22]

In general, it is quite possible to produce functional packaging materials which possess good resistance to fungi and bac-

terial growths. Foil and certain films are resistant in themselves, and paper combined with suitable coatings, laminants,
and saturants will also possess the required resistance without
any problem of odor, taste, or toxicity. The base paper can be
treated in the beater or on the paper machine.

FLAME-RETARDANT PAPERS

The flameproofing of papers, cloth, and films is a problem
which has occupied many individual researchers and research
organizations for many years and there has been much literature
and many patents on the subject. As a result of all this work,
however, there have been very few really effective new agents
produced.

There are three basic materials produced by the converting
industry which require attention from the standpoint of flameproofing. Foil is not considered since it is a fireproof material
and will not burn or support combustion.

1. The plastic and cellulose-base films offer a wide range
of combustible properties. Some, such as nitrocellulose and
polyethylene, are inflammable; others such as treated Cellophane,
ethyl cellulose, and cellulose acetate will burn but not support
combustion. The vinyls, Pliofilm, and Saran are nonflammable.
A great deal of work has been done on the use of special
plasticizers which possess flame retardant properties, and most
cellulose base films, other than nitrocellulose can be formulated
so as to possess a certain degree of flame retardency.

2. The printing or coating material, the laminant, or the
saturating agent used in the finished sheet must be made flame
resistant or at least flame retardant. There are many flameproofing agents, fire retarding plasticizers, and noncombustible
synthetic resins which are suitable for this purpose. It is beyond
the scope of this work to go into the details of the subject.

3. The base paper or cloth, which, being cellulosic in nature,
will burn and will support combustion. It has the further disadvantage that it is in an ideal physical state to burn, since it

offers a great deal of surface area for a given weight. The flameproofing of the paper is the convertors problem and an understanding of flameproofing methods is of basic importance.

Fundamentally, no material can burn unless its temperature is raised to the ignition point in the presence of oxygen or oxygen-containing compounds. The material must decompose and liberate combustible gases and it is these gases which are first ignited when burning occurs. Chemical instability alone will not cause combustion; it is also necessary that the liberated gases are flammable. It is apparent that in any consideration of flammability the chemical nature of the materials plays a vital role.[27] Cellulose is a material which is flammable and which supports combustion, and as a result it is practically impossible to combine another material with it which can make the resulting product flameproof or fireproof. It is possible, however, to treat the paper so as to make it difficult to inflame and alter its properties so that it will not support combustion. Such a treated sheet is called "flame retardant."

The mechanism of flame retardancy is still a debated subject. There are certain flameproofing agents, such as ammonium chloride and borax which have been used for many years, but there is still no agreement as just how they protect the sheet. Fordyce [27] describes the following three concepts:

1. The first explanation is that ammonium salts and the like decompose to give off noninflammable gases, such as ammonia, and exclude oxygen from the paper. If this were the entire story, however, certain other salts such as carbonates and bicarbonates would be expected to be much more effective than they are.

2. A second group of investigators postulates that a low-melting material like borax melts at elevated temperatures and spreads out over the surface as a thin protective skin preventing free access of oxygen to the combustible paper material. In the case of borax this is probably true.

3. The last possibility is that the flameproofing agent alters the course of the combustion, i.e., during rapid oxidation less

flammable gas is produced and more carbonaceous (charred) material and more water are formed. In the case of acidic materials like diammonium phosphate and ammonium sulfamate a reaction is possible with cloth or paper and this tends to support this last theory.

There is no question that each and all of these factors are important, but it is also possible that there may be cases where one of the three is preponderant to the practical exclusion of the other two, while in other cases the three may possess equal importance. It must be again emphasized that cellulosic materials treated with these compounds are flame-resistant as tested by standard methods and are not fireproof in the sense of foil or asbestos. All will burn if heated to high enough temperatures. The effect of the flameproofing or fire-retarding agent, regardless of the mechanism, is to greatly reduce the rate of combustion of the treated material and reduce afterglow to a minimum.

Flame-Retarding Agents

Some of the oldest flameproofing agents have been previously mentioned; these are soluble salts such as borax and ammonium chloride. Other soluble flameproofing agents are diammonium phosphate and diammonium ethyl phosphate, both of which are applied from water solution and require about 15% on the weight of the paper to give adequate fire protection and prevent afterglow. Another agent which can be applied from a water solution is a boric acid-sodium borate mixture and this must be added to the sheet in amounts of 25% to obtain fire retardency, but it does not protect against afterglow. A more recent development in this class is ammonium sulfamate, which is added in amounts of 15 to 20% by weight to the sheet and gives excellent flame-retardency and fair afterglow characteristics. These agents all have the disadvantage of being water-soluble, and any severe wetting reduces or eliminates the retardant characteristics.

A different type of flame-retarding compound is formulated

from chlorinated paraffin and/or antimony oxide. This agent is water insoluble, and imparts excellent flame resistance, good waterproofing, and fair afterglow properties. It has been noted, however, that when antimony oxide is used as the sole flame retardant, it is only effective when the amount of organic matter is less than 50%, i.e., when the pigment is 50% of the sheet.[28] The use of chlorinated paraffin is found to be most effective in the presence of antimony oxide.[28] Chlorinated rubber applied from a toluene solution has proved highly successful.

Other agents suggested by various investigators are ammonium sulfate, ammonium carbonate, aluminum hydroxide, zinc sulfate, magnesium sulfate, sodium phosphate, zinc chloride, and urea.[27, 31]

Zinc borate is a new retardant developed during World War II. This compound has good fire-retardant properties and also exhibits water resistance and a definite fungicidal action against common cellulose destroying fungi.[29, 31]

Nitrogen-phosphorus compounds are the basis of recently developed compounds, which are still in the experimental stage. They are claimed to retard flame propagation by chemical suppression of the flammability.[30, 31] The compounds owe their effectiveness to the expansion of the resin on exposure to heat and the protection against combustion of the charred frothy mass by the ammonium phosphates which are present. Such compositions can be made from urea-formaldehyde resins and ammonium phosphate.

According to Jones,[32] there are almost thirty-five chemicals which are good fireproofing agents. These are mainly inorganic in nature, but a few organics are also used such as hexachlorobenzene in o-dichlorobenzene. The compounds used most frequently are: chlorides of ammonia, calcium, zinc, copper, and magnesium; sulfates of ammonia, nickel and aluminum; sodium arsenate; boric acid and phosphoric acid. Some such chemicals are used alone and others in mixtures, such as 70 parts of borax mixed with 30 parts of monoammonium phosphate. Mono- and diammonium phosphates are excellent since they retard flame and afterglow even in low concentrations, have no corrosive action on metals, are not hygroscopic under normal working conditions, and, if well impregnated, possess a retentivity of 75% after water leaching.[32]

A new type of fire retarding coating, developed at the Forest Products Laboratory,[31] is composed of equal parts by weight of monoammonium phosphate and a 2% solution of sodium alginate. Another recommendation is a formula containing 50 parts of monoammonium phosphate, 5 parts titanium dioxide, and 45 parts of a 2% solution of sodium alginate. Other coating compounds containing borax, boric acid, phosphates, clay, as well as other suspending agents such as methyl cellulose, casein, and synthetic resins were also suggested. The work done by this group is very extensive and merits study.

The major weakness of most of the flame-retarding agents discussed in this section is their inability to retain their effectiveness after exposure to water, due to the leaching out of the water-soluble components. So far as is known, no water-insoluble compound has been found which is equal in its effectiveness to such water-soluble compounds as ammonium phosphate, borax, and sodium silicate. Water-insoluble compounds which possess flame retarding characteristics are zinc borate, chlorinated rubber, chlorinated paraffin, antimony oxide, and potassium pyroantimonate.[31]

PLASTICIZED PAPERS

by G. Schmidt

The modification of the paper web by natural or synthetic materials of resinous or elastic nature has not always been too successful without some greater or lesser change in the bending or folding characteristics of the untreated fiber mat. Most of the papers used for coating or impregnation can be considered stiff, rattly, or having resistance to bending when applied in certain functions. These characteristics can be modified with certain materials to produce limpness, softness, or low resistance to bending. Such alteration of paper is commonly called plasticization, and the materials are designated as paper plasticizers.

The theory explaining the mechanism of cellulose fiber plasticization is most controversial and has no place in this short discussion. For all practical purposes, however, it can be said that there is only one successful plasticizer of paper fibers and that is water. Water is the only lubricant which can cause each fiber in a paper to bend with less resistance than in the dry state. Surrounding the comparatively stiff dry fibers of paper with an elastic or plastic material does not in any great degree cause a change in the paper's limpness such as water does.

It is a well-known fact that cellulose fibers are somewhat hygroscopic, but the amount of water which is attracted at normal humidities by them is quite insufficient to make a noticeable change. Other hygroscopic materials having a greater hygroscopicity must be brought in contact with the fibers, so that the water they attract can be transferred directly to the fiber.

Glycerin was the first, and practically the only material, used to plasticize paper during the years preceding World War II. Some work in the use of invert sugar, either with glycerin or alone, had been progressing, but the evident changes wrought by a small amount of glycerin in comparison to a large amount of sugar made the glycerin first choice. Before the war, the application of these materials to paper could hardly be called very important, for only certain highly hydrated, poor-folding grades were treated. Some glassine and parchmentized grades were treated with glycerin, as were the first paper drapes and shades.

It took the widespread substitution of paper for other materials to accentuate the importance of the changes which can be attained through plasticizing. Without the incorporation of the characteristics of folding, bending, or being somewhat limp, many treated papers would fail in their end use. The solution of the problems of plasticizing has not been accomplished without much research and experimentation. The old stand-by humectant, glycerin, was found to be unsuitable in many cases. Its vapor pressure being somewhat high, glycerin evaporated from the paper in too short time and its humectant properties at low atmospheric humidities left much to be desired. Certain surface coatings on a glycerin-plasticized sheet were found to absorb the glycerin from the paper, rendering the coating tacky or too plastic. Some coatings had reduced cohesion to the glycerin-coated fibers. Invert sugar was found to be less efficient than glycerine, and of doubtful use below 30% relative humidity.

The research work that has been done in the field of paper plasticization has resulted in a considerably greater range of compounds adaptable to the art, each of which has its own sphere of use. Of particular importance had been the various glycols and polyglycols. These water-soluble or dispersable chemicals have wider humectant ranges than glycerin and have such vapor pressures that they remain in the paper for considerably longer periods. Certain classes of the polyethylene glycols can be formulated to resist migration into resin top coatings or impregnants. Certain hygroscopic salts have also been found to be good paper plasticizers. Potassium acetate, in the presence of small percentages of ammonium acetate or other modifiers, has been used to a great extent. The added flame retardant properties of the acetates have been used in applications requiring this desirable characteristic. In recent months, amine-sulfamates have been given a great deal of attention, particularly because of their excellent plasticizing efficiency and their inherent flame-retardant properties. The desirable characteristics of this salt as a low-humidity humectant are of added importance. There are many other chemicals which have been investigated as possible paper softeners, but due to their cost, nonavailability in quantity, or their effect on the paper fibers, they have been pigeonholed or discarded. Most of the new humectants have been judged toxic and cannot be used in papers in contact with foods. Glycerin and propylene glycol are not in this class. There is some possibility that some of the polyethylene glycols may slip into the class of nontoxic materials, but at this writing they are not accepted by the Food and Drug Act recommendations.

Paper plasticizers are usually applied after the paper web has been formed and dried. Since most of the chemicals are water-soluble and applied from a water solution, wet strength sufficient to hold the fibers together is usually necessary. Size tub, diptank and squeeze roll, spray, or fog are the usual methods of application. The paper may be subsequently dried, or it may be rolled up in a damp condition, depending upon its further treatment. All papers suitable for impregnation with waterborne chemicals can be plasticized. Wetting agents compatible with the plasticizer solution aid impregnation into sized or low water absorption papers, but unsized webs are in the most satisfactory class.

Not all plasticized papers are so heavily treated that the physical change is easily detected. High levels of treatment in ordinary papers usually result in strength reduction or sweating at high humidities, both of which may be detrimental to the end use. In some applications of plasticizing such as with greaseproof papers, the decreased resistance to fold attained with a few pounds of softener per ream can result in very high folded grease resistance with lower coating weights. Papers coated with resins, which stiffen the sheet, can be brought back to their original flexibility with a low level of plasticizer treatment. But some applications, such as in paper drapes, require very high levels of treatment and the flame retardant properties of certain of the plasticizers are directly applicable in this case. Noiseless confectionery bags, barber throws, hospital sheets and pillow cases, are further papers which require plasticizers, but only those softeners which are noninjurious to the skin or are nontoxic can be used.

Plasticizing has gained greater importance because of these wide and diverse applications of paper, and with research in the field progressing at its present rate, the ideal paper plasticizer may soon be found. It will have plasticizing action in itself, and will be independent of atmospheric humidity. A plasticized product will then be as soft at 0° as at 99° relative humidity.

PHOTOSENSITIVE PAPERS

by C. E. G. Thomson

The important processes to be discussed in this section are:

1. Blueprint processes
2. Direct positive processes, frequently known as diazo types
3. The Van Dyke process

There are many other photographic processes which are of interest but space would not permit their discussion.

Blueprint Papers

Base Stock. At one time 100% rag stock was the only paper used for blueprints in this country and it was thought until fairly recently that if any fiber other than rag were used, the resulting paper would not be suitable for the blueprinting process. Times have changed, however, and for the last 20 years, excellent blueprint stock has been made with the rag content varying all the way from all rag to no rag. In Europe today, practically no-rag-content blueprint paper is manufactured, while in this country the standard composition is 50% rag with the balance mostly sulfite.

Base stock for blueprint paper is essentially of bond type, and in this country, it is almost invariably manufactured by mills which specialize in rag bonds and ledgers. The stock must be fairly well beaten so that the paper will have a smooth formation. Great care must be exercised in the manufacture so that the paper has a minimum amount of curl during processing.

Blueprint stock is well sized in the beater and subsequently tub-sized with glue. The glue tub size usually contains formaldehyde as a hardening agent and the paper in most mills goes directly from the tub size through the dryers and is wound up immediately ready for use. Paper made in this manner is known to the trade as machine-dried paper. Machines making blueprint paper are frequently equipped with two calender stacks; one before the tub size and one before the wind-up reel. Blueprint paper is seldom supercalendered.

Since blueprints are made on a machine which subjects the paper to intermittent washing and drying while the paper is under tension, the base paper must possess great tensile strength and wet-rub resistance. This is usually achieved by the tub sizing operation. Blueprint paper must be relatively free from all impurities, especially iron. The pH should be in the neighborhood of 5. One of the absolutely necessary characteristics is an ability to absorb the sensitizing solution evenly across the whole width of the web. Soft spots, thin spots, or any variations from standard thickness make the sheet unsuitable for the coating operation. Blueprint base stock is usually sold in rolls weighing 250 to 350 pounds, although in exceptional cases mill rolls are sold weighing up to 1200 pounds.

Until fairly recently, many manufacturers of blueprint base stock ceased operation during the hot summer months because they were unable to size the paper properly. During the warm weather, the paper they did make was usually too soft to coat, since during the coating operation the chemicals frequently struck through to the back of the sheet. For the last few years, this trouble seems to have been overcome due, no doubt, to the appearance on the market of improved sizing materials. It also is true that as the rag content of the paper is decreased sizing troubles are minimized.

Coating Technology. Most of the equipment used to coat blueprint paper in this country is simple in design. The average blueprint coating machine is capable of turning out the sensitized product at a rate of from 400 to 1200 yards per hour. During the coating process, the paper passes over two or three rolls, approximately 5 inches in diameter, revolving in a bath of the sensitizing solution. These rolls apply the liquid to the felt side of the paper, the excess is scraped off with a glass or stainless-steel doctor blade, and the paper then travels into a drying box, where it is dried with air heated to approximately 200°F. It is wound up in 50 to 100 yard rolls and has a final moisture content in the neighborhood of 3%. It is then wrapped in waterproof paper, labeled and is ready for shipment.

There are two types of blueprint paper: 1. that produced by the ferro-prussiate process, and 2. that prepared by the ferro-gallic process. These both produce a blue or white print, but the first is a positive print where the lines of the print show up dark on a white background, while the second is the conventional blueprint where the print is a negative one and is white on a dark background.

FIGURE 26. *Blueprint-coating machine* (Courtesy of Drying Systems, Inc.)

1. *Positive Print Papers.*[34] The coating solution for use with this type of paper is a solution of ferric chloride, tartaric acid, and gelatin and it is laid down on the paper by the usual methods. After such a sheet is exposed behind a tracing, the

ferric salt is reduced to the ferrous by the light so that the unchanged ferric salt which remains behind the lines can be developed by a tannic acid wash. This produces a positive blue-black image of ferro-gallate complex. The sheet is then washed and dried.

There have been two other types of such papers produced for volume consumption. In the first type, or "water bath" variety, the gallic acid powder was dusted on the paper by the manufacturer so that the exposed sheet could be immersed in water for a few minutes and then washed. The resulting print was usually grainy in appearance, however, and not as sharp and dark as when the gallic acid bath was used. The second variety utilized a mixture of gallic, tartaric and other acids, and ferrous chloride which was coated on the paper and dried. The paper was fairly satisfactory when first made, but over a period of time the ferrous salt oxidized to ferric although there was no premature formation of color. In order to prevent the color formation it was found necessary to incorporate fairly high concentrations of mineral acids and sometimes even mild oxidizing agents. The result of this addition was the rapid breakdown of the paper strength so that few papers were still usable after a month's time.

2. *Negative Print Papers.*[33] The common blueprint papers have been made using many formulae, but practically all of them are simple variations of the original process suggested by Sir John Herschel. He discovered in 1840 that ferric salts, when exposed to light in the presence of organic matter, were reduced to the ferrous state. His experiment involved the use of a ferric salt coated paper which was then exposed and the paper treated with potassium ferricyanide to develop the image. The ferrous salt produced during the exposure period reacts with the ferricyanide to give blue ferrous ferricyanide. This undergoes molecular rearrangement to form ferric ferrocyanide or Turnbull's blue and the soluble ferric ferricyanide which still remains on the exposed portions is removed by washing with water.

In actual practice there is not much divergence from this basic reaction. Ferric ammonium citrate and ferric ammonium oxalate are used as the light-sensitive salts, either alone or in combination, and are coated on the base sheet along with potassium ferricyanide. A typical formula is as follows: [33]

	Parts
Ferric Ammonium Citrate	125
Potassium Ferricyanide	45
Water	1000

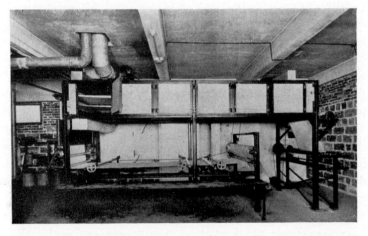

FIGURE 27. *Blueprint coater showing details of coating head*
(Courtesy of Drying Systems, Inc.)

Such a coated sheet must be dried in the darkness since the chemicals are photoreactive in the wet state. Such a paper is comparatively slow printing and will not age too satisfactorily. The addition of oxalic acid has been suggested but although it shortens the required exposure time, it also has a degrading effect on the paper and reduces the quality of the blue color. Citric acid has been added to help improve the clarity of the white.

A double-coated paper has been tried where potassium ferricyanide and gum arabic was used as the base coat followed by a second coating containing a ferric salt. Since the ferric salt is separated to some extent from the ferricyanide coating, the keeping qualities of the paper are improved, as the ferric salt is less likely to be reduced. With rapid or high-speed printing papers, the addition of potassium dichromate has been suggested as an intensifier for the blue color. The incorporation of neutral salts, i.e., sodium or ammonium phosphates, has been recommended as they are said to act as preservatives and as inhibitors to any reduction of the ferric to the ferrous state. The addition of acid ammonium oxalate instead of oxalic acid is said to increase the speed of printing without loss in aging qualities.

Practically all blueprint paper made today has as the basic light-sensitive compound ferric ammonium oxalate, while the color-forming compound is a mixture of sodium and potassium ferricyanide, known to the trade as Redsol. As a preservative, an alkali oxalate or citrate is generally used. The printing speed of the sensitized paper may be varied from slow to fast simply by varying the amount of Redsol in the formula.

It is of some interest to note that during the past few years, a new form of blueprint paper has appeared on the market. In this sheet the regular base stock is precoated with a compound consisting mainly of silica in colloid form. The colloidal silica in the presence of suitable binders is coated and dried on the base stock, which is then precoated with the blueprint-sensitizing solution in the usual manner. The resulting product usually gives richer blues and brighter whites. The process has certain drawbacks but appears to be gaining favor.

Diazo Process

Base Paper. Base stock suitable for the diazo process must, if anything, be made with more care than blueprint base stock. The presence of any impurities, especially iron, cannot be tolerated. Some of the best diazo-type base papers have been made by the Gelderland Company of Holland from rice straw, and others have been produced in this country prior to the war from a furnish which contained mostly hardwood and alpha pulp with absolutely no rag fiber present in the sheet.

During World War II, when wood pulp was scarce, most of the diazo-type paper made in this country had a high rag content, usually 50%, but this does not alter the fact that the less rag stock used in diazo-type paper the better.

Like blueprint base stock, paper for the diazo process must possess the following properties: 1. very uniform formation; 2. freedom from impurities; 3. extremely hard sizing; 4. low pH, preferably around 4.5; and a fairly high finish. The wet tensile strength and wet rub need not be so great as with blueprint paper, since diazo-type paper is not subjected to the prolonged washing and drying common to the blueprint process. The paper is almost always tub-sized and preferably calendered slightly before the tub, and again calendered before the final windup.

Practically all the diazo type paper and blueprint paper produced today is "machine made"; in other words, the operation is not broken into two parts as it used to be. In the old days, general practice was to make the paper first, wind it up and then, in a separate operation, tub-size it and dry it. Such paper was called loft dried. Very few mills make loft-dried diazo-type paper today.

Diazo-type paper is sized harder in the beater than blueprint paper, and in the tub-sizing operation, starch is used in place of glue. A small amount of urea-formaldehyde resin is usually added to the starch to harden it and to achieve a certain amount of wet strength. The paper is seldom, if ever, super-calendered and is usually fit for use as soon as it comes off the paper machine.

Since practically all the diazo-type sensitizing compounds impart a tint to the background of the prints, the general practice is to include some dyestuff in the paper furnish which will counteract the color imparted by the diazo chemical. Diazo-type paper which is designed to print black usually has a bluish-green dye added, whereas paper designed to print blue frequently has a pinkish dye added. The dyestuffs used must be highly resistant to both acid and alkali and the number of suitable dyestuffs is rather limited.

FIGURE 28. *Continuous blueprinting and processing machine* (Courtesy of C. F. Pease Co.)

Coating Technology. The diazo-type sensitizing solution is almost always very acid, the pH being in the neighborhood of 2, and it usually has a definite penetrating and wetting action. This means that the diazo-type raw stock must be quite dense and hard, and have great resistance to penetration. The sensitizing solution is quite thin, the Baumé reading varying from 2 to 6°, and is usually coated at room temperature. Most coating machines used for diazo papers, like blueprint coaters, are simple in design and operate at low speeds; the average being about 600 yards per hour. Some coating machines have been built which have been operated at 4000 yards an hour but these are very much the exception.

Practically all diazo compounds are more or less sensitive to light and one of the earliest suggestions for their use in photosensitive papers was around 1890.[35] This early sheet was made by dyeing a paper with primulin, a compound of sulfur and *p*-toluidine, and then treating it with dilute sodium nitrate in hydrochloric acid solution. A photosensitive paper was produced, but the diazotization of the primulin must take place *in situ* since the diazo compound is insoluble and the preparation of the paper is quite laborious. The sensitized paper had poor storage life and the background of the prints often stained a yellow color. The exposed paper was developed by treatment of the undecomposed diazo-primulin with alpha-naphthol in alkaline solution to couple and form an insoluble dye. Tetrazo compounds of benzidene, tolidine, dianisidine, and diamino stilbene are used in the manufacture of diazo-type papers by standard coating techniques, since the diazo compounds are soluble in water or dilute acids and the background colors of the prints are close to white. The papers have poor keeping characteristics, however, and so do not offer any extensive commercial possibilities.

The diazo compounds used must be heat-stable, unaffected by mechanical shock, and nonreactive with the base paper. They should be soluble in an inert solvent so that they can be satisfactorily coated on the paper in a sufficient concentration to produce a dark image. The resulting color must be insoluble in water and light-stable. The decomposition or solubilized products should be white or colorless and the diazo compound itself should be cheap.[35]

The real commercial application of the process followed the development of sensitizing solutions which are composed of a light sensitive compound and a coupling component which are coated together on the base paper. Premature coupling is avoided by incorporating a weak organic acid in the formulation. The paper is exposed and then the image developed by neutralizing the acid in the dry paper with ammonia vapor.

As the development of these papers took its further course, diazo compounds were discovered whose decomposition products after exposure to light were not affected by the presence of alkali. The result of this work was the introduction of papers which could be developed by merely sponging the surface of the exposed sheet with a suitable alkali-coupler solution. Such a paper need not be washed. Negative-image papers have also been studied and several methods have been developed for their manufacture.[35]

FIGURE 29. *Continuous whiteprinting and developing machine*
(Courtesy of C. F. Pease Co.)

According to Spencer,[35] the following types of diazo papers are possible:

1. Diazo compound A decomposed by light to substance B. Developed by the application of a coupler C in alkaline solution which reacts to give a colored product with A, but not with B.

2. Diazo compound A decomposed by light to substance B and developed by the application of a substance C which reacts to give a colored product with B, but not with A.

3. Diazo compound A and coupler C coated together but prevented from reacting by the presence of an organic acid. Such papers are developed by bathing in weak alkali or, providing they contain about 6% of water, by exposure to alkaline vapors, e.g., ammonia.

4. Diazo compound A and coupler C coated together but with one or both compounds modified by the formation of addition compounds in such a manner that they will not couple in neutral condition. Development is effected by breaking up the addition compound by heat, ammonia vapor, steam, etc.

5. Diazo compound A decomposed by light to substance D, capable of coupling with unchanged A on standing or on making the paper alkaline.

The diazo solution is applied to the felt side of the paper in the same manner as a blueprint solution; in other words, it is roll-coated and the excess is doctored off. In order to reduce curl in the finished paper, a back coating of water is usually applied to the sheet or it may be steamed. By varying the back coating and applying it before or after the sensitizing solution, or both, a certain amount of control can be exercised over the curling tendency of the finished paper. Some authorities prefer to sensitize first and then apply the back coating, preferably without drying in between. The proper drying of diazo-type paper is very important and for best results, the temperature of the drying air should be held below 200°F. and it should never be allowed to strike the wet coated surface. Final moisture content of diazo paper should not exceed 4% and preferably it should be in the neighborhood of 3%.

Diazo papers have been coated on almost every conceivable type of coating machine. Excellent results have been achieved at a speed of 600 feet per minute, using an air doctor of both the pressure and the vacuum type, and equally good paper has been produced on a machine which operated at only 3 feet per minute and which dried the paper at room temperature.

Van Dyke Process

Another interesting process which at one time was very important but which now has only limited application, is the iron-silver printing process commonly known as the Van Dyke process. The paper requirements for this process are very severe and only a few mills have succeeded in making an acceptable sheet. Van Dyke or negative raw stock invariably has a 100% rag furnish. The rag fiber is of the highest quality, free from harmful impurities, and should be as strong as possible. The stock is well beaten, heavily sized, and the paper machine is run at low speeds. An even formation is an absolute necessity as most Van Dyke paper is used in its final form as a tracing paper. Van Dyke paper is tub-sized with gelatin and formaldehyde and has high wet tensile strength and wet rub resistance. Much of the Van Dyke paper is still loft-dried.

The Van Dyke sensitizing solutions are very simple, consisting essentially of ferric oxalate, silver nitrate, and sodium citrate. The silver nitrate has a decidedly bad effect on the fibers of the paper, especially if the sheet has been overdried, so there is a tendency for most Van Dyke paper to become brittle in storage. To counteract this tendency, glycerin or other plasticizers are sometimes added to the sensitizing formula and the final moisture content held in the neighborhood of 4 or 5%. Van Dyke paper is coated on the same equipment as used for sensitizing blueprint paper, but it is slightly modified to accommodate the thinner stock.

References

1. Carleton Ellis. *Printing Inks.* Reinhold Publishing Corp., New York (1940), p. 406–407.
2. V. Bausch and A. Schroth. U. S. Patent 1,864,116. Production of Paper for Security Purposes (1912).
3. Id. U. S. Patent 2,112,756. Manufacture of Safety Paper (1938).
4. C. P. Foote and C. D. Guertin. U. S. Patent 2,402,542. Coated Paper and Method of Making Same (1946).
5. A. C. Shaney. *Elements of Magnetic Tape Recording.* Amplifier Corporation of America, New York (1947).

6. Anon. *New High Fidelity Magnetic Tape Recorders.* Circular No. 4901. The Amplifier Corporation of America, New York (1948).

7. Anon. "Magnetic Paper Tape Recorder." *Review of Scientific Instruments* (Jan. 1947), p. 72–73.

8. H. W. Rowe and Otto Kress. "Investigation of Anti-tarnish Paper." *Tech. Assn. Papers.* **23**, 332–336 (1939).

9. O. J. Schierholtz. *Pulp Paper Can.* **36**, 609–13 (1935).

10. R. H. Osborne. U. S. Patent 1,628,610 (1927).

11. J. Szott. *Papermaker.* **59**, 166–7 (1920).

12. W. G. Aurand. U. S. Patent 1,933,302 (1933).

13. A. E. Thurber and R. H. Scholtz. U. S. Patent 1,946,508 (1934).

14. A. D. Champlin. U. S. Patent 1,949,781 (1934).

15. Id. U. S. Patent 2,075,730 (1937).

16. O. J. Schierholtz. U. S. Patent 2,033,452 (1936).

17. Anon. "Anti-tarnish Tissue." *Paper and Twine J.* **21**, 9–10 (1947).

18. B. L. Kline and C. E. Mobius. U. S. Patent 2,400,544. Conductive Paper (1946).

19. B. L. Kline. U. S. Patent 2,425,742. Electrosensitive Recording Blank (1947).

20. J. E. Currah, E. M. S. Arthur, R. E. Thiers, W. A. E. McBryde, and F. E. Beamish. "Electrolytic Recorder Paper." *Ind. Eng. Chem.* **39**, 1286–1288 (1947).

21. A. Minich and M. Goll. "Mildewproofing Protective Coatings." *Paint, Oil, and Chem. Review* (Nov. 28, 1946).

22. L. Teitell and S. Berk. "Coatings on Kraft." *Mod. Packaging.* **21**, 165–167 (1947).

23. L. C. Barail. "Bacteriology of Food Packaging Materials." *Mod. Packaging.* **21**, 145–149 (1947).

24. C. G. Lavers. "Mold Control." *Mod. Packaging.* **20**, 185–187 (1947).

25. A. E. Michelbacher. "Insects and How to Control Them." *Mod. Packaging.* **20**, 143–145 (1947).

26. A. Goetz. *Mod. Packaging.* **17**, 113–115 (1944).

27. R. G. Fordyce. "Flameproofing Agents for Textiles, Paper, and Wood." *Chem. Ind.* **57**, 1069–1070 (1945).

28. L. S. Birnbaum and M. Markowitz. "Fire Retardant Paints." *Ind. Eng. Chem.* **40**, 400–405 (1948).

29. Anon. *Fire Retardant,* T.A.P.P.I. Bulletin No. 32, Technical Association of the Pulp and Paper Industry, New York (1944).

30. Anon. "New Flame Retardants." *"For Instance" No. 41,* American Cyanamid Company, New York (1948).

31. A. Van Kleeck. *Fire-retarding Coatings.* #R-1280. Forest Products Laboratory, Madison, Wisconsin (January 1946).

32. Anon. *Wood Fireproofing.* T.A.P.P.I. Bulletin No. 33, Technical Association of the Pulp and Paper Industry. New York (1944).

33. D. A. Spencer. *The Ferro-gallic Process.* Royal College of Science. South Kensington, S.W. 7.

34. Id. *The Ferro-prussiate Process.* Royal College of Science, South Kensington, S.W. 7.
35. Id. *The Diazo-type Process.* Royal College of Science, South Kensington, S.W. 7.
36. M. S. Kantrowitz. "New World War Papers and Their Uses." *Am. Paper Convertor.* **22,** 11, 12, 34 (1948).

Chapter VIII

COVER PAPER, SYNTHETIC LEATHERS, COATED TAG, AND BOARDS

by R. H. Mosher, F. A. Barr, and M. A. Park

THE heavier weight products of the paper-converting industry are the cover papers, imitation leathers, and various types of coated-tag stock and boards. Such products are manufactured from heavy-weight base paper or lined board or from stock made by laminating together several plies of boards and/or paper. The final product may be coated or printed on one or both sides, or the individual facing sheets may be coated or printed before laminating. The product may possess only decorative characteristics, or may also be functional in its applications.

The products can be grouped into four major classes:

1. Cover papers
2. Synthetic leathers
3. Various types of coated tags and boards
4. Photo mounts

Since the four types are so different in their characteristics they will be discussed in separate sections.

Cover Papers

Cover papers can be divided into two main types: uncoated covers and specialty coated or printed covers. The uncoated

241

types are generally given only a fleeting treatment by convertors, but the coated or printed covers undergo several converting operations before they are ready for use.

Uncoated Covers. The uncoated grades are generally converted through the application of an embossing pattern or
printed design on one or both sides of the sheet. The most
common grades of this type are made from a colored base
paper. Some of the most important characteristics of the sheet
are good folding strength and tear resistance, good resistance to
fading, and good wet and dry abrasion resistance. Such papers
have been print-embossed or spanished in order to obtain special effects.

Coated Specialty Covers. These are usually made from a
strong, long-fibered base paper, such as a kraft or sulfite sheet.
The final sheet may be a single ply or a laminated structure,
depending upon the desired weight and method of making the
final product and may be white, tan, or a color which is complementary to the coating. The sheet may be coated on one or
both sides, coated and waterproofed on one or both sides, embossed on one or both sides, or printed, print embossed, topped,
or spanished or two-toned, depending upon the requirements.

1. *Coating.* The base sheet may be coated with a pigmented
casein, glue, or other protein coating, or using a pigmented
synthetic resin (plastic) coating laid down by solvent, emulsion,
hot-melt, or organosol technique. Where a two-side-coated
product is required, two such sheets can each be coated on one
side and then laminated back to back in order to obtain the desired two-side-coated product. A heavy weight single sheet
can also be coated on both sides. The protein-based coatings
can be formulated to possess good flexibility and dry-abrasion
resistance, but their wet-abrasion characteristics, even when
waterproofed, are generally not completely satisfactory. The
plastic-coated sheets generally possess good flexibility and good
wet- and dry-abrasion resistance. The use of the newer synthetic resin latices together with the protein adhesives and the
new water-solubilized synthetic resin-base adhesives will no

doubt improve the results with water-base coatings. The coatings are pigmented to produce the required colors and the proper choice of pigments will result in the desired nonbleeding and light-fast characteristics.

2. *Waterproofing.* Where a nonwaterproof pigmented coating is used to give the required color and surface characteristics to the sheet, a clear, waterproof top coating or sizing is often applied. Such a sizing can be formulated with waterproofed casein or other protein or with one of the new water-soluble synthetic resins which can be insolubilized after application to the sheet. A synthetic resin (plastic) coating laid down by solvent, emulsion, hot-melt, or organosol technique also offers distinct advantages.

This waterproofing, or top-sizing operation, produces a durable, nonsoiling surface which will withstand handling and general abuse, fingermarking or scratching, as well as moisture and solvents. The base sheet can be coated on two sides or two single coated sheets can be laminated to produce the desired effect. When two waterproofed sheets are to be combined, however, the problem of water or solvent removal from the glue line may be important, and the use of special techniques involving coating and drying the adhesive before combining the sheets may be necessary.

Most specialty covers are embossed with leather designs, although various cloth and other special designs are also used. The embossed effects are usually obtained by one of three different methods.

a. *Machine Embossing.* The finished coated or uncoated web is run through an embossing machine, which is composed of two rolls, one of which is engraved with the desired design to produce the impression. The second, or supporting, roll acts as a backing for the sheet during the embossing operation and either a smooth or reverse embossed effect can be obtained on the back side of the sheet depending upon the type of backing roll.

The two rolls may both be steel-engraved and mate as they

turn and in this case both sides of the sheet will be embossed with the same pattern, the face design being depressed and the back design raised. An alternate procedure to obtain a similar effect is to use an engraved steel embossing roll and a paper-filled backing roll which are run in together under pressure without any paper in between until the steel roll has imprinted its design uniformly into the paper-filled roll. These two rolls can then be used to produce a two-side-embossed job similar to that obtained with matching steel rolls. When a smooth backing roll is used and only sufficient pressure to emboss the sheet, the face of the sheet will take the design and the back will remain practically smooth.

b. *Sheet Embossing.* Some mills have equipment for embossing cover papers in sheets rather than in rolls and this is accomplished by using engraved plates mounted in embossing presses. The process is slow and expensive, and the sheet size which can be handled is very limited. The effect is not as pronounced as when the paper is web-embossed.

c. *Plater Embossing.* The third method of producing embossed paper is known as plater embossing since the effect is obtained by the use of plating calenders. The cover paper is placed between a pattern sheet and a smooth metal backing plate and several of the units are made up and run in under smooth heavy-pressure application rolls. This kind of embossing is usually confined to cloth finishes where the actual cloth is used as a plate but a lumpy paper is often used to obtain a ripple finish.

Special effects can be obtained by printing the surface of the cover paper before or after coating and before embossing and particularly where the printed design is partially or completely synchronized with the embossing pattern.

Print-embossing equipment where the embossing roll carries an ink film and colors the embossed design with a contrasting or matching shade to produce a two-tone effect can be used to obtain interesting designs. Another possibility is to apply a coating or a surface treatment during the coating operation which will discolor on heating. The embossing roll is then heated so that simultaneously with the pressure high temperature is applied to the same area of the sheet. Such a sheet produces a unique two-tone effect with different degrees of shading where the pressure is varied by the depth of embossing. With such embossing rolls, a smooth backing roll is commonly used.

A spanished cover stock is obtained by embossing the sheet in the usual manner and then passing the embossed sheet through a coating unit where an excess of a contrasting or blending pigmented coating is applied, and then doctored off so that the applied coating only remains in the depressions. This technique can be used to produce some startling effects which cannot be obtained in any other manner. A knife coater is usually employed to produce this effect.

A topped cover is the reverse of the print-embossed or spanished sheet since a smooth roll or etched roll carrying a thin film of ink or coating is run against the previously embossed sheet so that only the high points are colored. Here again very unusual effects can be obtained and similar, blending, or contrasting colors can be used.

Some specialty covers are made with a high-gloss surface finish. Such papers can be produced by laminating a sheet of high-gloss paper to a cover base sheet. Another possibility is to laminate a sheet of coated or colored cellophane or acetate film with a clear laminant or a clear film, using a colored laminant to the face of a cover base stock. By this means, a high-gloss sheet can be obtained which possesses the flexibility and bulk needed in a cover. It is difficult to polish heavy papers to produce glossy surfaces in the normal manner without adversely affecting other necessary properties of the sheet. Other special surface effects are attained by using mica or velour coatings.

The desirable properties of a cover paper are good folding and tearing strength, good fade, mold and fungus resistance, and a soil resistant surface. Grease resistance is important if the fabricated product is to be handled by greasy fingers. The abrasion resistance, both wet and dry, must be exceptional, since the sheet is continually exposed to handling and scuffing. Printability, or the ability of the customer to print any desirable legendary or decorative characters on the surface of the sheet is extremely important. The surface should also, if possible, take the usual printing inks, as the small printers, who as a group are large customers of the specialty converting industry, do not like to have to use special inks. The acceptance of gold leaf is also very desirable.

The cover papers are produced in a wide variety of basis weights, from the light weight papers, known commonly as leatherettes, which are coated one side, up to double-weight, two-side-coated covers used on large brochures or manuals, and for the mechanical bindings which are becoming so popular.

The principal applications of cover papers are for displays, fancy box coverings, and wrap-around covers in the light weights or leatherettes. The medium- and heavy-weight products are used for catalog, booklet, folder, proposal, and instruction book covers; manual and reference book covers; and counter cards and other miscellaneous converted items. During the World War II, various government agencies recognized the importance and necessity of protecting their specifications and other printed matter. Cover papers were widely used in such applications. Printers, advertising managers, advertising agencies, and buyers of printed matter have long realized the importance of protecting their printed matter and have been large users of such cover papers.

Synthetic or Imitation Leathers

A great deal of work has been done in recent years on papers which were made to have the appearance, properties, and feel of genuine leather. Such papers are specially treated so that exceptionally high strength is built into the base paper. They are coated so as to simulate the surface appearance and properties of real leather and are embossed to look like leather.

The commonly used base papers are 10, 17, 20, 25, and 35 mils in thickness and are made from kraft, rope, sulfite, alpha, and rag pulps.

The major requirements in the base stock are high tear and tensile strength, good flexibility, and high bulk for good embossibility. Such properties can best be obtained by an increase in the internal bonding of fiber to fiber within the sheet while still maintaining low density and high bulk. The base paper is made from strong and long fibers, with an open structure, low density, and high caliper, and it is then saturated with a synthetic resin or natural or synthetic rubber latex. The rubber or resin particles possess the property of bonding the fibers together to produce the required physical strength while still retaining the open and bulky characteristics in the saturated sheet. High tensile and tearing strengths are obtained, and the sheet is flexible and bulky so that it will readily assume and retain the embossed pattern. The latex may be added to the sheet at the beater or on the paper machine, or it may be incorporated in a secondary converting operation.

The saturated paper is then coated with a synthetic-resin-base, pigmented, plastic-type coating. Solvent, dispersion, hot-melt, or organosol techniques can be used. The saturated paper makes a very poor coating base stock because of its high porosity, low density, and relatively rough surface, since the sheet, either before or after saturating, cannot be calendered or smoothed to any extent without reducing the bulk. Multiple coating operations are usually required to produce the desired surface effect and as many as five separate coats of lacquer have been used. Other techniques generally require fewer individual coating operations for an equivalent job, but water dispersions need at least three and organosols generally require at least two coats to obtain the desired surface effect. The final coating is grease- and chemical-resistant, ages satisfactorily, and resists scuffing and abrasion. By a proper choice of pigments, the desired colors, which possess light stability and fade resistance, can be obtained. If desirable, a leathery odor may be incorporated into the coating or base sheet, so that the finished product will smell like leather.

The coated sheet can then be embossed, print-embossed, spanished, topped, or otherwise treated in a similar manner to the regular cover papers. On account of its resiliency and bulk, however, the saturated sheet takes a deep embossing pattern easily and the proper base stock and coating and embossing treatment will produce a sheet which, in many ways, simulates real leather. The embossing patterns used are usually designed to simulate the real leather grain as closely as possible and special leathers are often used directly as the basis of roll design and reproduction.

These papers are used for the same purpose as the better grades of cover papers as well as for hat bands, belts, dress accessories, wallets, folders, parts for shoes, handbags, automobile accesories, chair and bar decorations and coverings, and luggage covering.

Coated Tag and Boards

Coated tag and boards are heavy coated papers and are usually produced in converting plants which specialize in handling the heavier weight papers. These products are usually manufactured to specifications as to caliper and finish, and the finished sheets are mostly printed before they find their eventual use. The coatings are usually applied to surfaces which are not as smooth and uniform as are common in lighter-weight base papers and as a result, the customary coating weights are heavier and often contain more adhesive than those used in the lighter-weight field.

The manufacturing problems are other than with the lighter-weight papers in that there is less footage of paper on a roll than with lighter-weight papers, thus necessitating more frequent roll changes and handling; two-side coating is common; the heavier-weight coatings require more drying capacity; and it is difficult to handle these sheets, which are stiffer and heavier than the ordinary coated papers, on festoon lines without getting streak marks and cracked paper at the sticks.

There is a distinct problem involved in producing such coated papers to uniform caliper on large widths, since the raw stock itself may vary widely in thickness across the web. The coated rolls are usually calendered at least once and often twice in order to achieve the desired uniformity of caliper and to obtain the required surface finish.

Coated Tag. Coated tags are usually made from base papers manufactured on the Fourdrinier machine, but many of the medium and heavy weights are made from cylinder stocks. The surface of the base sheet is usually rougher than is desireable, because of the thickness of the stock, and a heavy coating is necessary to level off the sheet surface and cover it sufficiently so that the base imperfections and sheet texture will not appear as a mottle after calendering. Such coating weights are also desirable in order to produce a satisfactory smooth printing surface and attain the specified sheet thickness. The base stock for converting purposes is usually fairly highly sized so as to hold up the applied coating and is white, buff, or manila in color. The thickness ranges from 6 to 20 points depending upon the use.

The requirements of the coated stock depend to a great extent upon the end use of the product and the specifications of the customer. The sheet should possess good folding and tearing characteristics and have a surface which is smooth enough to print readily. The formulation of the coating compound depends upon the abrasion resistance requirements of the customer and the type of printing equipment available to produce the finished tags. A sheet which will be made into laundry tags and must pass through a laundering operation is different from a tag which will be attached to a new shirt for identification or pricing purposes in a retail store. The printing requirements also vary as some tags are printed with surface drying inks by the rotogravure process while others are handled on the usual flat-bed presses using oxidizing oil inks. The amount of adhesive in the coating formulation may range from 18 to 30% and, in some cases, the coatings will be waterproofed by the addition of shellac or formaldehyde. The pigment composition may vary from English clay or a carbonate pigment for good ink absorbency to a fine domestic clay or satin white to produce smoothness and a glossy surface.

The fiber formulation of the base stock can vary from rope, jute, sulfate or sulfite to soda or groundwood pulp, according to the use requirements of the final tags. Some tags must be strong and resistant to tearing, while others must be easily torn in half for identification or verification purposes.

The manufacturers of tags have formed an association known as the Tag Manufacturers Institute and this group has drawn up a series of specifications for colors, fiber composition, and for the physical properties of the sheet which they purchase for their manufacturing operations. The specifications cover 15 colors as well as gold and silver. These are known as T.M.I. shades and are usually specified on orders to the coating mill. In the specifications are also outlined in detail their test procedures and tolerances, as well as the terms and conditions of sale to the tag-consuming industries. Tag stock is supplied either in rolls or in sheets depending upon the requirements of the customer.

Tag stock in sheet form is usually termed tough check. This product is usually made from a single-ply sheet, containing long, tough fibers and is coated on one or both sides in white or colors. Tough check is usually supplied in three-, four-, six- and eight-ply designations, which refer to 12/1000, 18/1000, 24/1000 and 30/1000 inch thicknesses. The standard stock is usually 22 x 28 inches in size and packed in 100 sheet packages.

Tag stock is used for making all kinds of tags, file folders, heavy envelopes, score cards, menus, tickets, identification checks, car signs, and in applications where its strength and rigidity are desirable.

Specialty Boards

Coated boards include those products which are made from base sheets manufactured on the cylinder machines and are 12/1000 inch or more in thickness. Coated boards, coated and specialty blanks, and display boards also belong to this group. The coated boards are usually made up in thicknesses ranging from 12 to 28 points and are based on a single- or multiple-ply base stock. The blanks and display boards are manufactured in thicknesses ranging from 12/1000 to 78/1000 inch and are also made from single- or multiple-ply base sheets.

Coated boards are generally made by coating with clay or other pigment and casein directly on to the board surface. The base stock may be made from waste paper and bleached or unbleached kraft or sulfite pulp and is generally lined on one or both sides. A fairly heavy coating load, 10 to 24 pounds (23 x 29—500), is applied since the board surface is usually relatively rough and may contain coarse matter or dirt which must be covered up to make a good appearance and printing surface. The coated sheet is always supercalendered to smooth out the surface and attain the desired caliper, and care must be exercised not to emphasize any imperfections in the base stock which may show through the coating.

The coated blanks are made from a cylinder-lined or multiple-ply pasted base sheet which results in good durability and a certain rigidity which is not present in the average coated board. The minimum-thickness blank is manufactured from a two-ply, cylinder-lined board, but the heavier weights, usually in excess of six ply, are made from a laminated structure composed of a middle and two liners or facings. The middles are usually made from waste paper, either plain or deinked; groundwood; bleached or unbleached kraft or sulfite; or some mixture of these pulps. The facings are either kraft or sulfite base and may be white or colored, depending upon the use requirements of the stock. There are several classes of blanks as follows:

    a. Uncoated Blanks—Middle of news or groundwood and bleached kraft or sulfite facings in either white or colors.

    b. Coated Blanks—Single or multiple coated on both sides and calendered to a high finish. The coating is usually white and shows a high whiteness, usually on the blue-white cast.

    c. Coated Railroad—A lined news middle with a two-side coating, usually in colors.

These blanks are almost always coated with a casein-base formulation which is pigmented to obtain the desired color shade. The coatings are fairly highly sized, but generally not to the extent of a tag stock, the top sizing ratio usually being in the neighborhood of 24%. The sheet is characterized by a certain stiffness and rigidity in the pasted weights, because of the multiple-ply structure made up by a starch or glue pasting operation. This property is particularly desirable in the blanks as their biggest use is in the display and mounting field where they must hold up without sagging.

The usual sizes of display blanks range from two-ply or 12/1000 inch in thickness to twenty-four-ply or 78/1000 inch. This stock is commonly sold in sheets packed 25 to 100 to a package, depending upon the sheet thickness, in standard sizes of 22 x 28 inches or 28 x 44 inches. The grain direction in these sheets is usually specified since it is important that in a show card or display card the grain should run perpendicularly to the base. Where the rigidity is not important, but the folding quali-ties are desirable, the grain should be specified so that the fold will run in the grain direction.

The principal uses for these coated blanks and boards are display cards, calendar backs, menus, car cards, tickets and checks, show cards and mailing cards.

Photomounts and Special Mounting Boards

Photomounts and other mounting boards are used to hold, mount, and frame photographs, calendars, and advertising mat-ter for display purposes. The stock is usually made by pasting two facing papers on a news middle. The characteristics required in the sheet are good rigidity, freedom from curl and warp, good folding qualities, and resistance to fading. The rigidity is needed since folders, mounts, or displays are usually set on their edge on a table or counter and it is necessary that the board does not bend or flex. The second major requirement is flexibility since photomounts must be opened and closed many times without cracks developing on the folds.

Mounting boards are made in three different grades as follows:

1. **Soft Folder.** This stock is made from special grades of long-fibered pulp which will produce a clean flexible sheet; sulfite, bleached kraft, or rag pulps are utilized. The stock is usually made up to 25 points in thickness, if a single sheet is required, but where the usual heavier, more rigid structures are needed, it is customary to laminate two or more plies to obtain the desired thickness. Flexible laminants produce the best sheet, and the multiple-ply structure can be made warp- and curl-free, yet to possess the desired rigidity. The sheet can be printed or embossed if either is desirable.

2. **Cylinder Mounting Boards.** These products are manufactured on a cylinder machine and are lined on one or both faces according to the requirements for the sheet. Such a board can be used for many applications where the use requirements are not too difficult to fulfil. The liners are generally a sulfite or bleached kraft, white or colored, and the centers are often ground wood, reused news stock, or chipboard. If desirable, the sheet can be printed or embossed. Such boards are often printed with an over-all design simulating an embossing or other special effect for special applications.

3. **Pasted Specialty Mounts.** The pasted mounts represent the largest field of application and are generally produced in either two- or three-ply construction, depending upon the thickness required and the end use of the sheet. A three-ply stock is produced by combining two plies of facing paper to a middle or center. The thickness of each ply is determined

by the desired thickness of the finished board. The final thickness is also related to the rigidity and also the flexibility of the board. The proper adhesives must be used and the stock properly dried and seasoned so as to avoid any curling or warping in the final product. The sheet is usually a balanced structure and the problem of warp or curl is thus minimized, particularly on heavier mounts. Proper seasoning is good insurance against curl and warp, however, and most mounting boards are held under standardized conditions for at least 3 days, and usually longer, before shipments to the consumer.

The two-ply mounts are generally made with one or both faces coated, printed or embossed, and after the sheet has been pasted, an over-all embossing pattern is sometimes applied. Such a sheet, if made properly, has a balanced structure, is flexible, and can be fabricated readily; yet because of its laminated structure, it still has a certain amount of rigidity, even in the lighter weights.

The three-ply structure is more difficult to engineer and to produce. A news middle, which is a cylinder sheet composed of pulp made from old newspapers, is generally used to supply the desired bulk and thickness to the finished mount, but since the folding and scoring properties of such a sheet leave something to be desired, the two facing papers must have extremely good folding and flexibility characteristics. Kraft facings are generally used and, if laminated properly, the finished mount will be flexible so that the photo mounts can be opened and shut many times without cracking at the hinge, yet the entire structure will be rigid and stand without warp or curl on a table top. A secondary, yet important, problem with the middles is their thickness. Since this is directly related to the mount rigidity, the larger the expected photograph or easel size, the thicker and heavier must be the middle used in the pasting or laminating operation.

The mounting boards are generally made with one side coated or printed and the reverse side with a plain or colored uncoated facing where they are used for display work. The photo mounts are generally made with both faces coated and/or printed as they are handled and viewed from both sides. The coatings may be pigmented casein or other protein or plastic resin-base types, and the nonplastic types are generally top-sized or coated with a clear, protective, waterproof and grease-proof coating film so as to give the desired scuff and abrasion resistance. A heat-sensitive top coating is often used which will discolor under heat and pressure so that special two-tone embossed or die-stamped patterns can be applied by the customer where this is desirable. Fine embossing patterns are often used to give the outside cover of the photo mount a special finish. The inside face or insert which holds the photograph or other decorative matter is generally white, buff, light-gray, or cream-colored with a smooth or lightly embossed surface finish to provide the most suitable background for the photograph, calendar, diploma, or other decorative or legendary matter.

It is also common practice to print an over-all design on the outside and inside of some less expensive mounts, a dark gray and white on the outside and a light gray and white on the inside which will blend with the black-and-white photograph. This is usually an unobtrusive shadow pattern which tends to make a more attractive appearance and will cover up finger-marks or other soiled spots which may tend to deface the mounting after long use. Such printed patterns may or may not be top-sized with a waterproof and greaseproof coating after printing.

The design and over-all coatings must be fade-resistant and the proper choice of inks and pigments is very important. Since one side is often embossed while the other side has a smooth, glossy or matte finish, the two facing sheets are usually coated or printed separately and then laminated to produce the finished sheet.

Display boards may also be built up with a foil or glossy film facing, and sometimes even with special phosphorescent or fluorescent coatings, where specific effects are desired. Such sheets are true specialties, however, and do not enter the general lines of most convertors.

The main application for these products is obviously photo mountings and display cards, but there are some more specific uses such as mountings for blueprints, charts, and graphs; greeting cards; diplomas; announcements; and the many miscellaneous items which can be displayed in the windows, showcases, or counters of retail and wholesale stores and business establishments.

Chapter IX

ASPHALT AND WATERPROOF PAPERS

by M. L. Downs

I N ITS broadest sense, the term "asphalt papers" covers any type of paper treated with asphalt, including roofing felt, roll roofing, asphalt-treated wall boards, asphalt- and pitch-impregnated fiber pipe, asphalt-impregnated fiber molded products, and a wide range of other fabricated paper products. However, this definition is probably too broad for the purposes of either clarity or convenience and it has generally been accepted in the paper industry that asphalt papers is a term used to designate those papers which are asphalt-infused, laminated, or coated, and which are sold in sheet or roll form. They have almost universally been utilized where protection against water or water vapor is required and, therefore, they have generally been called "waterproof papers." It is the general trade practice to assume that, when the term "waterproof papers" is used, one of the asphalt-treated grades is meant.

It is impossible, within the scope of this section, to outline completely all the grades of paper made by the asphalt-paper industry. A summary of many of the grades used for wrapping and packaging can be found under Federal Specifications [1] or listed in wartime packaging manuals, such as the General Army and Navy Specifications for Packing and Packaging Overseas Shipments.[2] The simplest product produced by the industry is one consisting of a single sheet infused or saturated with asphalt. Such single-ply, infused grades are usually considered as water-repellent or resistant, rather than waterproof or water-vaporproof. The next grade of asphalt-treated papers consists of those in which two or more sheets of paper are laminated with a discrete layer of asphalt as the combining medium between each pair of sheets. These combinations may utilize a number of grades of paper which may or may not be infused with asphalt before laminating. This grade may also embrace a variety of reinforcing material which is usually imbedded in the asphalt layer, although reinforcement, such as burlap, or cotton fabric, is also utilized as either a facing or an intermediate layer in such combinations. In the laminated grades are also included those combinations in which a metal foil, such as aluminum, copper, or lead, is combined with paper either as a facing or as an intermediate layer. In a third group of products a tack-free asphaltic coating is applied to one or both sides of a sheet. The base to which such coatings are applied may be a single sheet of untreated paper or it may consist of various combinations of asphalt-infused or laminated papers. All these papers may be produced in a number of variations by using paper-machine creped base stocks so as to increase the stretch of the finished laminate, or they may be creped during or after the laminating operation to produce higher ratios of stretch in the finished product. There are also various other combinations of creping and embossing or corrugating to produce grades with stretch both in and across the machine direction.

History and Present Importance of Asphalt Papers

Abraham [3] in his comprehensive work on asphalts gives a number of references which mark the beginning of the asphalt-paper industry. As early as 1790, composition roofing was made in a crude manner by coating heated wood tar on plain paper placed over rough boards, but it was not until 1820 that a factory was set up to impregnate paper with asphalt so as to produce a water-repellent grade for the manufacture of tarpaulins and packaging and similar materials. In 1845, a British patent was issued to Williams [4] covering the method of producing asphalt-laminated paper and the product itself. In 1887, a U. S. patent was issued to Childs [5] on the same subject. The first patent [6] on the creping of asphalt papers was not issued until 1901, and the first patent on the reinforcing of asphalt paper was issued in 1909.[7]

Very little reliable information is available as to the early volume of tonnage in the waterproof paper industry, but by 1936 approximate tonnage records were accumulated and it is estimated that, in that year, 66,000 tons were produced. By 1942, a trade association [8] record showed a total yearly production exceeding 182,000 tons. The pressure of war use increased that tonnage until it reached a peak of 362,000 tons in 1944, a major portion of this tonnage going to the packaging of overseas shipments of food and equipment for the armed forces. By 1947, the total tonnage production of the waterproof paper industry had gone back to 191,000 tons. While this is a marked reduction from the peak during the war years, it is almost double the prewar production and indicates the trend to the increased utilization of these papers, particularly in the field of protective packaging and containers. It would appear, from the limited tonnage information available, that the industry is increasing its output at the rate of about 8% a year and, based on wartime performance, sufficient converting capacity is available for some years to come, without the necessity for any marked expansion. This opinion might be modified, however, by the observation that, in the years just following World War II, the waterproof-paper industry has been somewhat curtailed in output because of the shortage of kraft papers, particularly since a number of producers are entirely dependent upon outside sources for their papers. It should also be noted that the types of packaging involved during the war used many heavier basis weight grades, and the present yardage production of the industry has probably not decreased in proportion to the tonnage figures.

Raw Materials

Base Papers. The terms "base papers" or "dry sheets" are used to designate the papers used for asphalt conversion. The characteristics of the base papers used may vary widely, depending upon the grades being produced. For some low-grade sheets, as for example competitively priced sheathing paper, waste paper, Asplund fiber, or even groundwood pulps may be utilized, but, for the more permanent types and, in general, for a large percentage of the total production of the waterproof-paper industry, papers made only with 100% new kraft pulp are used. Papers which are to be infused or saturated with asphalt are usually of higher bulk, more porous and absorbent, and have lower bursting strength than those which are to be laminated. In turn, those which are to receive high-gloss coatings are usually produced denser and less porous than the intermediate laminating grades. Table V illustrates the base-paper specifications. The ranges of tests listed in this table are for 30 pounds basis weight only (24 x 36—500), but they serve to illustrate the relative range for various types of conversion. The asphalt-paper industry usually converts base sheets ranging from 25 pounds basis weight to 90 pounds basis weight (24 x 36—500), although both lighter and heavier grades are converted for various applications.

Laminating Material. Asphalt derived from the refining of petroleum is almost universally used in the waterproof-paper industry. Small amounts of natural asphalts, coal tar, fatty acid pitches, and modifying waxes are used, but their application is generally limited to the blending of compounds for the roofing and shingle industry and to those segments of the asphalt-paper industry producing coated sheets. Some producers of waterproof papers purchase asphalts and blend them with or without the addition of fillers, but, in general, the

TABLE V

Typical Range of Tests on One Weight of Paper for Various Asphalt Conversions

Basis Weight Pounds	Asphalting Class	% Burst	% Tear	Caliper Inch	Gurley Density	T.A.P.P.I. Water Penetration	% Moisture	Finish
30	Infusing Grades	75	200	0.0032	6	25	4.0	Low
	Bag, Sack, and Container Laminating Grades	80	195	0.0031	13	30	4.5	Medium
	Standard Laminating Grades	85	190	0.0030	18	30	4.5	Medium
	Specialty Laminating and Gloss-Coating Grades	85	180	0.0029	22	40	5.0	High

Basis weight—24 x 36 inches—500 count
Burst in pounds expressed as percentage of basis weight
Tear average in grams for sixteen sheets expressed as percentage of basis weight
Gurley density as seconds for passage of 100 ml. air
T.A.P.P.I. procedure T-443m, reported in seconds.

asphalt is purchased on specifications and used as received from the producer. All the major oil companies in the United States produce one or more grades for some segment of the water-proof-paper industry, and it is difficult to rigidly define what asphalt grades are to be specified as to working temperature and viscosity of the asphalt because of the wide variety of treatments represented by infusing, laminating, and coating, as well as the types of equipment utilized. Asphalts are usually purchased on the basic specification of ring-and-ball softening point[9] and penetration,[10] at a range of temperatures. These two specifications fix approximately the flow point of the asphalt, its relative fluidity, and give some indication as to low-temperature embrittlement. More comprehensive specifications quite frequently include requirements as to Furol viscosity, staining or oil migration tendency, odor, low-temperature cracking, and loss of volatiles at specified temperatures. An approximate range of asphalts utilized by the asphalt-paper industry is shown in Table VI.

TABLE VI

Approximate Range of Tests on Grades of Asphalt Generally Used by the Asphalt-Paper Industry *

Application	A.S.T.M. D36–26 Ring and Ball Softening Point F.°	A.S.T.M. D5–25 Penetration Test 77°F. 100 Grams Load 5 Seconds
Infusing and Saturating	60–120	Above testing range
Laminating	140–190	20–50
Coating	200–250	5–15

* These test ranges are very broad and specifications for any one application must narrow the limits shown to a considerable extent.

Reinforcements and Other Materials. A number of materials are utilized for reinforcing certain types of asphalt-laminated sheets, the principal reinforcing materials being jute and sisal. Jute is usuallly spun into cord having a tensile strength most commonly in the range of 6 to 12 pounds and either run in as longitudinal strands, woven into diamond-like patterns by means of special attachments on the asphalting machine, or purchased as prewoven scrims in rectangular weave in meshes ranging from $\frac{1}{4}$ inch to 2 inches. Sisal and related fibers are usually added in unspun form in an operation similar to carding. Other fibers, such as hemp, cotton, rayon, and glass fiber, are sometimes used in the form of cords. In the past, a wide variety of burlaps was utilized, particularly in heavy-duty grades, such as for the wrapping of coiled steel, but since World War II little burlap has been available from producers in India. Some highly specialized reinforced sheets have been produced with reinforcements consisting of plastic filaments, steel wire, and more recently a grade reinforced with steel strap.[11] A number of producers manufacture combinations of paper and asphalt with metal foils, particularly aluminum foil of 0.0003 to 0.0005 inches thickness.

Shipping and Application Equipment

Asphalt is received in paper cartons, steel drums, or tank cars, the last being the most economical and generally used by the larger converters. If received in paper cartons, the containers are usually hand stripped from the contents and the asphalt thrown into a melter in the form of large lumps. Steel-drum shipments are sometimes stripped by rolling off the steel drum after slitting, although in other cases, the drums are emptied by means of inverting the open drums over receiving tanks and heating by means of canopies or steam coils until the contents flows out of the drum, or by placing on heated racks. Asphalt tank cars are equipped with steam-heated coils. The cars usually leave the producer's plant at temperatures ranging from 350° to 450°F. and are, under most favorable conditions, received by the user ready for pumping, although cars must be often reheated up to 350°F. to produce a viscosity sufficiently low for pumping. Usually gear pumps are used and the lines are jacketed. Steam is the most common heating medium, although hot-oil systems and diphenyl-vapor heating systems are also employed. The asphalt is usually held in storage tanks at the temperature required for the particular type of converting equipment and either pumped to the treating tanks of the machine with overflow provisions back to circulating tanks, or pumped to the machine intermittently.

Asphalt application equipment, in general, is somewhat similar to the equipment used in the waxing and hot-melt coating industry, with the exception that quite frequently the construction is much heavier and built to handle much wider sheets. The simplest type consists of a submerging bath, or flooded nip, followed by a pair of squeeze rolls. Such machines are adapted only to saturating. The type most generally used consists of a pickup roll running in a bath of molten asphalt, which, in turn, carries the asphalt either to a transfer roll or directly to the underface of the sheet being treated. The excess is then removed and metered to the desired weight either by means of a pair of squeeze rolls or by means of rods or blades. Usually the pickup bath, the pickup roll itself and the metering equipment are all heated so as to maintain a suitable application temperature and asphalt viscosity. A typical asphalt-laminating machine is shown in Figure 30. For laminating, one or both meeting faces of the sheets are coated with asphalt. Then the sheets enter a pair or a series of combining rolls or press rolls, which are quite often oil-resistant rubber-covered, and either weight, spring, or hydraulically loaded to get the required combining pressure. These combining rolls may or may not be heated. The laminated sheet then passes over cooling drums prior to being wound into rolls. For saturation or infusion, the press section is eliminated and the sheet passed over heated drums so as to drive the asphaltic material into the body of the sheet. For producing an exposed coating, the sheet usually travels sufficient distance so as to partly set the coat. Then it passes over brine- or water-cooled drums or is carried by means of carrying sticks or belts through a cooling tunnel to chill the coat so as to prevent "blocking" or adherence in the finished roll. Where reinforcing material is incorporated in the laminated sheets, it is either applied to the face of molten asphalt on one of the sheets travelling over the machine or is continuously fed between the two sheets just prior to the combining rolls.

FIGURE 30. *Asphalt application section of vertical asphalt coater and two-web laminator* (Courtesy of John Waldron Corp.)

Various types of specialized machines are utilized, as for example equipment for producing two saturated plies by heating a lamination to the infusing point and separating the layers.[12] Numerous patents cover methods for producing two-way-stretch grades, and one particular group of patents [13] covers a method of creping at a 45° angle to the sheet travel, with asphalt as the adhering medium so as to produce a true two-way crepe. Standard one-way crepes are most frequently produced by means of regular creping equipment which causes the sheet to adhere to the surface of a polished roll by means of glue or other adhesive and removes the sheet in creped form by means of a doctor blade riding against the surface of the creping roll. Other auxiliary equipment may consist of slitters or circular cutting blades used to divide the trim of the machine into a number of specified smaller width rolls. In some cases, the machine is also followed by formers and folding rolls to produce sheets with prefolded flanges for special uses, as for example rock-wool backing. Other auxiliary equipment consists of the usual rewinders and sheeters common to the paper industry and automatic rewinders to produce measured length rolls for small-consumer use, as for example the building and lumber-supply industry. Some asphalt-converting includes dual operations applying wax or another material to one face or one ply and asphalt to the other, but such operations are not generally considered part of asphalt-paper conversion.

Grades and Applications of Asphalt Papers

It is almost impossible to give a complete tabulation of all the grades of paper produced by the asphalt paper industry and their applications. Therefore, only typical applications of some of the more common combinations will be discussed here.

Saturated and Infused Sheets. A continuous film in the form of either a lamination or coating is necessary in order to obtain good water- and water-vapor resistance. Sheets, the body of which have been infused with asphalt short of coating, are not water- and water-vaporproof and are used principally where water shedding, resistance to softening by water, and scuffing and wear resistance are desired. In fact, in certain cases, as for example in the "breather sheet" or sheathing paper on the outside of buildings, the water-vapor permeability but water shedding properties of an asphalt-saturated sheet are desirable so as to resist occasional wetting from outside rain but still permit free exit of any water vapor trapped within the wall structure or insulation. This application is shown in Figure 31. A considerable part of asphalt-infused paper is used within the industry itself for recombining as laminations so as to enhance the wear and wetting resistance of laminated sheets. The weight of asphalt in infused sheets usually ranges between 20 and 60% of the original basis weight of the base paper. A typical use is a preformed bag-type case liner, the outside surface of which is protected from excessive abrasion by means of a light asphalt infusion.

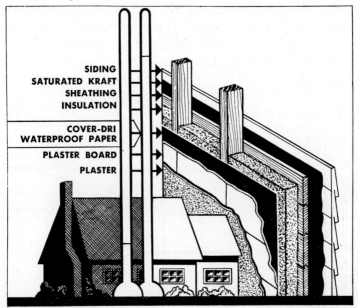

FIGURE 31. *Diagram of wall-insulated frame house showing positions of asphalt-saturated sheathing paper and asphalt-lminated vapor barrier* (Courtesy of Thilmany Pulp & Paper Co.)

Laminated Sheets. Laminated combinations represent the most diversified range, so far as weights and types of asphalt papers are concerned. So-called plain duplex sheets

usually consist of a sheet of kraft, a layer of asphalt, and another sheet of kraft designated in order by numbers indicating
basis weight, as for example 30-30-30 indicates 30 pounds of
kraft, 30 pounds of asphalt and 30 pounds of kraft in this
order. The lightest combinations usually do not run much below
25-25-25, and the heaviest combinations rarely exceed 90-90-
90. Such sheets, if properly designed, are excellent as vapor
barriers and are used wherever protection against the loss or
gain of water vapor is desired, or where protection against
water is needed. Basis weights of paper in the combinations
are selected largely according to strength requirements, whereas
asphalt weights are selected largely on the basis of water-vapor
resistance requirements. Figure 32 shows the approximate average water-vapor transmission in grams per 100 square inches,
per 24 hours, as tested in the General Foods water-vapor trans-

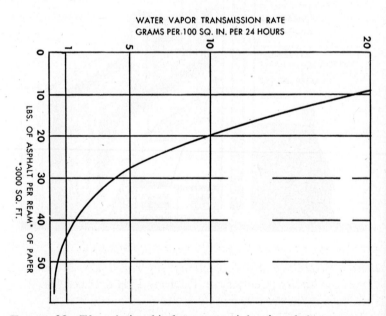

FIGURE 32. *The relationship between weight of asphalt, as a paper
laminant, to water vapor transmission rate* (Courtesy of Thilmany
Pulp & Paper Co.)

mission cabinet, in relation to the basis weight of asphalt in pounds per 3,000 square foot ream in a regular asphalt duplex combination.

This curve represents an average values for machine-finished kraft papers. If higher-finished sheets are used, lower basis weights will be needed to obtain the same resistance to water vapor. Likewise, if very rough finished, e.g., machine-creped sheets are used, several times the weight of asphalt may be necessary to obtain equal water-vapor resistance.

Plain duplex grades of laminated asphalt papers are frequently used as vapor barriers on the warm side of insulation in housing, in the walls of fiber drums as a vapor barrier for the packaging of high-moisture products, moisture-sensitive materials such as photographic printing paper, and chemicals, and as protective overwraps on small machinery and equipment. It is at times advantageous to incorporate aluminum foil in such laminated grades to enhance the decorative and water-vapor resistance properties.

Reinforcing strands are added to asphalt duplex combinations where handling requires good tearing resistance. In the case of reinforced asphalt papers, it is necessary to increase the basis weight of asphalt so as to completely enrobe the reinforcing strands and prevent wicking across of moisture along the reinforcement itself. It is common practice, therefore, to utilize three to four times the basis weight of asphalt in reinforced grades in order to produce the moisture-vapor resistance which is common to plain duplex grades. Typical application of reinforced sheets is for protection against the rough handling encountered in shipping upholstered furniture, or for the protection of concrete during curing where the sheet requires high resistance to tear, both from the standpoint of the original application and for subsequent exposure.

Coated Sheets. Coated sheets are adapted to individual applications and, therefore, no average basis weight can be given for the paper normally used. However, the water-vapor transmission of gloss coats has been restudied and it has been established that gloss coats transmit water vapor at basis weights ⅓ to ½ of that required for laminations because of the elimination of the possibility of cross wicking common in laminated form. Coated sheets are often utilized as a backing and vapor barrier on rock-wool insulation, purchased by the insulation manufacturer in the form of a prefolded, flanged backing suitable for application to standard stud widths. Figure 33 shows a coated sheet used as one layer in a multiwall bag for protection against excess free acids in fertilizer, and also to prevent moisture penetrating the fertilizer bag where it might give rise to objectionable caking. Coated sheets do not supplant asphalt laminated grades because of their limitation

FIGURE 33. *Asphalt-coated ply in multiwall bag construction*
(Courtesy of Thilmany Pulp & Paper Co.)

as to appearance, blocking at higher temperatures, and possibility of rub-off but, where application permits, they provide excellent protection at minimum asphalt weight.

Creped Sheets. Creped grades of asphalt papers find their widest use in specialized wrapping and packaging where it is desired to have a good measure of water or water-vapor resistance along with properties which enable the sheet to stretch and conform to the contours of irregular objects. Typical uses of creped waterproof papers include barrel and case liners, bale shrouds, coil wrapping, and interior packing to protect nursery stock and plant material. A considerable volume of creped grades go into the manufacture of thermal-insulating material where the asphalt paper usually serves as both an enclosing wrap as well as a vapor barrier. Creped grades are also used as temporary shrouds over machinery and in place of drop cloths during painting and sand blasting operations.

Special Uses. While the volume may be smaller than in the protective packaging field, asphalt papers find wide use in industrial fabrication and a few illustrations will serve to show the scope of use in this field. Special asphalt sheets are fabricated by means of a twisting operation into tacking strips used for fastening interior automobile upholstery to the steel body. Asphalt laminated sheets of various kinds are used in the construction of dry batteries as cell separators and in certain types of electrical coils as separators between the primary and secondary windings. Shims and gaskets of various types are die cut from asphalt-impregnated or laminated sheets and asphalt-coated or laminated sheets are commonly used as auxiliary vapor barriers for the protection of the insulation in refrigerators and frozen-food cabinets. Asphalt duplex or duplex reinforced sheets form the base for special water-resistant gummed tapes and are also used for water-resistant sewing strips for the closure of certain types of multiwall bags.

References

1. Federal Spec. for Paper; Kraft, Wrapping, Waterproofed UU-P-271a.
2. U. S. Army, Spec. No. 100–14A, General Spec. for Packaging and Packing Overseas Shipments (issue of Feb. 15, 1943).
3. Herbert Abraham. *Asphalts and Allied Substances,* 5th Edition, Vol. I, D. Van Nostrand Co., Inc., New York (1945), p. 49.
4. T. R. Williams. British Patent 10,774 (1845).
5. W. H. Childs. U. S. Patent 361,050 (1887).
6. J. Arkell. U. S. Patent 670,393 (1901).
7. A. Wendler. German Patent 222,959 (1909).
8. Communication from The Waterproof Paper Manufacturers Assoc., New York.
9. American Society for Testing Materials Standard Method D36–26, Volume III-A (1946), p. 280.
10. American Society for Testing Materials Standard Method D5–25, Volume III-A (1946), p. 255.
11. Signode Patent Grain Door, Brochure of Signode Steel Co., Chicago.
12. W. M. Wheildon. U. S. Patent 1,595,637 (1926).
13. W. C. Kemp. U. S. Patents 2,008,181 (1935); 2,008,182 (1935); and 2,071,347 (1937).

Chapter X

WAXED PAPERS

by A. M. Worthington

THE development of waxed paper, which dates back some sixty years, may be ascribed to two important industrial developments: the manufacture of paper from wood pulp, and the manufacture of paraffin wax from petroleum. These two developments, which occurred at about the same time, made possible the production of paper designed especially to be water- and water-vaporproof. Waxed papers were introduced commercially by the National Biscuit Company for the inner wrap of their Uneeda Biscuit package, and they were early used for the inner wrap for Crackerjack boxes.[8]

Paper, which is a mat of felted cellulose fibers of higher or lower degree of purity, embodies the properties of the individual fibers themselves, one of which is that of being hygroscopic, or being able to absorb moisture from the air. Cellulose will also permit desorption of the moisture it holds to the air, if the air is dry. It is a carbohydrate, containing hydroxyl radicals which are hydrophilic or "water-loving." When paper is exposed to moist air, these OH groups attract water molecules; when paper is exposed to dry air, these water molecules are again given off to the atmosphere. The amount of water which may be absorbed is 6 to 8%. It appears that water is absorbed more readily than it is given up.

Natural waxes had been used for many centuries as decorative and/or protective coatings.[11] It was known that waxes could be used to impart waterproofness. When paraffin wax was developed, its cheapness and availability made it ideal for impregnating and coating paper to render it waterproof and water-vaporproof. Waxed paper and paperboard are now widely used for wrapping and packaging materials where protection from moisture or dryness is desired. Perhaps the largest and most important group of materials thus protected are foods; bread wrap as well as wrappers for cakes, meat, sandwiches, delicatessen foods, butter, cheeses, frozen foods, dehydrated foods, crackers, tea, coffee and candy consist of waxed paper.

Most of the paper used for the manufacture of waxed paper is made from bleached sulfite pulp. To a lesser extent, unbleached sulfite and sometimes sulfate pulp is used. The sulfite sheet may be either plain or loaded with an opaque filler. Greaseproof krafts, glassines, manilas and several grades of twisting papers, may also be used.

Where a grade of paper such as glassine, which is practically impervious to wax, is converted, the process is simply one of coating either one or both sides of the sheet with the wax forming a surface film. The waxing of sulfite and similar grades of paper is a process of either wax penetration or wax penetration and wax coating. The first is known as dry waxing, and the second as wet waxing. Figure 34 illustrates the differences. In dry waxing, the wax is driven into the sheet and fills the spaces between the fibers, with very little wax being left on the surface. In the case of wet waxing, most of the wax remains on the surface as a continuous film, with just enough penetrating into the sheet to bond the film. Water passes through paper by way of the spaces between the fibers, whereas water vapor is transmitted both through these spaces and through or along the fibers themselves. If the surface of a sheet of paper is not completely covered with wax, some of the fibers protrude and act as wicks for the transmission of water vapor through the sheet. Thus, a dry waxed sheet provides waterproofness, and a wet waxed sheet provides both waterproofness and water-vaporproofness. Lamination, as shown in the third part of Figure 34 provides water-vaporproofness with no surface wax film, by placing a film of wax between two similar or dissimilar sheets, which will act as a bond between them. Waxed papers are now commercially produced which have a water-vapor transmission rate as low as 0.2 grams per 100 square inches per 24 hours at a temperature of 100° F. and a relative humidity of 95% on the wet side of the sheet, or 31.0 grams per square meter per 24 hours.[8]

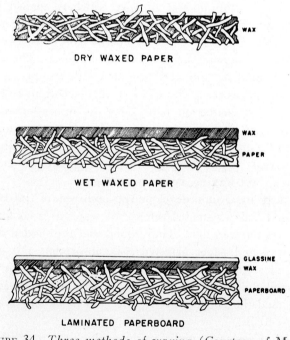

DRY WAXED PAPER

WET WAXED PAPER

LAMINATED PAPERBOARD

FIGURE 34. *Three methods of waxing* (Courtesy of Modern Packaging Magazine)

Most of the waxed paper is made on waxing machines. The history of such machines goes back to 1866, to Stuart Gwynn of New York, who was the first to patent the use of paraffin for impregnating paper.[13] In 1878, Siegried Hammerschlag, who has been called the father of the coating section of the waxing machine, applied a wax coating to one side of a sheet by running it over the top surface of a steam-heated roll which was revolving partly submerged in a bath of wax. The speed of the roll was variable, which, in turn, varied the amount of the coating. The surplus wax was removed by scrapers. A fan cooled the waxed paper.

In 1879, Hammerschlag went a step farther and developed the principle of the squeeze roll section as we know it today. This is a very important part of the machine, as this section mainly controls the amount of wax which is applied to the sheet. Hammerschlag patented a machine using two vertically mounted rolls, the bottom one of hollow iron to be heated by steam and the top being made of wood or rubber. The journal boxes were in slides and were provided with weights or levers to vary the pressure of the top roll on the bottom roll. The sheet was first coated on both sides by immersion in wax, passed through the squeeze rolls, and then the coating was smoothed by drawing the sheet over hot pipes. A cooling fan was also used. Hammerschlag was the originator of many of the steps in wet-waxing as we know them.

The next important development occurred in 1901 when Norris and Vavra patented the use of water as a cooling medium to set the wax film. They found that the sudden cooling of the wax and paper arrested wax absorption and gave a smooth, glossy appearance to the waxed sheet. In their work, they found the most suitable wax temperature to be 150° to 175° F., and the temperature of the bath of cooling water to be 32° to 40° F.

In 1915, Carter patented a machine which ran paper through a wax bath, over a set of hollow, heated, smoothing or ironing rolls (two of which were turning in the opposite direction to the travel of the sheet), and through a bath of cold water. The residual water was removed by an air blast in the direction opposite to the paper travel. In 1921, the speed of the

water-cooling machine was increased by the patent of Decker
and van Sluys for a device of vibrating rods bearing against
the paper across the web, followed by a set of scrapers against
the paper, and finally suction pipes between which the paper
passed. All these were designed to provide more rapid water
removal. In 1922, Carter patented and used a set of four cooling rolls to chill the waxed sheet. Liquid from a refrigerating
plant was used to keep the rolls at the desired temperature.

Further patents have not changed the basic principles of the
waxing machine. It is interesting to note, however, that in
connection with developments leading to increased production
of waxed paper per machine, in 1928, Nunez patented a duplex
waxing machine, comprising supports for a pair of dry paper
rolls, a wax pan, guide rolls to direct two webs of paper independently through the wax bath, independent chilling rolls for
each web, and two separate winders for the waxed paper rolls.[23]

An exception to the usual type of waxing machine is one
which can be considered almost completely as a coating machine. Either one or both sides of a web of paper can be wax-
coated by using this equipment. For one side coating, the
paper passes over an equalizer rod, a highly polished and accurately ground steel rod, 3/16 inch in diameter, wound with
fine-diameter steel wire. This rod is driven and is fed by a
driven roll revolving in a wax tank. A set of rods comes with
each machine wound with wire thicknesses ranging from 0.003
to 0.050 inch. The amount of coating is regulated by the wire
gage, the finer the wire the lighter the coating. For coating
both sides of the sheet, the paper passes over one equalizer,
then is reversed in direction and passed over a second equalizer,
operating from a second wax bath. The sheet is then drawn
over a cold roll to chill and solidify the wax coating.

Another development is the use of petroleum products other
than paraffin wax for the impregnation of paper to provide
waterproofness and grease resistance.[24] These products are
petrolatum, sometimes called soft-type microcrystalline wax;
white oil; and pale oil. Paper treated with these waterproofing

agents is comparable to dry waxed paper only, but the distinctive properties of these substances and their ease of application have caused them to replace waxed papers for some purposes, and to extend the use of petroleum-product-treated papers to new fields.

Types of Base Stocks Required

The principal advantage of a sulfite sheet for waxing is that it can be tailor-made to fit the specifications laid down for the use or uses for which it is intended. Several properties are controlled to produce a sheet which will respond in the ways desired when the paper is run through the waxing machines.

The main requirements of the raw or base stock for a sheet of sulfite or sulfate waxing paper are:

1. Proper finish
2. Correct texture or hardness of the sheet
3. Adequate physical strength of the sheet
4. Proper density or ratio of basis weight to thickness
5. Proper moisture content

Finish. The finish of the raw stock may be low, medium, high dry, and high wet, for machine-finished sheets. A high dry finish is made by passing the sheet through all the nips of one or two calender stacks at the paper machine, with no steam shower on the first stack. A high wet finish paper is made by using a steam shower on the first stack in order to put moisture into the sheet to obtain a higher finish. In addition, the sheet may be supercalendered for an even higher finish.

Of these finishes, the first three are part of the requirements of a sheet for dry waxing. The lower the finish the greater the ease with which the wax penetrates into the sheet. Decreasing wax loads are obtained as paper with a higher degree of finish is put through the waxer. The two other finishes, high wet, and supercalendered, are preferred where the sheet is to be wet or full waxed. Such finishes resist penetration of the wax, provide a smooth base for the external wax film, and thus help to impart a high gloss to the waxed sheet.

Texture. Closely related to finish in influencing the behavior of the wax during the waxing process is the hardness or
texture of the sheet. Everything in the papermaking process
affects this, from the raw pulp to final calendering. Strong
bleached, or unbleached sulfite pulp, or a mixture of the two
are generally used in the beater furnish, depending on the color
and brightness desired in the finished sheet. In some cases,
sulfate pulp, or a portion of it, is used. The sheet must be
well formed, but the fibers should not be too short, since the
sheet is to be used for wrapping purposes and must not be too
brittle. One way of judging the hardness of a sheet is by the
bursting-strength tear relationship. Low burst with high tear
indicates a soft sheet, i.e., one with a tendency to absorb too
much wax. Such a sheet, when waxed, would be reduced in
strength as the large amount of wax between the fibers would
have a lubricating effect which destroys the bond between
them. High burst with very low tear indicates a brittle sheet,
i.e., one which would tend to break and tear easily when used
for wrapping.

Strength. A sheet with the proper strength and degree
of hardness for correct waxing would be (a) for dry waxing:
one with a bursting test of 50% of the basis weight in numerical value, and an average tear test (averaging the tests with
and across the grain) equal in grams to the figure for the basis
weight of the sheet (basis weight: ream weight of 24 x 36
inches—480 sheets); (b) for wet waxing: the sheet would
need to be harder and the bursting strength requirement would
be 60% of the basis weight with the tear test almost the same
as before. The porosity of the sheet was formerly thought to
be a factor but more recent work has not shown any direct influence of this property on the waxing of the sheet.[17]

Soft sheets are indicative of insufficient treatment in the
beaters. Such sheets may be greatly improved for waxing purposes by supercalendering for giving them a high finish to
reduce wax penetration. In connection with the question of
soft texture, it should be noted whether or not the sheet under

consideration contains opaque filler. Such a sheet would have a softer texture than one made in the same way without the filler, and allowances would have to be made accordingly in the hardness requirements. The filler is mineral and since it occupies spaces between the fibers, will tend to reduce the penetration of the wax.

Density. The density of the sheet, which is the ratio of the basis weight to the thickness, or caliper, is also important. This is related to the other properties of the sheet already described, but it can also serve as a guide as to the waxing qualities of the sheet: since the higher the density, the more the sheet will resist wax penetration.

Moisture. The sheet should carry as much moisture as is practical. For dry waxing, where wax penetration is desired, 6 to 8%; for wet waxing, where penetration is to be restricted, more moisture, namely 7 to 9%, is required.

Printing of Waxing Paper

In many of the uses of waxed paper it is advantageous or necessary to have the paper printed, as a descriptive and advertising device for the product which is to be wrapped in the paper. Where printing is to be done, this step is carried out before the paper is waxed. Because of the texture of the sheet of waxing paper and the fact that it is subsequently to be waxed, all types of inks are not suitable. The inks and the printing methods described in the following paragraphs are among those generally used.[14]

Oxidizing Inks. These inks may be used in any of the three types of printing: letterpress, lithography or offset, and intaglio or rotogravure. They harden because the vehicle is a drying oil or drying-oil-modified resin which oxidizes in the air, aided by catalysts; usually organic compounds of cobalt, lead, and manganese. These inks take 1 or 2 days to harden sufficiently so that they do not bleed when the paper is put through the waxing machine.

Immediately after being printed, the back of the sheet may

be lightly waxed before it is rewound, in order to prevent offset. This is usually done by applying the wax by means of a roll, and then chilling the sheet by passing it over a cold roll. This corresponds to a one-side coating method. The wax used is of the same melting point as is to be used later when the sheet is waxed.

Aniline Inks. Aniline inks and presses were developed so that paper could be printed and converted to other forms in one continuous operation. This type of printing is now widely used for bread wraps. Aniline printing plates have extremely long life as a million impressions can be made from a single rubber plate. The solvents necessary with these inks are often toxic and flammable and must be vented from the press room for the sake of health and safety. Binders of various types are used with the solvents.

Heat-drying Inks. These inks were brought out in answer to a demand for higher production speeds for fast quality letterpress printing on web-fed presses. They use a binding resin in a solvent such as a mineral oil fraction which is essentially nonvolatile at room temperatures but very volatile at high temperatures. Because of these properties, the inks dry almost instantly upon the application of heat, which can be from an open flame. This literally burns away the solvent in the ink, leaving the binding resin and pigment on the paper. The flame temperature may be in excess of 1000°F. The inks may be dried by passing the web over large steam-heated drums, or through hot-air chambers with a large amount of super-heated, unsaturated air. Combinations of these methods may also be used. The paper then passes over chilling rolls to bring the temperature back to normal. These inks are being used in bag printing.

Moisture-set Inks. These are a comparatively new development.[15] The principle of drying involves neither oxidation, nor evaporation of solvents. It is based on the principle of precipitation. The ink consists of a pigment or pigments dispersed in a vehicle made of synthetic resin dissolved in a

high-boiling solvent; the resin being soluble in the solvent and
a limited quantity of water. The resin is insoluble in a greater
quantity of water mixed with the solvent and is precipitated in
the presence of this added water, thus "drying" the ink film.
Water may be added in one of four principal ways: (a) spraying after printing, (b) added to paper before printing, (c)
drawn from the moisture in the air, or (d) drawn from the
moisture already in the material. These inks are being used
on chewing gum wraps, bread wraps, and for similar applications where an odorless ink is necessary. Paper thus printed
can be waxed within 2 hours after printing.

Waxes

Paraffin Wax. Paraffin wax, the most commonly used
in the waxing of paper, is mainly derived from high-boiling
fractions of petroleum. Each year 500 to 600 million pounds
of this wax are produced in the United States, of which 80%
is used for paper, 10% for candles, and 10% for other purposes. It is not a chemically pure compound, but a white,
translucent, tasteless, odorless, solid, which consists of a mixture of solid hydrocarbons, chiefly of the methane series, when
in a refined state. The crude grades are odorous, greasy, and
contain volatile constituents, and as a result are not important
in connection with waxed papers. Refined paraffin wax is
soluble in benzol, ether, chloroform, carbon disulfide, carbon
tetrachloride, turpentine, petroleum, and fixed oils. It is insoluble in water and cold alcohol.

Petroleum (Paraffinic crude oils as distinguished from asphaltic crudes) is the raw material of paraffin. It occurs naturally and was formed by the decomposition of organic refuse
over a vast period of geologic time under conditions of low
temperature and enormous pressures. It consists of four types
of hydrocarbons: paraffins, olefins, naphthenes, and aromatics,
the paraffins being saturated open chain hydrocarbons, known
as the methane series.[2]

The refining of petroleum is carried out by means of distillation. Gaseous light ends, gasoline, naphtha, kerosene, and gas oil fractions, varying in boiling point and viscosity, are first removed in this order. The paraffin distillate, from which paraffin wax is obtained, is then removed. The still residues contain the heavier lubricating oil fractions and residue from which microcrystalline wax and petrolatum are obtained.

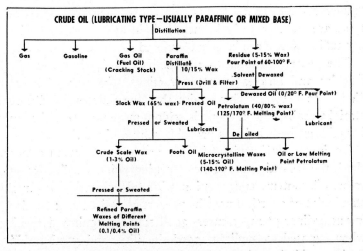

FIGURE 35. *Flow sheet of preparation of waxes from crude oil* (Courtesy of Modern Packaging Magazine)

The paraffin distillate is a mixture of light-bodied oils and waxy fractions, the former being more branched chain, and the latter nearly all straight chain hydrocarbons. This material contains 10 to 15% of wax; it is refined to produce paraffin waxes of various melting points, from 110°F. to about 150°F. Each grade covers a range of 2°F.

The composition of paraffin wax was not established until recently. The final analysis was made by Ferris, Cowles, and Henderson.[3] They chose a slack wax from a mid-continent crude, completely deoiled it, fractionally distilled it into narrow cuts, and purified these into twenty-six separated waxes, and then recombined the fractions having the same melting points.

These last fractions showed no change on further crystallization, and were assumed to be practically pure. The types of
crystals formed when these pure waxes were crystallized from
a solvent were carefully noted. Three series of compounds,
each with a characteristic crystal form were found. These were:
1. Plate type, representing straight-chain hydrocarbons.
Most of the waxes formed this type; 2. needle, and 3. called
"malcrystalline" as the form could not be identified. These two
types are assumed to be branched chain hydrocarbons. Microcrystalline waxes are largely composed of these types.

The generic formula of the methane series is $C_nH_{2n} + 2$.
Buchler and Graves isolated fractions with formulas from
$C_{18}H_{38}$ to $C_{32}H_{66}$. They claim that the number of different
straight-chain hydrocarbons is seldom more than ten; the number of branched chains is probably a little higher.[4]

To insure uniformity of their product, the manufacturers
check the following properties: melting point, tensile strength,
color, oil content, and reaction with sulfuric acid. From the
standpoint of practical use, the properties desired are: no blocking at ordinary temperatures, good stability against darkening
when exposed to sunlight, good ductility, and good stability
against oxidation when exposed to temperatures well above the
melting point.

The oxidation of waxes results in darkening, development
of acid and saponifiable bodies, lower tensile strength, lower
melting point, and lower hardness. The higher melting point
waxes are more stable; the refined waxes are more stable than
the crude scale waxes. In the case of paraffin, serious oxidation occurs at 250°F. after 3 to 5 days. Very small percentages
of pitches, asphalts, or asphalt-like substances are helpful in
preventing oxidation at temperatures of 235° to 240°F.[5]

Microcrystalline Wax. Microcrystalline waxes, sometimes incorrectly called "amorphous waxes," have found an
important place in the waxing of paper. They are paraffinic,
crystalline waxes, but their crystals are much smaller than

those of ordinary paraffin wax. These waxes can be used alone or blended with paraffin waxes. Microcrystalline waxes are made up of the methane series hydrocarbons of high melting points and high molecular weights. The work of Ferris, Cowles, and Henderson, and also that of Buchler and Graves shows that the crystals are in needle and malcrystalline forms. The formulas range from $C_{34}H_{70}$ to $C_{43}H_{88}$. The melting points may run from 140° to 200°F. They are not white but of varying degrees of brownish-yellow in color. Compared to paraffin they are tougher, have higher ductility and tensile strength, have greater tackiness, and are less lustrous and greasy. They have higher viscosities in the molten condition.

Paraffin vs. Microcrystalline Wax. These two waxes are widely used in the paper industry for the waterproofing and water-vaporproofing of paper. They are economical, easy to handle, and satisfactory in use. Each type has its advantages and disadvantages compared to the other. Blends of the two types may be made to produce a combination of desirable properties of both, or either may be used as a base to which other ingredients may be added to modify the original properties.

The advantages of paraffin wax are: whiteness, producing practically colorless wax films; hardness; non-tackiness; ability to achieve high gloss in a film; and low viscosities when molten, for production of lower wax loads. The disadvantages are: brittleness, poor aging qualities at elevated temperatures, and low grease resistance.

The advantages of microcrystalline wax are: greater ductility over a wide temperature range, making the wax useful where waxed sheets may be crumpled or creased, or used in the wrapping of quick-frozen foods; tackiness, making this wax useful in the laminating field; markedly greater grease resistance; higher viscosities in the molten state for high wax loads; good aging qualities at elevated temperatures; and good stability toward oxidation. The main disadvantage of this wax is its color, restricting its use to papers where light appearance is not so important, for coating dark-colored sheets, or for use in inner wraps.

Waxes do not in themselves render a sheet of paper grease-proof; this is generally the function of the base sheet of paper. Microcrystalline waxes do have the property of imparting much greater grease resistance to paper than paraffin, and a heavy coating of such a wax makes a sheet which passes some specifications for greaseproofness.

Petrolatum. Petrolatum, or soft type microcrystalline wax, is a purified semisolid mixture of hydrocarbons, of salve-like consistency, and transparent in thin layers. It is manufactured in various grades, ranging in color from dark-green to white. The highly purified grades are free from odor and taste, and suitable for use in food wraps as they will not become rancid. Petrolatum is freely miscible with other petroleum products such as waxes and oils, and these are often used to modify the characteristics of petrolatum as required for various treated papers. Applied to paper, it has a softening effect. Compounded with waxes and added to paper, a harder drier sheet is produced. Oils as additives have a softening effect on the paper.

Investigation indicated that petrolatum is a colloidal system of two phases, the internal phase being liquid hydrocarbons and the external phase solid hydrocarbons. The melting point ranges from 110 to 137°F. by the A.S.T.M. method. Its stability to oxidation is comparable to that of a fully refined paraffin wax.

White Oils. These are paraffin oils which have been additionally refined to remove practically all reactive and unstable components. They are light-bodied, extremely light in color, and have high stability against discoloration and rancidity.

Pale Oils. These also are paraffin oils. They are of low viscosity, and are practically free from odor. They may be used where the degree of purity need not be as high as with applications requiring white oil.

Wax Formulation and Compounding

The waxing of paper is usually carried out with a paraffin or microcrystalline wax of the desired melting point with no other added substances. Where certain effects not obtainable under such conditions are desired, compatible substances may be added to the wax in the molten condition. Any one or more of the properties of petroleum waxes may be modified by the use of additives, and marked changes may be obtained by employing blends of the waxes with other substances.[2] *Ductility, flexibility,* and *pliability* are related properties, and may be described as the ability of the wax to be distorted without breaking. In the case of paraffin, this can be increased by the addition of microcrystalline wax or petrolatum. Microcrystalline wax can be made even more ductile by incorporating an oil or petrolatum. Polyisobutylene, a synthetic thermoplastic elastomer, increases flexibility when added to wax formulations. It blends with wax with some difficulty, so that a concentrated mixture is supplied by the manufacturers which may then be diluted in the wax bath to a content of ½ to 2% polyisobutylene. Cyclized rubber, added to wax, improves pliability. Hydrogenated oils or fats, added to the wax, produce waxed paper of greater folding endurance.

Viscosity or Body. This may be increased by adding: metallic soaps, such as aluminum stearate; rubber; polybutenes, or polyisobutylenes; methacrylate polymers; cellulose ethers; Acrawax C; Strobawax; or butyl rubber. (Many of these are supplied as concentrated mixtures with paraffin, to be diluted during the waxing process to 2 to 5% butyl rubber in paraffin.) Increasing the viscosity of the wax decreases its penetration during waxing.

Viscosity may be decreased by blending the wax with substances of lower viscosity or solvents. Microcrystalline wax may be reduced by the addition of a small amount of paraffin. Penetration is increased by applying the wax at a higher temperature and thus lowering the viscosity. The addition of small amounts of fatty material such as stearic acid (5% or less) improves penetration.

Adhesiveness. This property may be increased where it is desired to have a tackier wax for a stronger heat seal, or a stronger bond in a laminated sheet. For this purpose, rosin, polymerized rosin, or hydrogenated rosin are most commonly used. Polymerized rosin is superior to the hydrogenated type. Other materials which may be used are: polyisobutylene, butyl rubber, and cyclized rubber.

Slipperiness. This is increased by hardening the wax with some additive. To microcrystalline wax, paraffin wax may be added. In the case of paraffin, carnauba wax, or some other vegetable wax, or hard resins may be used. Albacer, a synthetic wax, added to paraffin in a proportion of 5 to 10% prevents adhesion of the wax to sticky candies.

Tensile Strength. This property of paraffin is increased by blending it with microcrystalline wax. Stearic acid and ozokerite (an amorphous natural hydrocarbon wax) may also be used.

Hardness. In the case of paraffin, this property may be increased by the use of small amounts of the following additives: carnauba wax, Acrawax C, IG Wax S, IG Wax Z (the last three being synthetic waxes). Hardness is desired to reduce wax penetration into the sheet, and to stiffen the waxed sheet.

Melting Point. With paraffin, this may be increased by the addition of carnauba wax or ozokerite.

Luster and Gloss. Carnauba wax and rosin or its derivatives added to paraffin increase these properties.

Opacity. Opaque waxes may be prepared by blowing air or any other suitable gaseous medium into the molten wax to which a froth stabilizer, such as a soap, has been added previously. The minute bubbles trapped in the wax upon solidification render it more opaque. The froth stabilizer permits reheating of the wax above its melting point with retention of the greater part of the bubbles when the wax resolidifies.[2]

Other methods of increasing opacity are 1. incorporation of a suspension of titanium dioxide and a small amount of stearic acid or some substance with an acid reaction in the paraffin wax, and 2. addition of 0.5 to 5% of a hydrogenated vegetable oil. The methods of rendering waxes more opaque are patented, as are the uses of some of the substances mentioned in preceding paragraphs of this section.

Wax Blends. An example of a few of the wax blends which have been disclosed in the patent literature is given in Table VII.[23]

TABLE VII

Wax Blends

Formula No.	1	2	3	4	5	6	7	8	9	10
Paraffin	85	65	75	40	60	55	30–60	5–50	20	100
Carnauba	10			40	20		5–15			
Rubber	5	5	5	5	5	4			2–3	1–3
Candellila		30				25				
Gum Dammar			20		15					
Ester Gum				15				5–75	80	
Hydrogenated Castor Oil						16				
Pitch							10–25			
Rosin							10–30			
Petrolatum Wax								25–90		
Titanium Dioxide										5–15
Sodium Benzoate										5–15

Resin Wax Blends. Resins which are compatible with petroleum waxes are largely composed of hydrocarbons, such as polymerized terpenes, rubber-like polymers, and certain vinyl chloride resins. Some normal phenol-modified resins, ester gum and fused congo have also been found to be compatible with paraffin and other waxes. Under continuous heating, however, there is separation due to the oxidation of the oxidizable portions of the resins. If these portions are reduced to a minimum during the manufacture of the resin, greater compatibility is achieved, and such resins are more suitable for blending with wax for coating.

The addition of 20 to 25% resin to paraffin wax increases the luster, grease resistance, and water resistance of the wax. Such addition also reduces the tendency of the wax to smear and collect dirt, but it gives little or no improvement in the heat sealing qualities.[16]

Ethyl Cellulose. This resin can be used together with paraffin provided a mutual solvent is also present. Ethyl cellulose increases the toughness of wax films. Two of the formulas which are recommended are:[2]

	Formula 1		*Formula 2* [2]	
	Parts			%
Paraffin	10		Ethyl Cellulose	10
Montan Wax (derived			Stearic Acid	45
from lignite)	10			
Ethyl Cellulose	2		Paraffin	45

Waxing Processes; Impregnating and Coating on Waxing Machines

The three methods of waxing by means of waxing machines are: dry waxing, wet waxing, and laminating.

Dry Waxing. This method is designed to impregnate the sheet without leaving a surface film. On some machines, the sheet is unwound from the raw paper roll, and fed through the nip between two squeeze rolls, the bottom one of which is partially submerged in the molten wax. The pressure at the nip forces the wax into the sheet. A heated roll immediately following the squeeze rolls aids in the penetration. The sheet may then be passed over one or more chill rolls to cool and set the wax, or it may be passed over additional heated rolls and wound up hot, depending on the character of the impregnation desired. The finishing rolls may be used interchangeably as chill or hot rolls by having both steam and cold water connections. The first method leaves a waxy feel to the surface of the sheet; the second method gives the sheet a dry feel, as the wax is allowed an extended time for thorough penetration. For keeping the wax load down on this type of machine, a three-roll squeeze section may be used. The paper passes through the upper nip, where the amount of wax transferred from the bath is less than at the lower nip.

On another type of machine, the wax is applied by an "advance roll," a heated single roll of variable speed revolving in the wax bath. The paper passes over this roll. The amount of wax applied may be increased by increasing the speed of the advance roll. At all times the peripheral speed of this roll is less than the speed of the paper, so that the wax is applied by a wiping process. The distribution of the wax may be varied by changing the arc of contact between the paper and the advance roll. This is done by raising or lowering two rolls under which the paper passes before and after the advance roll. The paper then goes through the nip of the squeeze rolls, the bottom one of which is heated to increase penetration, but is out of contact with the wax bath. For heavier impregnation, the lower squeeze roll may be partially submerged in the wax bath.

Wet Waxing. The purpose of this method is to provide a continuous surface film or coating of wax either on one or both sides of the sheet of paper.

For one-side coating the method is like that for dry waxing. The wax is applied either by means of an advance roll, using the wiping process without squeeze rolls, or by means of squeeze rolls without an advance roll. The sheet then passes around the chill rolls to stop penetration and keep a film on the surface. The squeeze-roll method is not applicable to tissue sheets for coating one side as the wax penetrates through the sheet too readily. For heavier-weight sheets the paper itself prevents contact of the wax with the upper squeeze roll, and a one-side coating is provided by the wax supplied by the lower squeeze roll which is partly submerged in the wax bath.

For coating both sides of the paper, the sheet passes under a dip roll and is immersed in the wax. The sheet then goes through the nip of the squeeze rolls which regulate the amount of wax put on the sheet. If a heavier wax load than can be applied by the use of uncovered squeeze rolls is required, the rolls may be covered with woolen blankets. The bottom blanket is kept saturated with wax as the bottom roll revolves in the bath. The blankets cushion the sheet as it goes through, so that more of the wax is retained on the sheet, and at the same time the squeeze rolls serve to keep the wax load uniform. The sheet then passes over a hot roll to maintain the proper temperature for the polishing of the film. This is done by passing the sheet down between brass rolls which are revolving in the direction opposite to the travel of the paper.

The wax film is then set in one of two ways. The first and earlier method is to pass the paper around two or more cold rolls through which cold water or brine is circulated. Machines using this method are known as "cold roll machines." The second method is to immerse the paper in a bath of cold water to chill the sheet and set the wax film, followed by removing this water before winding the sheet into the finished roll. Machines using this method are known as "water waxers."

Water is removed by squeezing, blowing, suction, or scraping. In the squeezing method, the paper passes between two rubber-covered rolls like a wringer. Here the water removal is not 100%. In the suction method, perforated tubes connected to a vacuum pump are used. The sheet passes over these and the water is drawn off. The disadvantage of this method is that it is necessary to deckle the tubes in for various sheet widths. Constant checking against leaks is also required.

Two examples of the blowing methods are those patented in 1928 by Hayward, and in 1937 by Potdevin.[23] In Hayward's method, two vertical sets of box-like blowers are ar-

ranged in series on alternately opposite sides of the web of
paper. The tension of the sheet prevents it from blowing away
and the air blast keeps it from coming in contact with or rubbing against the blower heads, while the water is blown off
the sheet. In Potdevin's method, the sheet moves between air
streams directed against first one side of the sheet and then
the other in order to vibrate the sheet, and remove the water.

FIGURE 36. *Wet-waxing operation on bread wrappers* (Courtesy
of Marathon Corp.)

The scraping method is illustrated by that patented by
Howard in 1939, using the Howard water-removal tower.
After the sheet has been submerged in the water bath, it goes
upward past two water-removal doctors. These remove the
major part of the water, leaving only enough to act as a cushion. The sheet goes over a roll at the top of the tower, then
downward past two banks of knives, twelve to the bank. The

top bank removes the water from the lower side of the sheet, and the bottom bank does the same for the upper side. The water still being carried by the web protects it from too close contact with the knives. These blades are set at an angle and have edges so tooled that drainage is effected after the water is removed. From the tower the sheet may go to cooling rolls and then be rewound, or it may be rewound directly. This apparatus efficiently removes water from the sheet at speeds of over 1000 feet per minute.[13]

Carton Waxing. Carton waxers are like water waxers. The cartons are printed and stamped out before waxing, although sometimes they are waxed in sheet form. They are fed in, one at a time, by the machine operator. After the water bath the cartons pass through a series of felt squeeze rolls to remove the water. Endless belts conduct the cartons through the waxing machine.

Wax Load. Dry-waxed sheets usually have a wax load of 15 to 20% of the dry sheet. With wet-waxed sheets, the load is 40 to 50% or even higher, based on the dry weight of the sheet. In a dry-waxed sheet, it is desired to have the wax impregnated into the sheet. When wet waxing, only enough wax should be impregnated to anchor the surface film to the sheet.

Factors Controlling the Amount and Type of Coating

1. Speed. of Sheet. It is very important that the speed of the sheet is equal to the peripheral speed of the squeeze rolls at all times. With wet-waxed sheets, having a high percentage of wax on the surface, the wax film should be carried through the nip. Since hot wax acts as a lubricant, the paper has a tendency to pass through the nip of the squeeze rolls either too fast or too slow, when proper attention is not given to the running of the waxing machine—too slow if too much friction is applied to the dry roll shaft compared to the power of the winder, and too fast if too little friction is applied.

2. Speed of Machine. At higher speeds, the sheet carries more wax to the nip of the squeeze rolls. At higher speeds there is also less time for penetration of the wax into the sheet before it is chilled.

3. **Pressure Exerted by Squeeze Rolls.** In this roll section, the bottom roll is of chilled iron, either solid, or bored with a hole for steam. During the operation, the iron roll, if solid, is heated by contact with the molten wax. The top roll is composite, having an iron core with an inch of rubber for covering. The density of the rubber is determined by local conditions. In the newer machines the rolls are mechanically, rather than manually, adjusted and are held in position to compensate for the pressure of the wax at the nip. An air-operated loading device is used, with gages to measure and record the pressure at both ends of the nip. The difference in pressure is made possible to compensate for any variation across the dry sheet. With pressure indicators and recorders, the degree of pressure can be determined for each grade of waxing, kept substantially uniform throughout each run, and repeated on the next run of the same grade. In general, a tighter squeeze is necessary to keep the coating down to specifications at higher speeds. With machines which have no gages, there is a danger of using too much pressure and damaging the rubber roll.

In a three-roll squeeze section, the bottom roll is chilled iron and the two top rolls are hard-rubber covered.

4. **Density of the Rubber Roll.** In general, relatively soft rubber will apply more wax to the sheet than a harder covering.

5. **Melting Point of the Wax.** In dry-waxed sheets, a low melting point (under 130°F.) grade is generally used as these grades are less expensive, and the melting point is not important where the wax is thoroughly impregnated. At the other end of the scale, glassine requires wax of the highest melting point to produce the hardest possible surface, and best possible finish.

In the case of most wet-waxing processes, a wax of higher melting point may be used in summer than in winter to reduce danger of blocking in hot weather. It has been also suggested to reduce the blocking tendency by the addition of 15 to 20% microcrystalline wax to paraffin. (Above 20% the tackiness of the microcrystalline wax becomes effective.)

6. Temperature of the Wax Bath. It is not good practice to have the wax-bath temperatures too high. For wet-waxing, 15 to 20°F. above the melting point is recommended. Temperatures above 175 to 180°F. for paraffin are not advised since there is a danger of oxidation where the waxes may be continuously mixed with air through agitation.

Molten paraffin wax is a thin liquid, and the viscosity drop with temperature increase is only slight. Higher wax bath temperatures are, therefore, not so important in securing better penetration or decreasing the wax load. Microcrystalline waxes, which are more viscous than paraffin when molten, also show a greater rate of viscosity increase with decrease in temperature, so that, for these waxes, the temperature of the wax bath is a more important factor in determining degree of penetration and wax load in the sheet.

Accurate control of the temperature of the melted wax is important. For close control, one plant uses recording-controlling instruments, and two wax tanks for each machine. The first tank has the wax heated to the approximate temperature level, and the second tank, through which the paper passes, has the temperature maintained within one degree fluctuation. The temperature of the bath is regulated at the start of a run by setting the controls at the desired temperature. The wax baths are heated by steam coils or a steam jacket in the bottom of the tanks. Close control prevents overheating and oxidation of the wax.

7. Presence or Absence of Blankets. The wax load can be increased by the use of blankets. Newer blankets generally produce heavier wax loads. Blankets are not needed in the wet waxing of light weight sheets. They cannot be used for dry waxing.

8. Chilling by Water Bath or Cold Rolls. For good gloss and opacity in the wax coating, the water bath is recommended.

Water waxers chill the sheet quickly from both sides, and produce a coating consisting of small crystals and needles, which reflect light. The temperature of the cooling water should be between 32° and 40°F. Refrigeration systems are necessary to maintain this temperature range the year round.

The cold-roll machine is better suited for the manufacture of transparent types of paper. The slower cooling rate, first from one side of the sheet and then from the other, permits formation of large plate-type crystals (in the case of paraffin) which transmit light.

Air Conditioning. One modern waxing plant has installed an air conditioning system to reduce the danger of having the wax block in the rolls in summer.

Heat Sealing. In some types of packaging, especially bread wraps, it is required that the waxed paper is self-sealing. This is done by heat sealing. The parts of the paper where the seal is to be made are pressed together and heated until the wax melts. The heating is discontinued, and the paper is held together until the wax solidifies, at which time the wax will have sealed the parts of the paper together. This seal is not very strong with paraffin wax alone, but is usually strong enough for the purposes required. If a stronger bond is required, certain materials may be added to the wax bath, as previously described under "Wax Formulation."

For good heat-sealing qualities, the surface wax film must be of sufficient thickness in relation to the finish of the paper. The paper must not absorb too much of the wax during the heating process or too little wax will remain to provide a seal. A high-finish sheet of low wax absorbency does not need as heavy a wax film as a lower-finish sheet of greater absorbency, but under the proper conditions, the latter produces a stronger seal.

Petrolatum and Oil Processes. There are two ways of applying petrolatum to paper. The first method is the same as that used for the dry waxing of paper, where the chill rolls are converted to hot rolls to produce thorough penetration of the impregnant. The second method is to apply the material at the calender stack of the paper machine either by using a special "water" box or by means of a bath below the stack. The roll in contact with the impregnant and the roll directly above act as squeeze rolls. Steam coils heat the bath to keep it fluid. One or more of the rolls of the calender stack may be heated to improve penetration.

Methods of applying oil are the same as for petrolatum. The oil bath may be unheated or warmed slightly to improve penetration. Reduction of the oil load in the paper may be brought about by the use of scraper bars arranged in the form of a comb.[25] These bars remove part of the oil which is brought up from the bath by the bottom squeeze roll. The amount of oil can be controlled also by varying the width and number of the bars. The streaks in the sheet produced by this method can be eliminated by winding the finished roll tightly and allowing it to stand for 24 hours or more. The oil then becomes evenly and thoroughly distributed. The oil load in such cases may be as low as 5%. (Oil or petrolatum load in most cases is of the order of dry waxing, namely 15 to 20%.)

Laminated Papers. Laminated papers are those which consist of two or more layers, or plies, of paper, which have been combined into a single structure by means of an adhesive between their inner surfaces. Cost and other considerations, as a rule, limit the number of plies to four; two is the usual number. The plies may be of different types of paper or film or foil so that the distinctive properties of each may be combined to give a product of wider usefulness. Where the adhesive composition or laminant used is wax, advantage is taken of its water-vapor-proofing qualities so as to produce a sheet of high water-vapor resistance, without the presence of wax on the surface.

The many combinations of paper and laminant fall into three main groups: (a) two hard-surfaced sheets, (b) a hard-surfaced and an open sheet, and (c) two open sheets. Group (a) consists usually of glassine, cellulose acetate film, or Cellophane,

which are useful in food packaging because of their transparency or translucency. Group (b) includes glassine or parchment bonded to paperboard, kraft, or sulfite papers. The glassine or parchment is used for its greaseproofness. In this group
would also be included combinations such as foils and sulfite
or other papers. Group (c) generally includes light-weight
sulfites or krafts laminated with wax to produce a water-vapor
resistant sheet without wax on the surface.

There are four main types of laminants: aqueous solutions,
latices, solvent solutions, and hot melts. The last are waxy,
asphaltic or resinous mixtures, of which the most important
and most widely used is wax. The wax used is generally of
the microcrystalline type because of its tack, and its ductile and
flexible nature. The wax bond is a continuous film, and so
provides a combination with a high degree of water-vaporproofness. For some applications, the wax may be compounded
with other materials. There are many patents covering such
mixtures, and also covering equipment for laminating, and
methods of operation.

The wax bond must be strong enough to prevent easy separation of the plies or slipping of one ply on the other. In the case
of a two-ply sheet, there are five possible separation points,
namely: in either layer, at the bond between either of them and
the wax, or in the wax layer itself. In the case of group (a),
which requires a wax of high adhesiveness because the surfaces
are hard and smooth, splitting would occur in the wax layer,
if the sheet is properly bonded. With group (c), the opposite
is true. Here high wax tensile strength rather than high adhesiveness is important, and rupture will normally occur in either
paper layer. Group (b) is intermediate between the other two,
and rupture will normally take place between the wax and the
hard-surfaced paper.

Two basic rules have been given for laminating.[9] These are:
1. The wax should always be applied to the harder surface of
the two sheets. If both are equal, the relative ease of handling
would govern the choice. 2. Temperatures should be so adjusted

that by the time the waxed sheet reaches the combining rolls, the wax is only slightly above its solidifying point. If the temperature is too low, the wax will not penetrate the unwaxed sheet sufficiently for a good bond. If the temperature is too high, too much penetration will result and the layers may spring apart after leaving the nip of the combining rolls. If the wax temperature is correctly controlled, contact of the waxed layer with the cold unwaxed layer serves to solidify the wax at the junction point of the plies. This means thermostatic control in the wax preheating tank and in the waxing pan. Heat is not applied at the combining rolls.

In the laminating operation, the underside of the harder-surfaced sheet is waxed by passing the sheet through the upper nip of a three-roll stack of waxing rolls. This method provides for more uniform application of the wax. The bottom roll revolves in the wax pan, transfers the wax to the middle roll, and this, in turn, transfers it in the form of a continuous film to the underside of the sheet. The waxed sheet then passes through the nip of one or more sets of combining rolls where it meets and is bonded to the other sheet, and finally passes to the winder. Good grades of paper should be used, especially in the case of the open-type sheet so as to provide greater coverage by the wax and more economical operation. It also results in the production of a sheet of higher general quality.

Other Means of Applying Waxes to Paper

The principal method of applying wax to paper is by means of waxing and laminating machines. In addition there are other techniques [8, 18] and these include the following methods:

1. **Beater Sizing.** Wax emulsions which are compatible with pulp and rosin size are added to the pulp during the stock preparation. These emulsions are so formulated that they can be precipitated on the fibers upon the addition of alum so as to provide proper distribution and retention of the wax in the finished sheet.

2. **Top Sizing.** By this method, the wax emulsion is applied

to the surface of the sheet, usually in a size press or by means of water boxes on the calender stack during the manufacture of the paper.

3. Dacca Method. Empty cartons, glued at one end are completely immersed in a molten bath compounded of pale crepe rubber or synthetic resins and a blend of waxes, the compound being tasteless, odorless, and nontoxic. The cartons are drained to proper weight under controlled temperature conditions and cooled.

4. Single Dip-Method. The cartons are first filled and sealed, then immersed once in the wax bath. The cartons must be completely sealed to prevent the flow of wax into the filled package.

5. Flushing or "Enrobing" Method. Filled and sealed packages are passed twice by sets of nozzles so arranged as to flush the packages of molten wax from all four sides. The packages are held so that the excess wax drains from one corner, rather than from one edge. The excess wax from the nozzles and packages drains to a sump tank where it is strained and then passes to the pump section and returns to the nozzles.

6. Double-Dip Method. The containers are first filled and sealed. On the first dip, the package is partially submerged to a controlled distance. The package is then inverted and given the second dip which slightly overlaps the first.

Applications

There are literally hundreds of applications for waxed paper. Practically every industry has some uses for this product. It can be in the form of transparent or opaque wraps either put directly around the article or around cartons holding the articles. It can be employed as a liner for cartons, boxes, bags or cans; in laminated wrappers; bags; separator, interleaving, or slip sheets; or protective papers of other kinds. It is sold to the consumer either in rolls or sheets depending on his requirements.

The Waxed Paper Institute, the association of the waxed paper manufacturers, with headquarters in Chicago, has compiled a list of the principal uses. The largest part of the waxed paper production goes to the food industry. Most of this goes to bakeries, for bread, cakes, pies, cookies, crackers, and doughnuts. Butter and cheeses, oleomargarine, candies, meats and fish, quick-frozen foods of all kinds, vegetables, and yeast are other food products for which waxed paper wrapping of one form or another is used.

The metal goods industries use waxed paper for wrapping automotive and machinery parts, razor blades, tin-plate products, and as separator sheets for batteries. The textile industry uses it for wrapping black friction tape, thread, rayon, and nylon. In hospitals, it is used for sanitary sheets, compresses, wraps for surgical specimens, and gauze bandages.

Waxed paper slip sheets find an important use in connection with printing, mimeographing, and decalcomanias. The United States Government Printing Office uses these sheets for stamps, both in book and sheet form.

Cake glue, soap, candles, chewing gum, plants and shrubs, rubber heels, tires, and tubes are other products which are wrapped in waxed paper. Trimmings and shreds are used for packing purposes. Water-vaporproof cartons, baking cups, household rolls, and soda straws are made from waxed paper or board. Many other uses could be named in addition.

Petrolatum- and oil-treated papers, or papers treated with a blend of these and wax, are used for meat wraps, dusting papers, metal parts packaging papers, fruit wraps, "parchment" lamp shades, tympan papers, and paper specialties.

REFERENCES

1. J. N. Stephenson. *The Manufacture of Pulp and Paper, Vol. V, Third Edition*. McGraw-Hill Book. Co., New York (1939).
2. H. Bennett. *Commercial Waxes*. Chemical Publishing Co., New York (1944).
3. Ferris, Cowles, and Henderson. *Ind. Eng. Chem.* **23**, 681 (1931).
4. Buchler and Graves. *Ind. Eng. Chem.* **19**, 718 (1927).
5. Vore. U. S. Patents 2,325,085 and 2,325,167 (1943).
6. Killingsworth. "Waterproofing of Kraft Papers." *Paper Ind.* **8**, 526 (1943).

7. Leinbach. *Modern Packaging.* **16**, 85 (1943).

8. Anon. "Petroleum Waxes." *Modern Packaging* (Jan. 1944).

9. Anon. "Petroleum Waxes in Paper Packaging." *Technical Bulletin.* Lubricating Dept., Socony-Vacuum Oil Co., Inc., New York (Aug. 1945).

10. Anon. "Making More Jobs for Paper." *Oil-Power Magazine.* Socony-Vacuum Oil Co., Inc., New York (Jan. & Feb. 1947).

11. Anon. "Use of Petroleum Waxes in the Paper Industry." *Ibid.*

12. G. C. Borden, Jr. and S. S. Gutkin. "Resins for the Paper Converter." *TAPPI Monograph Series, No. 5.* Technical Association of the Pulp and Paper Industry, New York (1947).

13. E. E. Ferguson. "Waxed Paper Machines, Their Development and Operation." *Paper Ind. and Paper World* (Oct. 1946).

14. R. G. MacDonald. "New Developments in Inks." *TAPPI Bulletin, No. 60.* Technical Association of the Pulp and Paper Industry, New York (Oct. 15, 1945).

15. R. G. MacDonald. "News Ink News." *TAPPI Bulletin, No. 80.* Technical Association of the Pulp and Paper Industry, New York (Aug. 11, 1947).

16. J. F. Maguire and J. G. Rote, Jr. "The Trend in Resins." *Technical Association Papers.* Technical Association of the Pulp and Paper Industry, New York (1941), p. 487.

17. T. W. Noble. "Factors in Quality Control of Thermoplastic Coated and Waxed Papers." *Technical Association Papers.* Technical Association of the Pulp and Paper Industry, New York (1941), p. 392.

18. Anon. "Developments in Waxes." *Modern Packaging Encyclopedia.* Breskin Publishing Co., New York (1946-47), p. 601.

19. Anon. "Waxed Papers." *Ibid.,* p. 632.

20. F. W. Padgett and R. B. Killingsworth. "Tensile Strength of Paraffin Waxes." *Paper Trade Journal.* **122**, 19 (1946).

21. Anon. "Paraffin Wax Absorptiveness of paper." *TAPPI Tentative. Standard T 467 m 45.* Technical Association of the Pulp and Paper Industry, New York (1945).

22. A. Kinsel and H. Schindler. "Flexibility of Microcrystalline Wax." *Paper Trade Journal.* **126**, 13 (1948).

23. Anon. *Bibliography of Proofing of Paper.* The Institute of Paper Chemistry, Appleton, Wis. (1943).

24. Anon. *Engineering Bulletin No. AP-97.* Standard Oil Company (Indiana) Chicago (1937).

25. Anon. "Products for Paper Converting." *Technical Bulletin.* Lubricating Dept., Socony Vacuum Oil Co., Inc., New York (August 1944).

Chapter XI

GUMMED AND SPECIALTY TAPES AND LABELS

by F. W. Farrell

T HE manufacture of gummed paper is one of the major converting processes. The base paper is bought in the form of rolls from the paper manufacturer and the adhesive is applied at the gumming plant. The basic function of the industry is to supply adhesives in a more useful and economical form than in the uncertain and wasteful manner of the olden days. The old glue pot and mucilage have given way to controlled adhesives applied to the proper paper, which is selected according to its specific use.

The gumming industry, however, as far as production is concerned, is relatively new, and its active expansion probably began around 1900.

Two factors contributed to this expansion. One, the Tobelman process of flattening gummed papers; and the second, the introduction of the corrugated fiber shipping case. Prior to the Tobelman patent, it was almost impossible to print the curly stock produced in gumming. By the process disclosed in this patent, the paper can be flattened so that it is possible to successfully feed it into the press. The flattening is accomplished by breaking or cracking the gum so that the tension between the gum coat and the paper is eliminated to a great extent. By proper humidification this flattened stock can be printed today on fast, automatically fed presses. The introduction of the

305

corrugated box is responsible for the newest branch of the industry, since kraft-sealing tape is used in sealing these boxes or cases. In addition, the manufacturer's joint for these cases consumes important tonnage of cloth-based gummed material.

The previously mentioned two events are also responsible for the growth of the two main branches of the gummed-paper industry. The first branch is concerned with the manufacture of white stock for label use and, therefore, its product is mainly a sheeted one; the other branch is engaged in producing kraft base stock which is generally sold in the roll form for sealing purposes. There are no reliable records of the production of flat or sheeted gummed papers, except for the war years, when reports were required for the Chemicals Division of the War Production Board. Tables VIII and IX listing the tonnage of several lines of the industry indicate its growth and present position.

TABLE VIII

Annual Shipments of Gummed Sealing Tape

Year	Pounds
1939	116,652,847
1940	114,232,672
1941	158,404,214
1942	110,097,218
1943	146,288,440
1944	167,054,340
1945	162,424,168
1946	147,565,423
1947	206,830,077

TABLE IX

Estimate of Poundage of Paper Used for Sealing Tape

Year	Pounds
1939	91,453,959
1940	89,403,300
1941	123,973,807
1942	86,108,059
1943	114,796,534
1944	130,370,532
1945	126,906,572
1946	115,856,841
1947	

The following table summarizes these reports:

TABLE X

Annual Tonnage Production of Sealing Tape

Year	Tons of Gummed Product
1939	11,006
1940	11,378
1941	16,273
1942	14,226
1943 (Jan. 1 to Sept. 1)	10,310

The preparation of the adhesive and the processes of gumming are much alike, but the two branches differ after the gumming operation. The label stock, if it is to be sheeted, is flattened, calendered, sheeted, sorted and packed; usually in a humidified atmosphere. The roll stock, for either label or sealing application, is flattened, calendered, slit into individual rolls, and then packed for shipment.

The machines used for applying the adhesives may be of the

FIGURE 37. *Guming machine* (Courtesy of John Waldron Corp.)

usual three-roll system: i.e., a lifting roll, a spreading roll, and an applicator roll; or they may be more complicated such as the reverse-roll coater.

The more elaborate and expensive coating methods and machines are not necessary for the gumming operation because of the natural mobility of the adhesive solutions which permit them to flow evenly after application.

As the adhesives are most often applied hot, the gumming machine has a jacketed glue pan heated either by hot water or by steam. For uniform and dependable results, these pans should be fitted with suitable thermoregulators.

The gummed sheet, as it leaves the machine is dried in a number of ways, but usually by passing through heated chambers. On account of the inherent curl produced when the gummed sheet dries, it has to be kept under tension. It may be supported on a carrier belt, passed over a revolving wheel, or it may be supported on rolls positioned at either end of a drying tunnel. A blast of hot air is applied to the gummed side and often means of humidity control are positioned near the wind-up unit.

The very light weight of the white-label stock often requires a bare edge to offset the breakage produced by nicks in the edges of the sheet. Dry gummed paper is very brittle and will not withstand much tension.

The drying temperature varies with the type of adhesive used and the speed of drying desired. The faster the machine operates, the higher the permissible heat, but the gummed stock should never be dried to less than 4.5% moisture. This is particularly true of glue-gummed sheets, which may otherwise lose the necessary rapidity of retack. When drying the glue-gummed stock, precautions should be taken that the outer layer of adhesive is not dried before the lower layer, or two detrimental effects may be produced: The steam or moisture escaping from below may cause bubbling or pitting; or when the stock is later held in the roll, the moisture will diffuse from the wet underlying layers and cause serious blocking. The equipment used should be supplied with the proper unwind and rewind assemblies, with tensioning controls.

Adhesives

The most common adhesives used in the gumming industry are glue and dextrin. Others used to a less degree are starch derivatives, water-soluble natural resins like gum arabic, asphalt emulsions, etc. The present trend is toward synthetic resins, modified starches, lignin and similar adhesives.

The glues used are made from either hide fleshings or animal bones. They are graded and sold on the basis of their viscosity or jell strength. In the gumming industry, hide glues of about 150 grams jell strength and bone glues of about 70 grams jell strength are used. The average viscosity, expressed as milli-poises, is 70 for hide glue and 40 for bone glue. The process of manufacturing glue is a simple hydrolysis, the hide fleshings or bones being cooked with boiling water. After thoroughly cleaning the hides or bones they are cooked either in open or pressure tanks and the solutions run off. After this first extraction, it is customary to make several further ones. The first extraction yields the higher test glues. The products of additional extractions are of decreasingly lower quality. The extractions are mixed and then concentrated by evaporation under vacuum. The concentrated glue is run into pans and chilled. The resultant jell is sliced into slabs which are spread on wire trays. The resultant dried cakes are ground and packed in bags for shipment. In addition to the ground glue made as indicated, a high tonnage of the so-called "wheel" glue is produced. This is made by running the concentrated extract on the surface of a heated drum from which it is scraped off by a doctor blade after it is dried. Ground glue has a moisture content of 11 to 14% while "wheel" glue contains 8 to 12% moisture.

Dextrin is manufactured from starch by heating it in the dry form in steam-heated jacketed kettles. During the roasting process, the starch is constantly stirred. Usually the starch is sprayed or mixed with a small percentage of a volatile acid such as hydrochloric, nitric, or a mixture of both prior to the roasting operation. The grade of dextrin produced is governed by the time and temperature of roasting and the amount of acid used. By varying these factors, one can produce a very soluble product or one of low solubility. The lower-solubility products are usually of lighter color and, in fact, may be nearly pure white, while the more fully converted ones are tan to brown in color. Two other starch products are used to some extent, i.e., British gum and chlorinated or oxidized starches. When the conversion point is reached, the slurry is diluted, and the starch washed and then dried.

Gum arabic is the most commonly used of the natural water-soluble resins. It occurs in the Mediterranean area as a resinous exudation of trees of the acacia family. The nodular masses are collected by the natives, sorted and graded as to color and freedom from dirt, sand, bark, etc. The most commonly used grade is known as grade No. 1 which is light tan in color and is sold in lump form.

Synthetic and natural rubbers and resins, lignin, asphalt emulsions, etc., are used in lesser amounts, and their preparation and compounding are mostly trade secrets or covered by patent applications at this time.

The resin- and rubber-base coatings are generally used on label papers and may be of the moisture seal, heat sealing, or pressure-sensitive types. Since these adhesives are more expensive than those used for gummed labels, they are often laid down on more expensive base sheets than the sulfite-soda base of the average gummed label. Aluminum foil, Cellophane, and even plastic films are used as well as white or colored label papers. Some of these specialized coatings are also used in the pressure-sensitive sealing-tape field to produce items such as Scotch tape.

Preparation of the Gumming and Coating Mix

The best method for dissolving animal glues is as follows:
A jacketed kettle is used. The jacket contains water which
is heated either with live steam led into the water, or, preferably, the jacket is equipped with steam coils. Cold water is
run into the kettle, the weight of cold water being the same as
the weight of the glue to be used. The glue is slowly sifted into
the water while the agitator is revolving so that no lumps of dry
glue are formed. Agitation is continued for 10 to 15 minutes
to wet all particles of glue; then the agitator is stopped and the
glue permitted to soak for 45 to 60 minutes. Then steam is
applied to the jacket and the agitator started again. The temperature of the glue solution is brought up to 140° F. and kept
there until the glue is entirely dissolved. Modifying ingredients
are added at this point: fish glue; plasticizers, such as glycerin,
glucose, invert sugar, etc.; preservatives; scent, etc. The mixture is agitated until all ingredients are incorporated; then the
glue solution is ready to be drawn off through a strainer. It
is important that the glue solution is not heated above 140° F.,
as higher temperatures for prolonged periods of time will break
down the protein molecule and lower the adhesive qualities of
the glue.

To dissolve dextrins for flat gumming and as extenders for
glue mixes, the same type of equipment is recommended. The
procedure is almost the same, with the following modifications.
Add only about 90% of the water to be used in the kettle, start
the agitator, and sift the dextrin slowly into the water, breaking up the lumps as much as possible. After all the dextrin has
been added to the water, part of the dextrin will usually float
on the top of the water. Add the remaining water to it at
this point so as to wet all the dextrin, continue agitating for
about 15 minutes, and turn on the heat. To obtain best results,
heat the solution to 185° to 190°F., turn off the heat, stop the
agitator, and let the solution stand for 30 to 60 minutes with
the lid tightly closed. This will permit the foam to rise to the

surface and break up almost completely. If modifiers are used, add them to the hot solution before stopping the agitator. If the dextrin is to be used as an extender, cool it to 140°F. before adding it to the glue solution. If it is used for flat gumming, draw it off through a strainer into a storage tank and let it stand for at least 24, but preferably 48, hours before using it on the machine.

To make sure that the gumming mixes have been prepared properly and that the gumming machines can be operated efficiently without the need of constant adjusting, viscosity and solid content standards should be established for each gumming mix. The viscosity can be checked by running the solutions through a Zahn or Ford cup, or using a Brookfield rotational viscosimeter. It is most important to make these tests always at the same temperature; a few degrees difference in temperature will make a considerable difference in the obtained results.

For the determination of the solid content, a hydrometer graduated in Baumé degrees can be used. Be sure that the cylinder in which the mix is placed is at least 6 inches in diameter, so that the mix is not chilled too rapidly, and that the mix is drawn off the bottom of the kettle and not taken from the top, so that there will be practically no foam in the mix to be tested. The temperature again should be the same for every test. The hydrometer should be perfectly clean; it should be washed in lukewarm water after every test. The mix is placed in the test cylinder, which should be at least as tall as the hydrometer and the hydrometer is lowered into the mix gently until it comes to rest and the Baumé degrees are read off. If the hydrometer is dropped too rapidly into the mix so that it sinks and then rises again, the hydrometer should be cleaned and the test repeated.

A dry animal-glue film is quite brittle, especially if higher-jelly-strength glues are used in the preparation of the mix, and is apt to fly off the paper when it is broken or after the tape has been stored at low relative humidities for a longer time and the tape is used on high-speed machines. For this reason, a small percentage of plasticizer is used in the mix, about 2 to 4%, based on the dry weight of the animal glue. Glycerin or the glycols are best for this purpose, but, for reasons of economy, they can be partly replaced by glucose or invert sugar. When using invert sugar with animal glues, be sure that the grade is the one recommended by the manufacturer for this purpose; other grades contain aldehyde groups which will tan the glue and make the tape unfit to use.

It is generally accepted that fish glue will impart the quick tack which is needed for tapes used on high-speed, automatic machines. The quantity used depends on economies and the grades of glue used in the mix.

Glucose and invert sugar are used most generally for plasticizing flat-gummed dextrins. They reduce the brittleness of the glue film, which is important in the breaking operation, and render the finished sheet less apt to curl, i.e., they will extend the range of humidities at which the properly finished sheet will lie flat. The percentages used are about 2 to 6%, based on the dry weight of the dextrin.

Preservatives are used to keep the glue mixes from spoiling, especially if they are to be kept for a longer period of time, like shutdowns over the weekend, or to prevent the tape from molding when it is used in high humidities like those encountered in cold-storage plants. The most commonly used is zinc sulfate, which has been replaced largely by the chlorinated phenols like Dowicide and Santobrite. The percentages used are small, less than 1%, as some individuals are very sensitive to these chemicals, and break out in rashes on handling them.

Dextrins and extenders are used for two reasons: About 10% mixed with the animal glue will produce a tape which is wetted and becomes highly adhesive in a shorter time. The other reason is economy when dextrins are cheaper than animal glues, or when glues are scarce on the market. A British gum-type extender is the best kind of dextrin to be used with animal glues, and the percentages depend on the kind of British gum which is obtainable. It is generally accepted that Tapioca British gums are better adhesives than the ones made from corn, and the same applies to flat-gumming dextrins as well.

Scents are used to mask the odor of animal glue, and impart a better odor to labels with dextrin gumming. The most commonly used is methyl salycilate or oil of wintergreen; other scents are essential oils, like peppermint, sassafras, cinnamon, etc., and their use depends largely on the manufacturer's taste and preference. The quantities used are very small, usually fractions of 1%.

A number of other chemicals are used to obtain papers for particular applications, but their use is usually the manufacturer's secret, with the exception of the patented ones.

The Manufacture of Gummed Tapes and Labels

Gummed Flat-Label Papers. Gummed flat-label paper is used for all types of stamps, labels of innumerable types, pennants, posters, seals, window stickers, and many other such common items. Certain types of resinous materials are being used for labels, and their development has been rapid. Their use, at present, is generally limited to special cases, due to cost, but in the near future the water-insoluble adhesives will probably become increasingly popular. Many of the details of the water-soluble gummed paper to be discussed in this section will also pertain to the water-insoluble type adhesives.

Raw Stock

Many types of paper are gummed for use in the label trade, including coated paper of various colors and grades, such as metallic coatings of gold, silver, and bronze, as well as the plated and glazed sheets. Also used are the uncoated sheets, which include the various natural shade and colored krafts, mediums, and many papers of machine finish, English finish, and high-finish whites. In addition, water-soluble adhesives may be applied to metal-foil papers, glassine, Cellophane and the plastic films.

Weights

Even though we are not specifically concerned with sealing tapes in this section, we will mention various weights of brown, white, and colored krafts, gummed and processed successfully for the label trade. Weights employed for labels in the kraft line range from 35 to 60 pounds (24 x 36—500). Weights usually vary, for coated or uncoated paper, from 16 to 30 pounds (17 x 22—500). However, both lighter and heavier weight sheets are sometimes gummed for special purposes in both of the classes mentioned.

Specifications

The following specifications should be met to insure proper raw stock for gumming and processing. The paper should be properly sized to the extent that the adhesive used for gumming purposes does not penetrate unduly into the sheet. A poorly sized sheet will obviously require more adhesive which will, of course, increase manufacturing costs. A surface similar to that of a good printing sheet is usually acceptable as a good gumming surface. The sheet should also have a satisfactory printing and writing surface, e.g., a coated surface, for most of the gummed paper is used for printing purposes on the plain side. Needless to say that the paper should be smooth and free from dirt. Creases cause considerable waste in the manufacture of gummed papers, as they commonly do in other uses of paper. Uniformity of thickness should be rigidly met, especially in certain specialty items. This is particularly necessary because in the flattening process, uneven gages will cause slack edges which contribute to misgumming as well as irregularity of tension in the drying operation, which possibly could lead to a curled sheet. These slack edges would also prevent the manufacturer from obtaining the same degree of flatness across the sheet. Paper structure or formation is extremely important, as a sheet that shows a wild formation (i.e., irregular structure) does not absorb the adhesives properly or evenly.

The tests of raw stock for a gummed paper are the same as the regular methods used for evaluating a sheet for ordinary coating work. The most common tests will determine thickness, weight, tensile, and tearing strength. Dennison wax tests are made along with other sizing tests to be certain of proper printing and writing surface.

Gumming

Adhesives used are animal and fish glues, dextrins, and water-soluble natural gums or combinations of these. For ordinary flat-gummed papers, the amount of adhesive usually applied is 6 pounds (17 x 22—500) dry basis. For specialties, when the paper is heavy, the amount of adhesive used will reach as high as 10 pounds (17 x 22—500).

After the adhesive has been prepared in the mixing room, the proper temperatures must be maintained for correct application. This is usually done by using a glue pan which is steam- or hot-water jacketed. The correct working temperature is usually about 125°F. The adhesive is applied to the paper by the kiss- or squeeze-roll method in most mills. It has been found that for most types of work a 40%-solids adhesive is satisfactory, but the solids content varies with the type of raw stock or the type of adhesive. For example, a soft-sized paper should be gummed with an adhesive having a higher solids content than a raw stock which is hard-sized.

After the gumming operation has been completed, the next step is the flattening. Most of this type of paper is sheeted and later printed. For obvious reasons, these sheets cannot have the curl which results from the application of the adhesive. Gummed papers will curl to the gum when the moisture content is low, and toward the plain side when the moisture content is increased. This is caused by the fact that the gummed side is more hygroscopic and has a greater coefficient of expansion and contraction than the plain side of the paper. The film of gum must be properly broken to make the sheet flat enough to be fed into the printing presses under variable conditions of humidity at the high rate of speed at which these machines operate.

FIGURE 38. *Gummed-paper flattening machine* (Courtesy of John Waldron Corp.)

A roll of gummed paper, with the gummed side out, is passed over a bar under tension at a 45° angle. It is then necessary to pass the sheet over another bar, making a 90° angle with the first bar. Without the second bar, the sheet would curl from one end to the other. The second bar obviously removes this curl.

Care must be taken in the flattening operation that the ungummed side of the sheet is not roughed up and thus mar the printing surface. Caution should be also used to prevent the flaking of the glue film.

The typical finishing operations are similar to those which are used in finishing ordinary coated paper. Machine-finished papers are usually calendered, depending upon the customer's requirements, and upon the finish desired. The regular multiple cutters and trimmers are used for the remainder of the finishing.

Gummed sheets are usually tested for sticking qualities, hygroscopicity, flatness and writing quality.

Sticking quality of the heavier grades of paper is measured by the McLaurin tester. This measures the tack of the gummed paper after it has been moistened, and before it is dried. Other gummed papers are tested by moistening one-inch strips and applying them to the type of surface for which the adhesive is intended.

Hygroscopicity is measured by stacking two-inch squares of gummed paper and observing their action under the same pressure in various ranges of controlled relative humidities. Standard tests for blocking are given in Federal Specifications for Blocking UU-T101 A, March 3, 1939, and subsequent amendments.

Flatness is tested by placing the sheet in a room under controlled conditions and observing its behavior.

Writing quality is determined by a pen and ink test.

Odor, grease, and color of the adhesive are important, but are controlled in the adhesive preparation as well as in the gumming operation. However, inspection should be made of the finished paper to insure that it is free from grease and odor and that the color of the adhesive is correct.

The method of sorting and inspecting gummed paper is akin to that used in ordinary coating and paper mills. Sheets are inspected, and all that are dirty or below standard quality for the usual reasons are separated and placed in seconds. Both the plain and the gummed side are inspected, because, as stated previously, the plain side must have a satisfactory printing surface.

After the paper has been inspected and all imperfects removed, it is trimmed to size (usually 17 x 22—500 or 20 x 25—500). It is wrapped in waterproofed paper to protect the adhesive during shipment and storage. The utmost care should be taken in wrapping this type of paper, as the adhesive would cause blocking when stored in highly humid atmosphere. Obviously this is especially true during the summer months.

Conditions of storage rooms are extremely important for this line of paper. Every year there is considerable loss because of the failure of paper and printing houses to properly store gummed paper. Paper of this nature should never be placed near radiators, or any type of heating unit, nor near windows or openings that may allow rain or dampness to penetrate into the room. Once a package of gummed paper is opened, in order to remove only part of the contents, the package should be securely rewrapped to prevent the paper from taking up moisture.

Sealing Tapes. Sealing tape is made in three categories: light, medium and heavy weight. Light-weight sealing tape is designed generally for light-weight bundles and bags, such as are put out by retail stores. Medium-weight tapes are employed most extensively for sealing the flaps of corrugated or fiber cartons. Heavy-weight tapes are designed for heavier packages and cartons.

Because strength is a prime requisite in such a tape, the backing material is almost wholly of kraft, which may be brown (or natural shade), or white (bleached) or any of a wide variety of colored kraft papers. It may be printed or plain.

For light-weight sealing tape, a basis weight of 35 to 45 pounds (24 x 36—500) is employed. For medium weight, a 60 pound paper is standard. For heavy weight, a paper of 90 to 120 pounds is employed.

Because this product is usually cut to narrow widths, the width of raw stock roll is limited only by the capacity of the gumming machine and the economical utilization of the paper machine capacity in width. The diameter of the roll is dependent on space for handling and ease of handling at the gumming machine. The diameter may run from 24 to 36 inches.

The paper should have the strength of a number one grade

kraft in bursting, tensile and tear resistance. In uniformity it should conform to recognized trade customs. The paper should be of good density, uniform in thickness. It should be adequately sized, and at least one face should be smooth, suitable to maintain an effective and economical film of glue.

Adhesives are largely of the animal glue type, applied hot, and as concentrated as possible. The amount of adhesives (dry basis) will run from 12 to 15 pounds per ream (24 x 36—500) for light-weight tapes, from 15 to 18 pounds per ream for medium tapes, and from 17 to 20 pounds for heavy-weight tapes.

Gumming speed is limited principally by the rate of drying, which, in turn, depends on dryer capacity, amount of glue, proportion of water and the nature of the adhesive. Speeds of 200 to 600 feet per minute are employed.

The dried gummed paper passes to a rewinding mechanism where it is wound usually in a large roll corresponding to the raw-stock roll used for the gumming operation. The rewinder here is usually of the center-wind type and friction driven.

Slitting may be done on two general types of machine, shear-cut and score-cut types. The first is equipped with a pair of circular knives for each cut, which overlap and cut much like a pair of shears. The second machine has a single circular knife which cuts by pressure, the knife bearing on the gummed paper as the paper is carried partly around a cylinder.

The large roll of gummed tape, usually in the width in which it has been gummed, is slit, usually in one operation, to a series of narrow coils of the specified width.

Directly from the slitting knives, the gummed paper (now in narrow tape form) passes to the rewinding mechanism. This, again, is of two general types. One is the center-winding type where a shaft-driven core winds up the tape. The second is the surface winder, in which the winding tension is frictionally imparted from a driven roll which rests directly on the winding coils of tape. Winding improvement is sometimes effected by a combination of center and surface winding.

The width of light-weight tape runs from ¾ inch upward, that of medium-weight tape from 1 inch upward, and that of heavy-weight tape from 2 inches upward, 1½ inches being perhaps the most common width for light weight, and 3 inches the most common width for medium- and heavy-weight tapes. Coils are usually packaged in bundles which are approximately 30 inches in diameter. Light-weight tape is wound in 500 and 800 foot coils, medium weight usually in 600 foot coils, and heavy weight in 375 foot coils.

Since remoistenable gummings are, to a certain degree, hygroscopic, they are affected by change in humidity. They are more difficult to moisten in excessively dry weather and tending to block in excessively moist weather. For this reason, the coils are customarily double-wrapped, with a moisture-resistant waxed kraft inside, and over this the usual strong kraft wrapper. This assures delivery of a tape that is uniform and of unimpaired quality. Tape removed from the original bundle should be stored away from excessive heat or moisture, and preferably wrapped again in protective paper.

The finished product must be suitably strong, commensurate with the raw paper employed. Because it may be subjected to splitting or tearing strain in the length as well as in the cross direction, it should be made from paper of adequate strength in both dimensions.

The adherence of the tape, after suitably moistening and applying, should be such that upon drying and attempting removal, any rupture will be in the paper, either of the tape backing or of the surface to which the tape was applied.

Stay Tape. Stay tape is employed for the corner sealing of "set-up" boxes. In set-up box manufacture, the box blank, usually of chip board, is die-cut to size with the corners cut away so that after scoring and folding the sides meet with no corner overlap. Stay tape is used to join together at each corner the four sides of the shaped box.

A section of tape in length equal to the height of the box (or cover) is automatically moistened, cut and applied to the box corner. Single stay machines apply the four corner pieces successively; quad stay machines apply the four corner pieces simultaneously.

A number one grade kraft is required. Since splitting or tearing strain, after application to the box, occurs parallel to the length of the tape, it is important that the paper is sufficiently strong in this dimension. A paper in which the fibers lie predominantly lengthwise will be inferior for this application.

The common brown kraft shade and gray (to roughly match the chip board) constitute the colors generally supplied for stay usage.

The raw paper is relatively heavy. In most cases, weights of 90 to 105 pounds (24 x 36—500) are employed.

Like sealing tape, this stock is eventually slit to narrow widths, so that the raw stock width is limited only by the gummer width and the practical utilization of the paper machine capacity in width. The usual range of raw stock widths are 36 to 48 inches.

The roll diameter, as for sealing tape manufacture, may run from 24 to 36 inches.

The strength of a number one grade kraft is required in bursting, tension and tear resistance. In uniformity, it should conform to recognized trade customs.

Minimum thickness for a given weight is important; the box manufacturer does not want a thick patch over his box corners. It should be well sized, and smooth, as for tape gumming, to maintain an effective and economical film of glue.

The adhesive for stay tape is similar to that employed for gummed sealing tape. Since, however, sometimes very short sections of tape are employed (for instance, on a shallow box or box cover) the feed of moistened tape may be very slow and the glue formulation is generally adjusted to yield a relatively long period of tackiness after moistening.

For stay use, a glue coat of 17 to 20 pounds per ream (24 x 36—500) is desirable.

Since the adhesive is similar to that employed for sealing tape, the gumming of stay tape will not differ greatly from that of gumming heavy-weight sealing tape.

For stay use, a clean, nonfuzzy edge is required and shear-cut slitting is favored. Well-wound coils are also required, and a combination center and surface winder is preferred.

Stay tape runs usually from ¾ inch to 1 inch in width, and is wound in coils of 10 inch diameter with paper cores having a 1¼ inch inside diameter.

This tape, like sealing tape, is usually double-wrapped with moisture-protective paper inside and strong kraft for an outer wrap. It should likewise be protected from excessive heat or moisture. It should be strong, commensurate with the raw paper employed, with special regard to resistance to lengthwise splitting or tearing. The adherence of the tape after drying should be such that any rupture, on attempted removal, will lie in the box board.

The adhesive should be of strong tack to prevent slippage from the box corner while the tape is still moist. It should be of sufficiently long tacky range so that on shallow boxes or covers, where tape feed is slow, the adhesive will not become too dry for good application.

Filled Cloth Tape. Filled cloth tape, generally in a kraft color, is employed both for the corner sealing of cartons and for diverse uses where a cloth instead of a paper gummed sealing tape is advantageous. In the field of carton corner sealing, filled cloth tape is largely superseded by tapes with other types of backing material.

The backing material is supplied by cloth processors as a clay-filled, starch-sized cloth. The type of cloth and amount of filling may vary rather widely, but in general it should be of suitable strength in each dimension and of fair flexibility, but not too limp. In weight, the filled cloth may vary for different requirements from 75 to 150 pounds per ream (24 x 35—500).

The raw cloth generally employed by the cloth processors is 40 inches wide. Shrinkage involved in filling brings the width approximately to 38 inches for the gummer's use. The roll diameter, as for paper tape manufacture, may run from 24 to 36 inches.

Specifications will vary widely. In general, the user should see that the advantages of cloth over paper are suitably maintained in this filled-cloth product. Of these, tearing resistance in each dimension and flexibility are important. The filling should be adherent and should provide a dense foundation for the adhesive that is to be applied without open areas. It should not be unduly absorbent or softened upon the application of the adhesive.

Because this material still retains much of the roughness and unevenness of a cloth product, much greater amounts of adhesive must be employed than with paper; 35 to 40 pounds per ream are customary, usually in two successive applications. The adhesive is usually an animal glue of greater strength than is required for paper tapes. The gumming operation is, in general, similar to that for gummed paper, but usually it is carried out at lower speeds as the cloth-backed tape is more difficult to dry. In general, slitting may be satisfactorily done on the equipment used for gummed-paper sealing tape. Coils are usually 1,000 feet in length, the lighter weights in a 2-inch width and the heavier weights from 2 to 3 inches in width. Cores are of paper with $1\frac{5}{16}$ inch inside diameter. The coils are packaged in cartons, usually of 6 to 9 coils, depending on the width of coil.

The finished product should be strong, commensurate with the filled cloth employed, with special regard to tearing resistance. It should be flexible, but at the same time stiff enough for feeding on automatic equipment.

The adhesive should be sufficient to compensate for the cloth roughness and to provide a smooth layer. It should be of strong tack and of fairly long tacky range to insure "grab" consistent with the more severe requirements for cloth tape. The adherence after application and drying should be such that failure, if it occurs, will not lie in the glue layer or in too ready separation of the filling from the cloth.

Duplex backed tape, a lamination of cloth and paper, is used extensively by carton manufacturers for sealing the open corner left after a corrugated or solid fiber carton is die-cut, scored and folded flat for shipment. Laminating is usually performed by the gummed tape manufacturer, the most common laminant being a modified-starch adhesive. The paper is a relatively light weight kraft 20 to 30 pounds per ream (24 x 36—500). It should be strong in both dimension and resistant to splitting apart from the paper layer.

The cloth is usually of two varieties: 1. A sheeting of evenly balanced strength in the long and cross dimensions is used for the lighter-weight product; 2. a cloth called Osnaburg of heavier construction, with the fill (or cross) threads stronger than the warp (or long) threads is especially suited for the manufacturer's sealing of the carton corner.

A thread count of the order of 36 warp threads and 40 fill threads per inch is typical of the lighter weight sheeting. The weight of this material is of the order of 5.55 yards per pound in a 40 inch width. This is roughly equivalent to 54 pounds per ream (24 x 36—500). This cloth is usually marketed in 40 and 46 inch widths.

On the heavier Osnaburg goods, a count of the order of 32 warp threads and 26 fill threads per inch is typical. It should be noted that these fill threads, while fewer, are considerably heavier than the warp threads. The weight of this material is of the order of 3.65 yards per pound in a 40 inch width. This is roughly equivalent to 82 pounds per ream (24 x 36—500). This grade is usually 40 inches wide.

The laminant may be of animal glue or modified starch or any other suitable adhesive. It is essential in laminating that a balance in flexibility is maintained. The flexibility of the cloth must not be lost, but a sufficient degree of stiffness must be imparted so that the finished tape may be fed readily on automatic moistening equipment. From 15 to 25 pounds of laminant per ream (24 x 36—500) may be employed, depending on the nature of the laminant.

The laminated product will vary (on a ream basis) from 100 pounds for the lighter grade to 140 pounds for the heavier grade. The 40-inch cloth will shrink to about 38 inches width in processing. A 46-inch cloth will shrink to about 44 inches.

Roll diameter, as for other forms of tape gumming, may run from 24 to 36 inches, depending on space and facilities for handling.

A good laminated product should be of suitable strength, particularly in respect to tearing in the longitudinal direction. For uniformity of adherence and economy of gumming, the cloth should be even, free from bunches and excessive variation in thickness. The product should be resistant to delamination or weakening of the laminating bond under the tension and wetting involved in gumming. The paper surface (to which the adhesive is applied) should be suitably smooth. Thin material is more economical of adhesive than filled cloth. A coating of 20 to 25 pounds per ream is customary and is usually applied in one gumming operation. The commonly used adhesive is an animal glue and of greater strength than required for paper tape. The gumming operation is similar to that for gummed paper, but, owing to the thicker backing material and the generally greater amounts of adhesive, lower speeds are customary. In general, slitting may be satisfactorily done on the equipment used for gummed-paper sealing tape. Coils are usually 1,000 feet in length, the lighter weights in 2 inch width and the heavier weights in 2 to 3 inch widths. Cores are of paper with an inside diameter of $1^{15}/_{16}$ inches. The coils are packaged in cartons, usually of 6 to 9 coils, depending on the width of tape.

The finished product should be strong, commensurate with the cloth employed, with special regard to tearing resistance in the longitudinal direction. It should be flexible, but at the same time stiff enough for feeding on automatic equipment.

The adhesive should be sufficient to compensate for the roughness of the laminated product and to provide a smooth layer. It should be of strong tack. The adherence after application and drying should be such that failure will lie in the cloth or the carton material and not in the glue or in the cloth-paper lamination.

"Sisalkraft," a patented product, comprises a 50 or 60 pound kraft backing (24 x 36—500) and a 30 pound kraft face, laminated with asphalt in which sisal fibers are distributed. For carton manufacturers' use as a corner tape, these sisal fibers lie crosswise; for other uses, Sisalkraft can be obtained with the sisal fibers lengthwise.

This material, as sold to gummed tape manufacturers, has a total ream weight of about 200 pounds. It is supplied in widths of 40⅝ and 42⅝ inches and is generally sold in rolls of a diameter of 26 or 28 inches.

For carton corner sealing, as noted, "Sisalkraft" is supplied with the sisal fibers lying crosswise. This material is relatively weak to lengthwise strain, but such strain is not a factor in this specific application. Against crosswise strains, the product is so exceptionally strong that the only concern of the tape manufacturer is that the sisal fibers are well bonded by the asphalt so that failure will not be due to fiber slippage.

The asphalt employed should be tough and so compounded as to avoid excessive brittleness, especially in cold weather. There should be no seepage of the asphalt at temperatures to be expected during the gumming operation or on long standing under summer conditions.

Since the raw stock, with its sisal fibers, presents a rather uneven surface, it is necessary to employ 25 to 30 pounds of glue per ream to assure an adequate adhesive surface. An animal glue of high strength is suitable. The gumming operation in general is similar to that for gumming paper. In drying, the material should be kept below the critical temperature of the asphalt (about 200°F.) and for this reason, the rate of drying will be slower than is common with gummed-paper sealing tape. After gumming, the sheet is usually embossed in a fine, all-over pattern.

This is advantageous for several reasons. Under the embossing pressure any local areas that have separated during gumming may be relaminated. Surface distortion from gumming and from the underlying sisal fibers is minimized and a useful flexibility is imparted to the product. With this backing material, slitting is more difficult than with the ordinary paper tapes. A special rewinding mechanism, with a rubber-surfaced drum rewinder, is recommended. The tape width is 2 to 3 inches, and the product is usually marketed in coils of 1,000 to 2,000 feet. The cores are of paper with an inside diameter of $1^{15}/_{16}$ inches. The coils are packaged in cartons containing 2 to 6 coils. To prevent sticking from possible exudation of asphalt, the coils are separated by waxed paper.

There should be no delaminated areas in the finished product. The sisal fibers should be suitably spaced to provide a non-bunchy product of even resistance to tearing in the length. It should be flexible, but at the same time stiff enough for feeding on automatic equipment.

The adhesive should be sufficient to compensate for the uneven surface of the backing and to provide a smooth adhesive surface. It should be of strong tack. The adherence, after application and drying, should be such that failure will lie in the carton material and not in the glue or in slippage of the sisal fibers.

Gummed Holland Tapes

Holland cloth is a starch-sized, pigment-filled product, mechanically glazed to a high finish on one side. It is produced in a variety of colors and is characterized by its finish and density and by absence of the openness and roughness normally inherent in a cloth. Its principal use is in binding, such as for paper tablets, note books, passepartout, etc.

Two general grades are prevalent, generally known as "number one" and "number two." "Number one" is the better grade, and is characterized by a higher thread count, a closer weave and a lesser amount of filling. The finished weight of Holland cloths will vary, roughly, from 60 to 90 pounds per ream (24 x 36—500) Holland cloths are marketed in 36 and 42 inch widths, and are usually put up in 2500 yard rolls.

No precise specifications are available. The thread count and weight, amount of sizing and pigment are largely in the hands of the cloth finisher. The most important qualities are appearance, smoothness, and the adherence of the filling. In this latter respect number one grade is pronouncedly superior to number two grade.

The gumming of this material differs little from that of gummed paper tape. About 20 pounds of adhesive per ream are applied, the adhesive being usually an animal glue of a grade similar to that employed for gummed-paper sealing tape. Gumming may be applied either to the glossy face or to the dull-finished back of the Holland cloth, depending on the finish the user desires on the ungummed side.

Slitting is not significantly different from the method employed for gummed-paper sealing tapes, a shear-cut slitter being preferred. Coils are 150 to 300 yards in length and $3/4$ inch or greater in width. Wooden cores of $9/16$ inch inside diameter are employed. The coil diameter may run from 7 to 10 inches. The coils are packaged in bundles of approximately 28 inches in diameter with a waxed paper inner wrap and a kraft outer wrap. This bundle is usually shipped in a carton.

Appearance of the finished product is important and the filling should not loosen in handling or in applying the moistened tape. The adhesive should be of good tack, and sufficient to provide good adherence.

The Uses of Gummed Papers

Gummed papers are used for labels, stickers, sealing tape for corrugated shipping cases and packages, stay for the corners of set-up boxes, veneer, tape tablet binding, etc.

The largest tonnage is used in the label stock and a sealing tape. The label stocks are sold to the printers. The standard sizes are 17 x 22 inches and 20 x 25 inches and the quotations are based on these sizes. Most of this stock is white, although

FIGURE 39. *Container band sealer* (Courtesy of Vertex Company)

there is, of course, considerable demand for colored stock either as coated or as plated or medium papers. As has been pointed out, gummed papers may be printed on fast, automatically fed presses so that the requirements as for the put-up, flatness, etc., are the same as with any stock that is to be printed.

While the label stock is processed to be substantially flat, it is nevertheless more susceptible to humidity changes than plain papers and a wide spread of relative humidity will produce curling and misregister.

In a dry atmosphere the curl will be to the gummed side, and

in a high humidity it will be to the plain or "back" side. If
several impressions are made, as in multicolor printing, care
must be taken to have the atmospheric conditions the same each
time the sheet is printed.

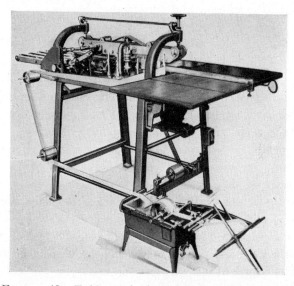

FIGURE 40. *Tablet stripping machine* (Courtesy of
John J. Pleger Co.)

Sealing tape is used in packaging for the closure of corrugated boxes. The moistened tape is applied to the closed
flaps and along the edges of the flaps. As corrugated cases are
subject to the rules of the Interstate Commerce Commission, the
proper procedure for applying the tape should be strictly adhered to.

Methods of Applying Tapes & Labels

From the time sealing tape was first produced, moistening
machines have been provided for its use. The original devices
were not much more than moistened felts, sponges, or rolls,
with a saw-toothed edge provided to sever the tape. From these

primitive methods, we have now advanced to the automatic machines which deliver predetermined lengths uniformly moistened and clearly cut off. These machines are provided with means for warming the water supply. While these machines are relatively costly, they are vital to economical results, both as to speed of operation and satisfactory bondage of the tape.

The stay tape for the corners of set-up boxes is applied by machines made for this purpose. This tape is supplied in rolls of ¾ or ⅞ inch widths and 9 inches diameter. There are two types of machines, the single stayer and the quad, and, as the names indicate, the first applies the stay on one corner at a time and the second all four corners simultaneously.

The choice of the type of machine used is usually governed by the depth of the box. The deeper boxes which require a longer stay are usually run on the single stayer, and the shallower ones on the quads. The "throw" on the single stayers may go up to 5 or 6 inches, while that on the quads may be as low as ¼ inch. A shoe box, for instance, would be run on a single stayer, while a handkerchief box would be run on a quad. Often the covers of shoe boxes requiring a shorter "throw," or shorter length of tape, are run on quads.

Veneer tape is applied by taping machines which make possible the assemblage of many strips of veneer into large sheets such as would be needed for desk tops, furniture panels, etc. The veneer strips are accurately cut so that adjacent edges are butted true and even, and run under two toed-in knurled rolls, one on each side of the joints, and the moistened tape is rolled on as the veneer is held between the pressure rolls. The several sheets thus made are applied to the core stick upon which the proper adhesive has been spread, and then this assembly, together with others, is placed on the platens of a veneer press. Pressure, and often heat, is applied to get the necessary bond.

The gummed stock used for the manufacturer's joint of a corrugated box may be paper on cloth. The rolls are 2 inches in width and up to 24 inches in diameter. The cloth tapes are usually made from various gray goods and are obtained by the mill suitably filled and finished to give a good smooth gummed surface and in rolls of over 2,000 yards, up to 40 inches wide. As the strain on the box corner is at right angles to the edge, the cross or filler threads should be the strongest. Therefore, the tear strength of the tape in the running direction, or lengthwise of the tape, is the most important. Depending on the requirements of the box to be taped, a light or a heavy construction is used, and in the trade, there are usually two grades commonly available. For exceptionally heavy duty, extra heavy or strong backing materials are available.

As to the paper tapes used on the manufacturer's joint, some heavier-weight kraft and case-liner papers are used in quantity, but for shipping containers to be used in interstate commerce, these grades are not acceptable. For this purpose, it is customary to use sisal tape. This product is made by combining a 30-pound and a 40-pound kraft sheet with asphalt in which raw sisal fibers are embedded across the tape. This gives a less expensive tape than cloth, and one which is very strong. It is not as pliable as cloth and therefore requires more care in application.

This tape is most commonly applied to the boxes on automatic taping machines. The corrugated boards cut to box size, creased, slotted, and folded flat so that the edges of the joint to be taped are adjoining and on the upper side are stacked in the magazine of the machine between two belts which pull the folded box forward. At the proper moment the tape is automatically reversed. The belts are about 12 to 18 feet long and 5 inches wide. They are maintained under substantial pressure.

Tablet stripping or binding uses coils of gummed material in a width of 1 inch and diameters of 7 to 10 inches. There are various machines available for this purpose, and they all use an unusually large throw or length of moistened tape before adhering the stock to which they are applied. Illustration of the type product in which they include school and stenographers' notebooks and pamphlets.

Much sealing tape is used in sealing parcels and packages in stores, laundries, etc. This tape is usually made from 35-pound kraft in colors and may be printed or plain.

A large tonnage of sealing tape is printed. Most of this is printed at the gumming plant. However, there is some printed by sealing tape jobbers both in machine rolls or trimmed rolls and in coil form. At the gumming mill, both methods are followed, but the machine roll method is both economical and efficient, because the production is higher and also because there is less danger of trouble from ink being offset on the back.

It is, of course, more economical to print in the coil form on small orders and these are printed on the gummed stock. Care must be exercised in using the proper inks so that offset is minimized; otherwise the oily ink will seriously waterproof the adhesive, a prolific source of complaint in this class of goods.

In most cases, these gummed products go to other manufacturers. Very few, e.g., some sealing tapes, are used by the general public in office or home. They are handled usually, if not always, by automatic machines. In fact, much sealing tape, and more each year, is applied by automatic moisteners such as the "tape shooter," which pushes out or throws a predetermined length of tape and at the same time moistens and cuts it. This point is stressed, as any product used in machines, which year by year are fitted with more delicate mechanisms and controls, must be more and more uniform. This refers not only to the character of the adhesive or coating, but also to the diameter, thickness, and the type of unit, whether roll or sheet.

Chapter XII

CARBON PAPERS AND OTHER DUPLICATING PAPERS

by R. R. Wissinger

A T THE turn of the century, copies of any business paper that was considered important were hand written. The procedure was to use a copy-writing ink with high color strength which when pressed against a thin sheet of dampened tissue produced a legible copy.

As industry and business advanced, it soon became apparent that a more suitable and faster method of making copies of business communications was necessary. The first attempts to develop a faster copying method resulted in a transfer paper which produced copies readily enough, but because of the thick, greasy dope that was crudely applied by means of a brush or scraper to a heavy absorbent paper, the copies usually became so smeared with the soft ink that they were practically useless. After the transfer sheet aged a few weeks, the absorbent base paper caused the ink to dry, with the result that a legible copy was no longer obtainable. It became obvious that something must be added to the ink, first to prevent smearing and second to prevent the ink from becoming too dry. This was accomplished by the incorporation of waxes into the ink which resulted in a new product.

The new industry soon cloaked itself in secrecy, however, in regards to its manufacturing and formulating processes so

335

that formulating of carbon dopes was an art rather than a science. Although this secrecy is still maintained in the present-day industry, science has been edging into the picture to control quality, increase output, and to develop new manufacturing procedures, products, and raw materials. The chemist has gathered considerable information regarding many of the raw materials of the carbon paper industry, but there still remain some facts about raw materials and the finished product that are not known. Therefore, it is an exception rather than a rule that the technical man can make a carbon dope and predict exactly its properties.

Types of Carbon Papers and Their Properties

When carbon paper was first introduced, the use specifications were quite simple. These earliest carbons merely had to produce a legible, nonsmeared copy. However, the rapid advance of industrial and business techniques has so changed the picture that today, there are more than a hundred kinds of carbon papers ranging from the simple one-time carbon to the nonfreeze carbon. The requirements of a carbon paper vary from the single hand written copy to the multiple copies obtained on complicated business and recording machines.

Throughout the carbon paper trade, there are four generally recognized types of carbon papers; one-time carbons, typewriter carbons, pencil carbons, and the special carbons such as pen, tabulating, nonfreeze, register-roll, spot, Cellophane, salesbook, and hectograph carbons. The above classification is somewhat erroneous as a one-time carbon may be either a pencil, typewriter, or hectograph type, whereas a typewriter carbon may be a one-time carbon or a regular typewriter carbon that is used many times. This classification, however, follows a logical pattern. One-time carbons are those papers which are common and are used only once and discarded. The typewriter carbons are designated as those that are used many times for making copies on a typewriter. The pencil carbons, similar to the typewriter carbons, are used many times except the copies are made by hand either with a pencil or a ball point pen. The special class of carbons are designated by a specific name so as to distinguish them from the general carbons, and in most cases they are either one-time, typewriter, or pencil carbons.

One-time carbon paper is the most important type made today. It has climbed to the top in the quantity produced and consumed. This has been due to the fact that business correspondence has been streamlined by the use of business forms which are printed and manifolded with interleaved carbon paper into the predetermined "set" or "form." After a form has been filled in with the proper information by a clerk or typist, the original and the copies are separated from the carbon paper which is then discarded. This carbon is a single use item and must be produced at as low a cost as possible. The paper base is generally the cheapest carbonizing tissue obtainable and the manufacturing process the fastest and most economical. The object is to obtain a fairly uniform quality with a very thin film of dope just sufficient to give a legible copy. For this purpose, the carbon dope must contain sufficient coloring matter to give a legible copy from a very thin film, and in addition the dope must have a high fracture or brittleness so that the reproduced images will be as sharp and distinct as possible. The base tissue must be of such quality as to prevent excess penetration of the dope into the paper to prevent binding it to the surface so that as much dope as possible will be released at one time on the copy sheet.

The typewriter carbons, which form the next important class of carbons, are usually the most expensive and of the best quality. These carbons are made in all grades and some are quite inexpensive. A typewriter paper is designed for multiple use, and a good carbon will have a life of forty to fifty reproductions. The production of a carbon of such high quality requires top-grade raw materials; the carbon dopes are, in many cases, very complicated and high in cost, the base paper is usually the best carbonizing tissue available, and the manufacturing process is much slower with more precision and additional treatments to impart special characteristics and longer life.

Since typewriter carbons are used many times, they must possess properties considerably different from the one-time types. The principle of such carbons is that only a small amount of carbon dope is transferred from the relatively thick carbon film to the copy sheet each time a copy is made. The carbon dope must have a certain amount of toughness or binding power within itself, it must have a high color strength so as to give legibility when a small amount of ink is transferred to the copy sheet, and the carbon film must be sufficiently thick and bound to the base tissue firmly so as to permit only small amounts of ink to be removed at one time.

Although the quantity of pencil carbons produced is considerably less than that of one-time and typewriter carbons, they are of great importance. The principle of these carbons is somewhat similar to that of typewriter carbons in that only a small amount of carbon dope is transferred from the carbon film to the copy sheet each time a copy is made. The main difference between them is that the pencil carbon dope is formulated in such a manner as to reproduce an image when subjected to the steady pressure of a pencil or similar blunt instrument, whereas the typewriter carbon is formulated in such a manner as to reproduce an image under the instantaneous pressure impact of a typewriter key. The cost of the raw materials for pencil carbons usually falls between that of the one-time and typewriter carbons. The outstanding difference in pencil carbons is that the base paper is the thickest paper used and a thicker film of carbon dope is applied to it.

Sales book carbons are one-use pencil carbons. The carbon dope is applied to the back side of original sales slip, and in the case of more than one copy the back of each copy sheet is also coated with carbon dope. In other words the actual sales slip is also the carbon paper. The carbon dope of these carbons is very inexpensive and in many cases they have a lower cost than one-time carbon coatings. These dopes are formulated so as to give a copy from a thin film of ink under the steady pressure of a pencil with the purpose of transferring as much ink as possible from the film to the copy sheet.

Pen carbons are very similar to pencil carbons, but pen-carbon dope is considerably softer than pencil dopes. Pen carbons are designed for the conventional pen whereas the ball-point pen can be used exactly like a pencil with a pencil carbon paper.

Nonfreeze carbons are usually of the one-time pencil type although they may also fall into other classes. The foremost requirement of these carbons is the formulation of a carbon dope which will not freeze in extremely cold climates. It is well known that ordinary mineral oil will become very thick and viscous at low temperatures, and for this reason a common carbon ink will freeze with the result that no copy can be made. To overcome this difficulty special low-pour-point mineral oils are used since such oils are unaffected by low temperatures.

Register-roll carbons are also known as oil-soluble pencil carbons. They are pencil carbons that must be designed to be absolutely tack-free to permit the removal of the original and copies from a register machine without tearing. Instead of using insoluble pigments to obtain the color, a dyestuff is employed by dissolving it in an oil such as lard or castor oil.

Spot carbons for one-time use are made to be used with a pencil or typewriter. The carbon dopes for spot carbons are very special and different from the conventional carbon ink. They are usually of high quality and compare with the typewriter carbon ink in cost. This is mainly due to the method of applying the carbon ink to the base paper. Spot carbons are applied to the back side of the original and copy sheets in specified spots where it is desired that only certain information is transferred. To apply carbon dopes in certain spots of any desired size and shape requires an entirely different coating procedure. The process is an actual printing method on a printing press, the carbon dope being printed to the spot from heated plates. For this reason, the carbon dope must possess a body approaching that of a regular printing ink and still remain a carbon dope. Spot carbons are not usually made by the manufacturers of conventional carbon papers.

Hectograph carbons are in an entirely separate classification. These carbons are not used for producing permanent copies like a regular carbon paper, but instead are used to make a duplicating copy which, in turn, is used as a printing plate to produce more copies. Hectograph carbons are used by placing the carbon so that the coated side is against the back of the original sheet. In this position a reverse image is formed on the back of the original sheet when the front side is typed or written upon. The original sheet is commonly called the master sheet or copy. This master sheet is then placed in a duplicating machine where sheets of copying paper are dampened with an organic solvent mixture and pressed against the reverse image on said master sheet thus dissolving a small amount of dye out of the carbon image and transferring it to the copy paper as a positive image.

This duplicating principle requires that the carbon dope contains a highly concentrated basic dyestuff. The amount of dye employed is usually between 50 and 60% and it is incorporated into the wax and oil vehicle as a pigment instead of a dye thus requiring the carbon ink to be ground on a grinding mill to break down the dye crystals into very small particles. The finished carbon ink is then applied to special base papers on conventional carbon coating machines. The speed of application is very low but otherwise the coating operation is similar to that of typewriter carbons.

Another important requirement for hectograph carbon ink is that the ink must be so formulated as to prevent large amounts of dye from being dissolved out of the carbon image onto the copy sheets during the duplicating procedure. Only sufficient dye should be dissolved out of the image as to give a legible copy. A properly designed hectograph carbon should produce up to 600 legible copies. This is not only accomplished through the proper formulation of the raw materials, but also by the use of special dyes which have been developed for this principle.

The hectograph carbons have grown to considerable importance after the slow method of producing hectograph copies by the water and gelatin process had been replaced by the spirit duplicating process where a mixture of organic solvents is employed to dissolve the dye through direct contact with the carbon image. This enables copies to be produced at a much greater speed using an automatic machine. The carbons are available in various colors such as purple, red, blue, and green. Many attempts have been made to produce a black hectograph carbon but none has proved to be very successful. The reason for the lack of success in making a black hectograph carbon lies in the fact that there is no true basic black dye. The black dyes used are a mixture of various colored dyes which give the appearance of black. Since each dye in these mixtures has a different solubility rate in the specific organic solvent, the hectograph image will soon give green, red, blue, or violet copies depending on the predominance of the dyes. The most important color for hectograph work is violet or purple. This is largely due to the fact that a violet dye is available which allows the reproduction of several hundred copies. The other factor is that purple was considered the next best color to black which was not available.

The one-time carbons and the typewriter carbons, in particular, are supplied in many grades and colors with no trade standards for the formulation of the dopes, their hardness, or the thickness of the dope that should be applied to any specific paper. Some brands of typewriter carbons are supplied in as many as six different grades such as soft, medium soft, medium, medium hard, hard, and extra hard. Each grade may be supplied in as many as six different colors with each color of every grade on five different weights of base papers. One brand of typewriter carbon may thus have as many as 180 different grades, colors, and weights of carbon papers. The one-time carbons are usually supplied in the three basic grades of soft, medium, and hard and the common colors of black or blue. Some companies also make purple, red, green, brown, yellow, orange, and white one-time carbons. Although there are no trade standards for the hardness of carbons, the general rule is that the hardness of the coating on the paper determines the suitability of a carbon paper for a particular job. The rule specifies that the carbon should become softer as the number of required copies increases. The exceptions are usually the desires of the user or the peculiarity of the job.

Within each class or type of carbon papers, the reproduction qualities will vary to quite an extent. This is due to the fact that some manufacturers will concentrate on the color strength as the most important quality while others may consider the sharpness and legibility of the copies more important. The demands of the consumer usually set the precedent for each manufacturer in determining what quality is of most importance.

In spite of the standards of quality and performance and of the rigorous controls most manufacturers impose upon their products, consumers of all types of carbons find it advantageous to make their own tests. The manifolding test, weardown, copy strength, and/or legibility or sharpness tests are usually made to verify their needs and the manufacturers' claims.

Base Papers

As a paper base or carrier for satisfactory carbon papers, various types of special carbonizing tissues have been developed such as the kraft and sulfite tissues that are made from wood pulp and the high-grade all-rag-stock tissues. The kraft and lighter-weight sulfite tissues are used for one-time carbons since they are the lowest-priced carbonizing tissues available. The heavier-weight sulfite papers are used for pencil carbons, and the rag-stock tissues are usually employed for typewriter carbons although pencil carbons are sometimes coated on lower-grade rag papers. There is an intermediate grade of paper which is a mixture of rag and wood pulp that is used for low-grade, less-expensive typewriter carbons, and for pencil carbons.

The specialty carbons are each coated on specific types of papers; the hectograph is ordinarily applied on a paper that is a mill-coated stock of fairly heavy weight. Spot carbons are applied to various types of papers such as regular bond and safety check paper. The sales-book carbons are applied to either a bond paper or a high-grade news stock both of which are wood-pulp papers.

Carbonizing tissue is generally available in basic weights ranging from 4 to 16 pounds per ream (20 x 30—500). The lightest-weight kraft paper is 5 pounds per ream, and the lightest-weight sulfite paper is 8 pounds per ream. Some of the bond papers, high-grade news stocks, and book carbonizing papers have basic weights as high as 28 pounds per ream. The all-rag four-pound tissue used for typewriter carbons has a thickness equal to a cigarette paper which is about 2.5 mils, whereas the twenty-eight pound book papers will be as much as 15 mils in thickness.

Since the carbonizing of paper is a continuous process, the tissue is obtained in the form of rolls which vary between 12 and 24 inches in diameter, more frequently, between 17 and 20 inches, and up to 44 inches in width. Each paper manufacturer has a set standard for winding his paper with the wire-side either inside or outside, and for making charge allowances on the wrapper, core, and/or plugs. The kraft tissues are available in a brown or tan color whereas the sulfite and all-rag tissues can be obtained in various shades of white, blue, red, purple, and black.

There are several specifications that are very necessary in order to obtain a good carbonizing tissue. One of the most important requirements is that the paper should have high density. The fibers of the paper should be sufficiently close together and the sheet contain the right amount of sizing to prevent the carbon dope from penetrating through the paper to the back side. Too much penetration of coating means an excessive amount of dope so that a messy carbon results which may produce a reverse image on the back of the top copy sheet.

A tissue of low density means that the paper will have less durability in the case of pencil and typewriter carbons. The carbon manufacturer must also know which side of the tissue is the wire side since the wire side is considered the hardest and smoothest and when coated this helps prevent an excess of carbon ink from penetrating into the paper. From the standpoint of the coating operation, the Mullen or bursting strength of the tissue is very important since if this is too low, the paper is weak. As a considerable tension is applied to the paper web while it is being coated, a weak paper can cause serious difficulty by continuous breaking. The tissues must be free from pin holes which permit excessive amounts of carbon dope to pass through the sheet and form a heavy deposit over each hole. This not only produces a messy ink-flaking carbon but will also cause the paper web to break during the operation if the pin holes are too large. The tissue must be uniform in thickness within specified limits, not only across the web of each roll, but also for different shipments or lots of paper. If a web of paper is too thick on one side, it will cause the coated web to be rewound into a very tight roll on one side which as a rule will cause the ink film to offset to the back of the paper next to it. Another requirement is that the tissue should be free from slime spots which often break through and allow an excessive amount of dope to smear over the back side of the paper, sometimes breaking the entire web. Felt hairs are sometimes picked off the felt blanket used on paper making machines and are embedded in the paper. These hairs in the paper should be avoided as they cause many paper breaks on the coating machine, particularly in the lighter-weight tissues. The moisture content of carbonizing tissue is also of considerable importance for if the paper is too dry, it will be brittle and result in an excessive number of paper breaks. Too much moisture in the tissue will cause a blistering or cockle effect to the ink film. When the jumbo rolls are slit and rewound at the paper mill, care must be taken that the cut edge of the paper is not permitted to split due to dull slitting knives, and all splices must be secure. Split edges which are caused by improper handling and poor splices are another source of paper breaks.

Most of the above specifications and requirements deal with those flaws which produce breaks in the paper web during the coating process. Paper breaks are very serious since they increase the cost of the carbon paper through the loss of tissue and carbon dope, as well as the reduction in output.

Waxes in Carbon Inks

As the carbon paper industry grew into a major chemical process industry and the requirements for various types of carbon papers became more complicated, more attention was paid to the chemical and physical properties of carbon inks and their raw materials. The raw materials for carbon inks are divided into two sections: the colors and the vehicles which carry the colors.

The vehicle consists chiefly of waxes and oils formulated so that the finished ink will have exceptionally good flow qualities which permit its smooth application to the carbonizing tissue. The writer found that good flow is the first and foremost requirement for a good carbon dope. Without flow it would be next to impossible to have the various types of carbon papers that are available today. Instead we would have rough and heavily coated papers that would be unsuitable for most purposes. A freely flowing carnauba wax has, with a very few exceptions, become a necessity in carbon dopes. The presence of waxes in the carbon ink necessitates that the mixing, grinding and application of the dope to the paper are carried out in heated equipment at about 200°F. Carnauba wax has a peculiar property, unique within itself, of imparting flow when melted into a mixture of colors and oils. Flow means that the dope should run freely in a continuous stream very similarly to a paint that has been thinned and is ready for brushing. The flow of carnauba wax is quite often called wetting property, but this term appears to be erroneous from the standpoint that colors can be thoroughly wetted with various oils and yet the mixture will not have flow although it is heated to 200°F. When a small amount of carnauba wax is melted into the color and oil, the resultant mixture will have good flow. In addition, it has been found that carnauba wax does not meet the flow requisite in every case. Certain mixtures have been formulated in which the carbon ink was very short and buttery although carnauba wax was present in the formula. It was also discovered that a small amount of a basic dyestuff, e.g., as little 0.5% methyl violet base, when added to the mixture, produced the desired results of good flow. Further experimentation showed that neither the wax nor the dyestuff by itself would produce flow in these particular cases.

As carnauba wax is very brittle and hard it cannot be used alone as the vehicle to carry the color and, for this reason, must be plasticized or softened with oils and/or greases. Carnauba has a very important and unique property of absorbing the oil by having a high oil retention. This permits the ink film to set or freeze at room temperature to such a point that it will be quite firm and not excessively oily or greasy. When one part of carnauba wax and one part of 100 viscosity mineral oil are melted together until homogenous and allowed to cool to room temperature, the resulting mixture will be very brittle and dry. If one tries to cut this wax-oil mixture it will break or fracture; this fracture being one of the requirements for a good one-time carbon. There will be no oil beads lying on the surface of this mixture and when rubbing the finger across the surface it will feel firm and dry. It is commonly assumed that in order to have a good, hard, dry carbon ink, a very hard wax is necessary. This is true only to a certain extent. There are waxes that are considerably harder than carnauba yet they are not satisfactory for carbon inks because their oil retention and flow properties are very poor. These two characteristics have made carnauba wax the most important wax in the carbon-paper industry.

Carnauba wax belongs to the vegetable class of waxes and is composed of a mixture of various high-melting-point fatty

acids, alcohols, and esters. Its melting point is 185°F., saponification number 88, acid number 2 to 9, and iodine number 13.
These values will vary for waxes coming from different sections
of Brazil.

There are several other waxes that are similar to carnauba
wax in respect to their suitability for use in carbon-paper inks.
Shellac wax obtained from the dewaxing of shellac; ouricury,
a vegetable wax, which comes from the ouricury palm tree in
Brazil; and esparto, another vegetable wax, which comes from
esparto grass that grows in northern Africa can be substituted
for carnauba with fairly good success in some cases. However,
none of these waxes has the flow and oil retention of carnauba
wax. They are often used as extenders for carnauba wax
when they can be obtained at a lower cost.

There are other waxes, such as candelilla, ozokerite, beeswax,
montan, Utah, and paraffin wax, that are usually incorporated
with carnauba wax. The purpose of these waxes is either to
temper the carnauba by softening, or to make the carnauba wax
tougher and less brittle.

There are six classes of waxes: vegetable, mineral, insect,
petroleum, animal, and synthetic. Carnauba, ouricury, candelilla, and sugar cane wax are in the vegetable class. Ozokerite,
montan, and Utah are mineral waxes. Beeswax, shellac, and
Chinese insect wax fall in the insect class. Paraffin wax is a
member of the petroleum class. Spermaceti wax from the
sperm whale is in the animal class.

There have been many synthetic waxes offered to the carbon
paper industry as substitutes for carnauba wax. A large number
of them are only mixtures of natural waxes which generally
contain a certain amount of carnauba or ouricury wax. Many
of these mixtures can be used in carbon inks. Another large
group of synthetics are the chemically modified natural waxes,
such as the series of "I-G" waxes made from the natural montan
wax by a German chemical concern. One of the "I-G" waxes
very nearly matches the properties of carnauba wax for carbon
dopes and, in several cases, this "I-G" wax has been used to

entirely replace carnauba. Another modified natural wax, an oxidized paraffin, has shown great promise as a carnauba substitute. It has excellent flow properties, but does not show the good oil retention which is necessary for carbon inks. If the oil retention of the oxidized paraffin can be improved to compare with that of carnauba wax, a good synthetic carnauba wax will be available at a reasonable price. The true synthetics made from nonwaxy raw materials are not comparable to carnauba wax, but a few have been used to extend carnauba in some inks.

Oils and Colors in Carbon Inks

A very important property of a carbon ink are its drying and nondrying characteristics. Its drying properties are defined as the ability of the carbon ink to solidify or freeze at room temperature so that it will not be soft and smeary. In spite of the fact that a carbon ink must dry, it must also be nondrying or open. The ingredients in the ink must be such that they are not oxidized into a hard varnish-like film upon aging and lose the ability to be transferred to a copy sheet. To make a carbon ink nondrying, the open types of oils are used, i.e., mineral oil, peanut oil, castor oil, and red oil (oleic acid).

The mineral oils are the most widely used nondrying oils in carbon inks because of their low costs and because of the availability of various viscosities ranging from a very thin oil to a very heavy, thick oil. Oleic acid is used quite extensively, but only as a solvent for oil-soluble dyestuffs for if these dyes are not in solution when used in carbon inks they will not produce any color strength. In addition to the mineral oils, various grades of petrolatum are also used in large quantities. The consistencies of the petrolatums vary from the soft amber to the hard dark-green grade. The function of the oils and petrolatums is not only to soften or plasticize the waxes but to obtain specific writing characteristics in the carbon ink such as sharpness of write, wear, non freezing, and release of the ink from the paper.

The most important ingredient in carbon inks is the color

for without it, the transferred image would not be visible. There are two types of colors used in carbon inks: pigments which are insoluble in any solvent and oil-soluble basic dyestuffs. Because of the large demand for black carbon paper, carbon black is most important as a pigment. It is a general belief that carbon black is black, but close examination of a thin film of carbon black reveals that it is either brown or blue. For this reason, lake-pigment or dye toners are added to carbon blacks to produce a jet black. Large quantities of the lake-pigment toners must be employed to obtain the desired results since these toners are insoluble in the oils or waxes and thus do not yield a high tinctorial color strength. Only small amounts of dye toners are necessary to produce a jet black since the dyes are dissolved in either the oils or the waxes and a high tinctorial color results. The dyes are usually dissolved in oleic acid and in some cases castor or lard oil. When it is desired to produce a nonbleed black carbon, the dyes are dissolved in the carnauba wax if there is enough carnauba present in the ink to keep the dye in solution. The toners used to produce a jet-black vehicle are the basic violet and blue dyes or dye bases, iron blue pigments, and green and red pigments. Another important factor in carbon blacks is the oil absorption of the pigment. Carbon black with low oil absorption values is usually considered as the best for carbon-paper inks.

Other pigments used in large quantities are the iron blues. The basic iron blue used is generally of the Milori type with the toning iron blue added in varying amounts to obtain different shades. There has been much work done by the color manufacturers to develop iron blues of special quality for carbon paper inks with properties of low oil absorption, soft grinding, and high color strength. In addition to the iron blue toner, blue lakes are used to obtain an intense blue shade. Red and green pigments and dyes and their lakes, brown pigments, blue and violet dyes and lakes are also used in high-quality carbon paper and titanium dioxide type of pigments for white specialty carbon papers.

The main variable in the colors is the oil absorption because it will not only affect the hardness and the flow of the finished ink, but will also determine the amount of color that can be used and thus the resulting color strength. In the cases where only soluble dyes are used and there are no pigments which have an oil absorption, fillers, such as china clay, are usually employed to give the ink some body and a certain amount of hardness. A formulator will usually know what type of composition is necessary for a particular type of carbon and he will experiment until the desired result is obtained. Because of the difference in the size of laboratory and plant equipment, the chemist will make a plant batch of the experimentally developed ink and coat it on plant equipment. A laboratory ink may perform perfectly, yet, when it is applied to plant operations, it is quite often found that further modification is necessary to obtain the desired results. Another factor that must be closely checked is the aging of the coated ink on the carbonizing tissue. It has been found that a freshly coated carbon paper and one that has aged a few days will give different results. As a rule the aged carbon will produce a sharper and weaker copy than the freshly coated paper. This is caused by the further modification of the crystal structure of the waxes as part of the oils and greases is absorbed by the tissue. The original crystal structure of the waxes is formed during the coating operation when the coated paper is passed over chill rolls to solidify or freeze the thin film of ink. The temperature of the chill rolls determines the crystal structure of the waxes. During the aging process, the crystal formation is either modified or the size of the crystals increased thus causing the ink to become harder and resulting in a sharper image. The most pronounced aging generally takes place during the first 72 hours after which the aging process continues but at a decreasing rate. Most carbon manufacturers age all of their coated papers at least 3 days before they are permitted to be shipped and, in some cases, they are aged from 1 week to 1 month before shipment.

Formulation

Application of the ink to the tissue demands skill and special equipment. The ink is applied in a molten state by a machine which controls the thickness of the coating by careful adjustment of the tension on the paper web, and at the same time controls the rate of cooling so as to insure the formation of a uniform, smooth, hard coating. The ink formulas in themselves do not meet the demands of every manufacturer and should be considered as working bases for further experiment and improvement.

Since black one-time carbon papers are the most widely used they will be considered first. A typical carbon formula in this class is as follows:

	Parts
Carnauba Wax	11
Candelilla Wax	19
Paraffin Wax	17
Light Mineral Oil	32
Oleic Acid	3
Carbon Black	14
Methyl Violet Base	1
Victoria Blue Base	1

Ouricury wax may replace carnauba wax in the formula. This formula may be considered the medium type. If a harder ink is desired, the amount of carnauba and candelilla wax is increased and the amount of paraffin wax and mineral oil decreased until the correct hardness is obtained. For a softer ink this procedure would be reversed.

A typical blue one-time carbon ink may be made as follows:

	Parts
Carnauba Wax	8
Ouricury Wax	5
Paraffin Wax	20
Heavy Mineral Oil	9

	Parts
Amber Petrolatum	20
Milori Blue	10
Toning Iron Blue	8
China Clay	15

These two formulas are basic examples of one-time carbon inks.

When a typewriter carbon ink of high quality is formulated, many more characteristics must be incorporated into the ink with each one being carefully tested. A typical high-grade typewriter carbon is as follows:

	Parts
Carnauba Wax	32
Ouricury Wax	5
Beeswax	5
Ozokerite Wax	5
Light Mineral Oil	26
Amber Petrolatum	6
Good-Grade Carbon Black	13
Crystal Violet Dye	2
Victoria Blue Base	1
Pigmented Purple Toner	3
Oleic Acid	3

Typical of a black pencil carbon ink which is quite similar to the typewriter inks is as follows:

	Parts
Carnauba Wax	34
Ouricury Wax	10
Beeswax	5
Paraffin Wax	21
Petrolatum	25
Heavy Mineral Oil	36
Carbon Black (Brown Shade)	15
Carbon Black (Blue Shade)	8
China Clay	3

In this case a blue-shade carbon black is used in conjunction with a brown-shade carbon black to obtain a jet-black color. The blue-shade carbon black may be replaced by the violet and blue dye toners dissolved in oleic acid to impart the jet blackness to the ink.

The following starting formula for a blue pencil sales-book carbon ink appears somewhat similar to that for a "one-time" formula but the machine formulation is only arrived at after testing many characteristics of the resulting mix.

	Parts
Carnauba Wax	20
Paraffin Wax	6
Medium Heavy Mineral Oil	16
Heavy Petrolatum	11
Amber Petrolatum	11
Toning Iron Blue	10
Milori Blue	25

Blue Register-Roll and Sales-Book Oil-Soluble Pencil-Carbon Ink

	Parts
Carnauba Wax	23
Oleic Acid	15
Lard Oil	16
Victoria Blue Base	7
Talc	39

Black Spot-Carbon Ink

	Parts
Carnauba Wax	26
Heavy Petrolatum	20
Heavy Mineral Oil	10
Light Mineral Oil	14
Oleic Acid	3
Methyl Violet Base	2
Victoria Blue Base	1
Carbon Black	15
China Clay	9

Black Tabulator-Carbon Ink

	Parts
Carnauba Wax	28
Light Mineral Oil	28
Nigrosine Base	38
Auramine Base	1
Bismarck Brown Base	1

Violet Hectograph-Carbon Ink

	Parts
Carnauba Wax	9
Ouricury Wax	6
Blown Castor Oil	9
Amber Petrolatum	16
Light Mineral Oil	18
Crystal Violet Dye	75

Black Hectograh-Carbon Ink

	Parts
Crystal Violet Dye	8
Brilliant Green Dye	5
Erio Green Dye	5
Chrysiodine Dye	21
Bismarck Brown	21
Carnauba Wax	13
Amber Petrolatum	7
Castor Oil	2
Light Mineral Oil	18

The violet hectograph-carbon inks require a special crystal violet dye which has been developed particularly for this kind of work. In the formulation of black hectograh-carbon inks, mixtures of various-colored dyes that give the appearance of a black color must be used, since there is no true black basic dye. The problem in this type of hectograph ink is obtaining the right mixture of colored dyes which, when dissolved in minute quantities from a thin image film, will produce a copy in black. This is very difficult to achieve since most copies will come off in a violet, green, or brown color due to the fact that the various dyes used do not have the same solubility in the organic solvent.

In this section it has not been possible to give examples of the many carbon inks used, but only a formula typifying each of the more important and the more common classes of carbon inks.

Application Equipment

Because of the nature of the waxes used in carbon inks, most of the equipment employed is heated, usually by steam or hot water and occasionally by electricity. All heated equipment should be maintained at approximately 200°F. as this temperature is generally sufficient to maintain the waxes and finished carbon inks in a molten condition. In the cases where the finished carbon inks, particularly those that contain dye toners, are kept in a molten state for long periods of time, the temperature should not exceed 200°F. because excessive and prolonged heating has a tendency to destroy the dye toners. This not only eliminates the toning effect but usually causes the carbon ink to become thick and extremely difficult to apply. In many cases, the temperature of the ink-making equipment is maintained at about 220°F. for the purpose of releasing and removing any water which may be present in the raw materials. It has been found that when the water content of a finished carbon ink exceeds 1%, the ink is generally too thick for application and in many cases, it is very difficult to remelt the ink after it has once solidified.

In the manufacture of a carbon ink, all raw materials are metered in the predetermined proportions by weight and/or by volume into a heated, jacketed kettle. The wax is the first material added to the kettle and is allowed to melt while the remaining materials are mixed into the hot wax under constant agitation. After the crude ink has been thoroughly mixed, it is ground in a pot mill, roller mill, or a ball mill. The ball mill is the most popular and the best means for grinding carbon

inks. The advantages of ball-mill grinding are many and may
be summarized by the ability to produce the most uniform inks
at the lowest cost. The ball mill eliminates the human element

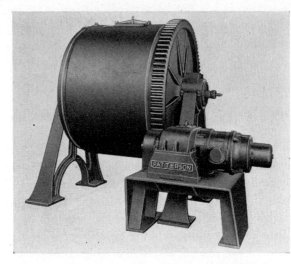

FIGURE 41. *Steam-jacketed ball mill* (Courtesy of Patterson Foun-
dry & Machine Company)

in grinding by removing the manual adjustment required on
other mill types and the major variable which determines the
quality of the grind is milling time. Inks ground in this manner are, in many cases, transferred directly into the mill instead of premixing in a heated kettle. The mill, which is
jacketed and heated by steam or hot water, is then run the
required number of hours after which the finished ink is discharged into trays and allowed to solidify. Where large quantities of a certain ink are used, it can be discharged directly
into heated storage tanks or kettles. In comparison with the
roller mill, a ball mill of the same size will produce more ink
faster with much less handling thus either reducing the amount
of equipment and personnel needed to make the same amount
of ink or increase production without an increase in the amount
of equipment and personnel. A comparison yields nearly the

same results for the pot-mill method of grinding. Some analyses have shown that the pot mill has the highest cost of production and the ball mill the lowest cost, with the roller mill falling in between these two.

FIGURE 42. *Three-roller mill* (Courtesy of J. H. Day Co.)

After the ink has been properly prepared, it is ready for application to the carbonizing tissue. This application is performed on special machines called carbon-paper coaters. The most common coating machine which applies carbon ink to only one side of paper is called a semicoater, whereas the machine that puts ink on both sides of the paper in one operation is known as a full coater. The semicoaters are usually of two types; one is the high-speed coater that makes one-time carbon paper, and the other a low-speed coater that makes the typewriter, pencil, and special carbons. The full coater is a slow machine which coats all types of carbon inks producing carbon paper in a special form known as full or double-faced carbons, and saddle-backed carbons. In some cases, the high-speed coaters are precision built to the point that they can be used to coat any of the semicarbon papers.

A carbon-coating machine employs a breaking system on the

mill roll of tissue as it is unwound and threaded into the coater. This breaking action is used to produce considerable tension on the paper in order to obtain a uniform film of carbon ink and to change the speed of the mill roll as it becomes smaller. The paper coming from the mill roll passes through a system of idler rollers and bowed, curved bars to remove any wrinkles that may occur in the paper and to straighten out the web as it passes over the inking roller. The heated ink roll, which

FIGURE 43. *Universal carbon-coating machine* (Courtesy of Haida Engineering Co.)

rotates in the opposite direction to the paper web, dips into a heated tray containing the melted carbon ink, picks up an excess of ink and deposits an excess on the tissue. The web containing an excess of ink then passes over an equalizer rod which removes the excess ink and at the same time meters a definite film thickness of ink on the paper. The equalizer rod rotates in an opposite direction to the paper web although most machines are constructed so that the ink roller and the equalizer rod may be rotated in either direction as may be desired. The paper, with the film of hot carbon ink, passes over a series of chilled rollers that are cooled to the desired temperature by city water, ice water, or a mixture of cold and hot water to obtain the desired chill temperature. The chill rollers cause the hot ink to solidify and at the same time remove the heat from the entire web of paper before it is rewound into what is commonly called a jumbo roll. The temperature of the chill roll in a large part controls the crystal growth of the waxes present in the ink. To impart special properties to some carbon papers, the coated web may pass over a chill roll, then a hot roll which remelts the ink to a certain extent, and it then is reset by passing over another chill roll. The cooled web passes on through the coater over more idler rolls and bowed, curved bars (dewrinkler bars) to the end where it is rewound into a jumbo roll. The rewinding mechanism contains a clutch arrangement which permits the roll to be wound as tight or loose as desired and at the same time changes the speed of the roll as it increases in size. It is most desirable that the coated paper is cooled to room temperature before it is rewound into a roll as it is the usual tendency for the hot ink film to transfer itself or offset to the back of the paper which it contacts.

Many of the coating machines in use today are specially built and contain many features designed to provide the utmost efficiency in the coating operation. Some coaters have special pressure rolls to maintain the paper web under constant tension. There is special equipment now available which controls the speeds of the unwind roll and the rewind roll automatically so as to maintain a constant tension on the web. There are automatic controls to stop the machine when the paper breaks. Most coaters have a variable-speed control to change the speed of the ink roll. Some coaters have attachments to slit the paper into narrower widths as it is being rewound. The coating machines that make typewriter carbon paper are equipped with a buffing roll that buffs the surface of the ink film to obtain certain special characteristics.

Much of the one-time carbon paper produced is sold in the jumbo rolls as it comes from the coating machine. There are large quantities of one-time carbon sold in slit rolls, i.e., jumbo rolls which have been slit and rewound into narrower rolls as specified. Where jumbo rolls are slit, a special machine is used to perform this task and the operator removes all the bad carbon and uncoated paper and makes good carbon to carbon splices. A small percentage of the other types of carbons are also released as jumbo or slit rolls, but more of them are sheeted into various ream sizes which are later trimmed and cut into smaller sizes as desired. This calls for further equipment such as the sheeting machine and the paper cutter. Carbon-sheeting machines are usually custom-built equipment, either semiautomatic with considerable manual handling, or fully automatic with very little handling until it reaches the paper cutters. The paper cutters are standard cutters used by paper manufacturers and converters.

Other equipment used by the carbon-paper manufacturer may include a printing press to print the back of a special line of typewriter carbons with a design where the printed back is coated with a thin film of a wax composition. With typewriter carbons of this type, the tissue is first printed and then either rewound and put on a coating machine or the printed web is passed right to the coating machine which should be a full coater so as to perform all the steps in one operation. The printed tissue may be coated on a semicoater and then rerun to apply the wax on the printed side.

Some carbon-paper companies make special carbon rolls such as teletype, adding machine, register, and billing machine rolls. In each of these cases, a special type-roll winding machine is necessary to obtain the desired type of roll.

Use Problems of Carbon Papers

The many complex variables encountered in carbon papers are a persistent cause for complaints from stenographic and clerical personnel in all organizations. Not only must the variables of the carbon paper be understood, but there must be an intelligent selection of the right carbon paper for a particular job and a knowledge of the work habits and mental attitude of the user of the carbon.

Typical carbon paper difficulties encountered and methods of correcting them are as follows:

Variation in Color of the Backs. This factor has no relationship to the quality of a carbon sheet. The color is actually dependent on the dyes used in the ink formula or on the actual color of the tissue before it is coated. The quality and finish of the carbons are the important considerations.

Buckling, Treeing, or Wrinkling of the Carbon Sheet. This may be caused by papers slightly wrinkled before inserted in the machine, too much pressure between platen and paper rolls, insertion of unevenly aligned paper sets in the machine, careless handling of the carbon sheets, carbon papers having been packed in too small a container, or the tension under which carbon is placed during the coating operation. Correction may be made by the use of a heavier-weight carbon sheet, adjustment of platen to allow for increased thickness of the paper sets, more careful handling of the carbon sheets, and more care during the coating operation, as many of these wrinkles will not leave upon aging.

Curling of the Carbon Sheet. This is undoubtedly the most frequently encountered difficulty in all carbon papers. There are many causes, and particularly to the expansion and contraction of the waxes and other materials used in making the ink. Warm, damp, or rainy weather promotes absorption of moisture by the uncoated surface and other weather conditions may promote the evaporation of moisture and/or free oils from the paper. Friction as produced by the manufacturing procedure on the coating machines, extreme surface tension such as that found on the harder coatings, and very light weight tissue, all can cause problems. The trouble may be corrected by laying the sheet aside until it took up the room temperature, by selecting a carbon sheet of heavier weight and/or softer finish, by notifying the supplier to replace unusable carbon, or by applying a wax compound to the back side of the coated sheet so as to counteract the expansion and contraction of materials in the ink.

Durability, Insufficient Carbon Life, or Erosion of the Carbon Sheet. This is usually an indication of a carbon finish not suitable for the job, e.g., a carbon with a too soft finish. Normally, the harder the finish and the heavier the sheet, the greater the life of the carbon paper.

Feathered Impressions. This is caused by a cockle-finish carbon paper, absorbent-finish copy paper, too soft a carbon finish, or too heavy a carbon sheet. It may be corrected by using a smooth or glazed-finished copy paper, a harder-finish carbon paper, or a lighter-weight carbon sheet.

Flaking of Carbon Coating. This may be caused by the storage of the carbon paper in a room which is too hot and dry, insufficient absorbency of the base paper, or improper formulation of the ink. Splotchy impressions which result from flaking carbon may also be due to irregular operator touch, cockle-finish copy paper, improper adjustment of the feed rolls or slippery paper-feed rolls. These possibilities should be examined carefully before pronouncing a carbon sheet defective.

Illegibility of Carbon Copies. This is caused by very absorbent copy sheets, cockle-finish copy sheets, too soft a carbon finish, too heavy a carbon sheet, light operator touch, or soft platens. Correction may be attained by using smooth or glaze-finish copy sheets, by selecting a lighter weight carbon sheet with a harder finish, by using a stiff backing sheet to secure a greater sharpness of writing, by using a machine equipped with art Gothic numbers for figure work, or having a hard platen installed on the machine.

Inadequate Manifolding of the Carbon Paper. This is caused by too hard carbon finish, too heavy carbon sheet, too thick ribbon, too heavy copy sheets, cockle-finish copy sheets, very light operator touch, or insufficient platen density. It can be corrected by use of lighter-weight, softer-finished carbon, use of thinner ribbon, use of smooth or glazed copy sheets, adjustment of machine action, or having a harder platen installed.

Offsetting of Carbon Paper. This is caused by excessive pressure between platen and paper rolls, rough- or absorbent-finish copy paper, too soft a carbon finish, carbon sheet too heavy for the manifolding job, improper insertion and removal of set from the machine, or carbon rolls rewound too tight or rewound with too much heat on the coating machine. It can be corrected by use of a harder-finish carbon sheet, use of a smooth- or glazed-finish copy paper, by adjusting platen according to the thickness of the assembled set, insuring that all the heat is removed from the coated paper before it is rewound, or rewinding loosely.

Stenciling of the Carbon Sheet. This is caused by too light a weight carbon sheet, too heavy operator touch, or too hard a platen. It can be corrected by selecting a heavier carbon sheet, adjusting the machine to the operator's touch, or installing a softer platen.

Tearing of Carbon Sheet. Its causes may be broken paper fingers or alignment rule, carbons too wide for the paper, or hyphens and underscore key may cut the carbon without injuring the original or copy sheets. It can be corrected by adjusting the machine, or selection of a heavier carbon paper.

Lack of Uniformity of Writing. Carbons of the same quality can and do give nonuniform writs. This may be caused by the carbon paper having been aged under varying conditions and for varying periods of time, variations in the absorbency of the base paper, variations in the manufacturing control, or some change in use conditions. Most of these factors are faults of the products themselves which should be replaced by the manufacturer. The first factor may be controlled by the facilities of the consumers supply room. The last factor is entirely a matter of consumer control since office procedure must be uniform if it is expected the performance of supplies to remain uniform.

Common Defects of the Machines that Cause Carbon-Paper Troubles

Platens. Hard, pitted or slippery platens will promote carbon paper troubles and will injure type face.

Feed Rolls. Slipping causes offset of carbon coating and when the feed rolls are improperly adjusted or when hard, they exert too great a pressure on the platen, again causing offset.

Machine Action. Noiseless, standard, etc., machines impose special problems and must be considered in selecting the proper carbons.

Maintenance, Oiling and Cleaning. These must be given periodic attention to assure best results and prevent machine depreciation.

Operator Peculiarities Causing Carbon Paper Difficulties

Personal preference for color of writing and sheet frequently makes necessary the use of a carbon sheet finished to suit this preference.

Care of Supplies. Carbons carelessly stored in a desk are subject to curling, wrinkling, treeing, buckling, tearing, etc.

Care of Machines. Type that is not cleaned regularly becomes gummy and produces an uneven writing.

Work Habits. Lack of care in handling and interleaving carbon sheets damages the carbon sheets and soils the work.

Paper Peculiarities Which Produce Carbon Paper Difficulties

Finish. Cockle, smooth, glazed or absorbent finish, each has its characteristic interaction with carbon-paper inks and must be studied by the supplier and user.

Weight. The weight of the paper determines the weight of the carbon sheet which should be chosen for the job. The lighter-weight sheets always make better copies.

Color. The paper color must be such as to provide the best contrast with the copy record; white, yellow, blue-green, cherry, and russet, in the order named, are the best suited.

Other Office Duplicating Methods

Of the four important office duplicating methods, the *carbon paper method* is the most important and the most widely used. Under this discussion of carbon paper the *hectograph duplicating method* has been discussed to some extent and nothing will be added here. The other two office duplicating methods are the Mimeograph process and the Multilith process.

The *Mimeograph duplicating process* produces copies on a highly absorbent copy paper by permitting ink to pass through the cut image of a stencil sheet. This method is carried out by means of a stencil or printing plate. The stencil is composed of a base paper of tissue called Yoshino, a substitute for the soft, very long fibered paper originally made in single sheets by hand in Japan, is now made by machine in the United States. This Yoshino paper is impregnated with a plasticized nitrocellulose of such a consistency as to permit it to be cut by the face of a typewriter key, or stylus, in a manner as to give a good clear image and at the same time prevent cutting through the base paper. The nitrocellulose in the form of collodion is mixed in the proper proportion with plasticizing agents such as triacetin, benzyl alcohol, and/or castor oil, and also with hardening and toughening agents such as waxes and solid fatty acids so as to impart the right consistency to the impregnation in the base paper. A special ink must be used with this stencil: an ink that will not have any interaction with the nitrocellulose film, that will readily pass through the Yoshino fibers which are exposed where the cut image is present, and that will be readily absorbed by the copy sheet. A properly prepared stencil and Mimeograph stencil ink will reproduce several hundred copies before the stencil breaks down.

The newest duplicating method used in business offices is the *Multilith process* with which any number of good, sharp, legible copies in any desired color may be obtained by the proper selection of the duplicating base or printing plate and the printing ink.

FIGURE 44. *Multigraph duplicator employing the "Multilith process"* (Courtesy of Addressograph-Multigraph Corp.)

The Multilith process employs the same method of reproduction as is used in the lithographic printing process by which some of the finest printing is performed today. The Multilith method uses metal plates for exceptionally long runs, but for shorter-run office work special paper plates have been developed so that a form may be typed on this plate with an ordinary typewriter using a special ribbon, inked with a greasy image ink. Two of the paper-printing plates which have been developed have proved quite satisfactory. A paper plate to be used in this process must possess high wet-strength so that when the paper is wetted with water, it will not disintegrate, but will remain in a firm uniform sheet with no stretching. In addition, the paper must be able to receive and retain a greasy image. Parchment paper meets most of these requirements with the exception of stretching, and this has been overcome by laminating it to a heavy waterproof backing sheet with a waterproof resin adhesive. The other good Multilith printing plate consists of a waterproof paper base, either single or laminated, coated with a mixture containing clay or silica or an alkali metal silicate that will precipitate silica. This coating is then treated to render it water-insoluble thus binding the silica or clay to the surface and forming a grain which functions in a manner similar to the grain that is applied to the metal lithographic plates. These paper plates are made so that they can be inserted into a type-writer and a typewritten image can be applied to the surface. The surface will also receive hand-written images by the use of a special writing ink.

These paper printing plates will reproduce several thousand copies from a properly prepared image on a small printing press designed for office use, which employs the lithographic principle.

Although the carbon-paper method is the most important for obtaining copies, the other modes of reproduction of business correspondence must be also considered because of the increased demand for a greater number of copies in a large organization. Carbon paper and the other three methods previously discussed all require specialty papers which are the basis for most office reproduction work.

Chapter XIII

PRINTING PAPERS

by R. H. Simmons

P RINTING is the act of reproducing a design on any surface. Generally, when we speak of printing, we think of the operation of a printing press. This concept of printing and its relation to paper properties will be the basis of this chapter.

The three fundamental forms of printing are (1) typographic, or relief, where the printing area is raised above the nonprinting area; (2) planographic, where the printing area is in the same plane as the nonprinting area; and (3) intaglio, where the printing area is incised below the nonprinting area. Because of these inherent differences in the manner in which ink is applied to paper, the nature of the ink used in printing must vary with the printing method. Since the ink and paper must be interrelated in the process, it is not hard to realize that the papers for each process must have certain definite characteristics.

There are several other methods of reproduction which are finding extensive use for short runs, among which is the silk screen process. Basically, this is not a printing process, but it can be used to reproduce a design and, therefore, falls under the heading of printing. There are also other methods of duplicating which are used to reproduce type and illustrations. The typewriter is used to produce copy for gelatin-pad duplicating, liquid or spirit duplicating, stencil duplicating and offset duplicating.

The method of printing to be used, whether by letterpress, offset or gravure, determines the basic requirements in choosing a paper for reproduction. It is considered good practice to submit to the ink maker, a sample of the paper to be used, together with the information relating to the kind, style and model of the press available so that the proper ink can be supplied. This interrelation between the press, paper and ink will be considered in discussing printing papers.

A paper mill, in manufacturing paper for the printing trade, has two factors to consider. The first concerns the requirements set by the purchaser. The second consideration is the paper, which is usually a standard grade and is sold under the mill's watermark, brand, or trade name. The order specifications are set up for a definite use and the sheet will be printed under reasonably uniform conditions. The mill specification is set up in order to meet any number of printing conditions. The paper maker and converter are, therefore, interested in knowing beforehand what characteristics should be built into a sheet of paper in order to meet the printing requirements.

Typographic or Letterpress Printing

This printing is done from printing areas which are in relief or raised. It is the oldest method of press reproduction. In the early days of printing, the characteristics of the paper used were not important. As the quality of paper had to be improved to meet the demands of higher speeds and improved illustrations, uniformity in structure, thickness, finish and ink receptivity of the paper became new and important characteristics.

Typographic printing accounts for the major volume of printing. It also uses the widest variety of printing papers. The presses used vary from the hand-fed platen press through the automatic, flatbed-cylinder, rotary sheet-fed, up to the high-speed newspaper and five-color two-side heat-set web presses.

The work may vary from a simple handbill, composed only of type, to high-grade four-color process printing.

Sheet paper used in typographic printing must have sufficient strength to withstand the mechanical action of the press, such as the pull of the grippers. The paper must have sufficient body so that it does not sag as it is fed to the guides. Light-weight papers tend to sag and catch while traveling down to the guides. This causes them to tear and feed out of line. A bad curl has the same effect.

In printing on web presses, the web of paper must have sufficient strength to withstand the pull of the press. The roll must be uniformly wound and must not have tight or loose edges. These cause uneven tension and tight edges may cause breaks while loose edges cause wrinkles. Nonuniformity in the winding of the roll of paper will also cause misregister on multicolor presses.

Planographic Printing

In this process, printing is done from a plane surface, i.e., the printing area and nonprinting area are in the same plane. A variation of planographic printing is the deep-etch process in which the printing area is etched slightly below the plane surface to resist wearing of the printing area during long runs. The process of printing is the same in other respects. A greasy image is developed on the printing plate. The plate is then dampened with a water solution or fountain etch and then inked. The water does not adhere to the inked portion of the plate and the ink does not adhere to the moistened part of the plate. In direct lithography, the printing is done directly from the printing plate or stone. In offset lithography, the next segment of the rotation of the plate cylinder brings the plate in contact with a rubber blanket which takes both water and ink from the plate. The blanket is then impressed upon a sheet of paper which also takes the water and ink.

Paper for offset and lithographic printing must lie flat and have a minimum of expansion and contraction. The fact that the paper, during impression, passes between two smooth rolls means that it cannot have any waves in it or wrinkling or fanning will occur.

A paper which shows considerable expansion due to moisture will tend to expand on contact with the moistened blanket. Offset papers are usually treated for offset printing by giving them a hard sizing or tub sizing. Where coated papers are used, the printing surface is given a waterproofing treatment to resist the absorption of moisture.

The very nature of offset printing makes it necessary for the paper to carry a fairly heavy, tacky ink. In full-strength colors, it is important to carry an ink as concentrated as possible and still maintain the proper working qualities. This is important because only a thin film of ink can be carried on an offset press and still give good impressions without filling in the printing areas. The ink is fed to the printing plates where the ink film is divided and part is taken by the rubber blanket. The ink film on the blanket is again divided when the paper takes part of the ink. The impression, therefore, receives only part of the ink brought to the plate by the ink rollers. The ink must be tacky and heavy in order to carry sufficient color. A thin ink may "grease" and cause trouble on the printing plate by producing a scum or printing in the nonprinting areas. Since the impression is made from a rubber blanket on a flat sheet of paper, there is no place for extra ink to go on impression except sideways or into the paper. The stiff, tacky body of the ink is necessary to prevent it from moving sideways under pressure.

It was first considered necessary for an offset paper to have a surface texture or grain in order to take care of extra ink on the blanket. The grain allowed the ink to compress into the hollows and allowed lateral flow of air trapped on the surface of the paper. Today considerable quantities of coated lithographic paper is being printed by offset. The addition of this class of paper seems to refute this theory of the need of surface grain on the paper. What apparently is necessary is a good surface ink receptivity. The oils or varnish used in the inks must penetrate rapidly into the surface of the coating and prevent a squashed effect on the impression. This rapid penetration, in turn, causes a rapid setting of the ink. A coated paper must be treated so that the coating does not pick, lift or flake. Coated paper often gives up the mineral coating as a fine powder. The mineral part of a coated paper is often found to lift from the paper and adhere to the rubber blanket as a fine powder. This condition is called piling and requires frequent wash-ups and may ruin the plate. Picking of offset papers, whether coated or uncoated, is extremely troublesome because the flakes or fibers adhere to the blanket, transfer to the printing plate, and then work back into the ink fountain. A spot on the blanket may not be in the printing area but when it works back to the plate the spot comes in contact with the ink roll, retains ink, and begins to print on the blanket and in turn on the impression. This necessitates washing up the plate and blanket, resulting in lost press time and also produces mechanical wear on the plate. The pressman may endeavor to soften his ink to prevent picking, but he is between two factors. If he softens the ink too much, he may get scumming or printing in the nonprinting areas.

Intaglio and Rotogravure

Intaglio printing is done from recessed plates or rolls. The printing area is cut below the surface of the plate. Intaglio printing is divided into two main classes; plate printing and gravure. The inks developed for this type of printing are the short, buttery type which wipe clean and lift readily from the plate.

The papers used for plate printing are dampened before printing in order to permit them to be depressed into the incisions of the plates so that intimate contact is obtained between the paper surface and the ink.

For rotogravure printing, an ink containing a volatile solvent is used. Most of the rotogravure printing is done on an absorbent paper which acts as a blotter for the ink, but due to the rapid evaporation of the solvent, the ink does not spread or feather.

Coated papers were originally not considered rotogravure papers but coated papers are finding an increasing demand in the converting industry and in the field for printing color work for magazines and mail-order catalogs.

Paper Characteristics in Relation to Printing

Let us consider what characteristics must be built into the paper for satisfactory operation with a view to the demands which are placed upon paper by the various printing processes.

Physical Strength. This characteristic is important in that the paper must withstand a certain amount of stress and strain in passing through the presses and the bindery operations. Strength is not as important in printing, on the other hand, as it may be for the ultimate use requirements of the finished product. In building a sheet of paper for printing, it is necessary to consider the use requirements of printed article and then consider them in relation to obtaining the printing properties. It is not possible to include maximum strength and still obtain a uniformly closed formation and a smooth finish unless a coated paper is used. The physical strength of the paper must also be considered in relation to binding operations such as folding, stitching and sewing. If the paper does not have the proper strength, it may break or crack in the folders and fall apart on the stitching machines.

Formation. This characteristic is basic for printing papers since the formation of the sheet is the foundation upon which many of the other printing characteristics depend. In preparing a letterpress for printing, it is made ready; that is, the packing and the plates are treated so that pressure is produced uniformly over the various printing areas. It is usually necessary to increase the pressure more on solid printing areas than on halftones, and type areas require the least pressure. The pressure should be uniform throughout each respective printing area. It is necessary that the paper is uniform in thickness to take uniform impression. A wild formation produces hills and vales in the surface of the paper which, when observed by transmitted light, appear as dark and light spots, and is not conducive to a uniform impression. The dark or thick spots will take the maximum pressure and thus act as bearers to prevent impression on the light or thin spots. This produces mottled printing. It is, therefore, necessary to increase the pressure of the printing plate in order to force the type into the low spots. This tends to emboss the paper and is detrimental to the plates and type. Crushing and rapid and uneven wearing of the type and plates can be expected when extreme pressure is used to make the entire form print. This effect is minimized in a coated sheet.

When a paper, which has a wild formation, is calendered, the high spots are polished down but at the same time they act as bearers and prevent a uniform finish. The paper has a galvanized appearance with shiny and dull spots across its surface. A good printing job depends upon a proper transfer of ink from the plate to the paper. These hard or shiny spots are not receptive to ink, while the low or dull spots on the surface of the paper may still be soft and porous and absorb the ink quite readily. A mottled print is the result. The hard spots resist the ink penetration while the soft spots accept it. The ink, due to slow penetration, remains on the surface and may set off on the next sheet. When dry, the ink, which remains on the surface, will usually appear glossier than the ink which penetrates. To obtain a uniform gloss or appearance, it becomes necessary to increase the heavier varnishes in the ink to prevent penetration in the soft or open areas.

Another effect of wild paper formation is the mottled or uneven show-through, and possible strike-through. The resistance to ink penetration by the hard spots prevents a strike-through at these points, but the soft or low spots permit the ink to penetrate further into the paper. The addition of extra pressure in printing aggravates this trouble. The soft spots are not as dense, and, therefore, are less opaque and may permit show-through.

Heavy calendering to reduce a wild formation to a smooth sheet has the fault of burning or blackening the sheet, resulting in a poor or dirty color.

Uncoated paper is very often two-sided in finish. Usually the wire side is more open and absorbent than the felt side. It is also rougher and it is customary for the papermaker to label the case or skid with a notice indicating the felt side as the better side for printing. Two-sidedness affects the ink receptivity as well as the color of the ink. It, therefore, becomes necessary to make changes in the amount of ink and, sometimes, in the color.

There are no instruments which have proven satisfactory for determining or rating formation. Thus far, the accepted method is a comparison with standard samples.

Smoothness. This characteristic of paper is very closely related to the formation of the paper. Smoothness is an important factor in printing papers. It governs many of the other factors used in printing. The smoother the sheet, the better is the contact between the paper and the printing plate. The degree of smoothness necessary in the paper is determined by the kind and quality of printing required.

Smoothness is closely related to the manner in which the pulp is handled in the papermaking process. Strength and smoothness are not fully compatible. In order to obtain strength, it is necessary to use the longer, stronger fibers. Long fibers in papermaking tend to clump as soon as agitation is discontinued. This clumping produces a wild formation with all the faults mentioned under this heading. Long, strong fibers are also flexible and springy, and not easily calendered. They tend to return to their original position. Unless properly bound into the surface by sizing or mechanical treatment, these long fibers may produce a fuzzy finish on the paper.

Smoothness and strength must be balanced to meet the use requirements of the paper. A sheet built for strength is not usually a good printing sheet. With the introduction of the synthetic resins, better strength of some printing papers is achieved, but the addition of stronger fibers and synthetic materials will increase the cost of the paper.

Increased smoothness can be obtained by the addition of high percentages of mineral fillers. A closed formation is obtained by the proper balance between long fibers for strength and short fibers to close the lattice formed by the long fibers. The addition of mineral filler then closes the very small interstices.

The use of the proper fillers results in a sheet which requires less calendering to produce a smooth surface. The ease of calendering depends upon the particle size of the filler used. Brecht and Pfretzschner [1] have demonstrated that in general the smoothness and the softness of a sheet increase with the increase in the amount of filler and the decrease in the particle size of the filler.

To overcome the effect of sheet formation, the converter manufactures a coated paper. Here a mineral pigment mixed with a suitable binder is added to the surface of the paper and the whole dried and calendered. The coating covers the surface of the sheet presenting a smooth even surface with a uniform ink absorption.

There are two grades of coated paper being manufactured today, machine- or process-coated paper and brush-coated paper. Machine-coated paper receives the coating on the paper machine during the process of drying the sheet. Brush-coated paper is coated in a separate operation. Coating is applied not only to paper but also to board stock.

Smoothness of paper [2] is measured by the Bekk,[3] the Williams or the Gurley S.P.S. [4] instrument. Each of these instruments operate on the air-flow method in which a definite quantity of air under a definite pressure is allowed to pass between the surface of the paper and a reference surface. The rate at which this amount of air passes between the two surfaces is considered a measure of the smoothness of the surface.

The Bendtsen instrument, also an air-flow instrument, is used for measuring the smoothness of paper especially in the field of newsprint.

The profilometer has found some use for measuring smoothness of paper and, with the proper head, gives an accurate measurement of actual variations in the profile or surface of the paper.

Softness and Compressibility. This factor in paper represents the ability of the sheet to compress and conform to the shape of the printing surface when under pressure. When we speak of softness and compressibility, we really think of elasticity or the ability of the sheet to compress and return to its original dimensions. Coatings containing rubber latex in their formulation have much to offer in this respect.

Softness in a printing paper is an advantage if it does not affect the other characteristics of the paper. A soft sheet tends to be bulky; the surface can usually be easily abraded and the finish is not as high as that of a comparable hard sheet. A soft sheet becomes fuzzy easily. A soft sheet does not have as high a strength as a comparable hard sheet.

Softness permits the sheet to compress under pressure, bringing all portions of the printing plate surface into contact with the surface of the paper. Thus, a better impression can be obtained on a rough, soft sheet in comparison to a rough, hard sheet. A rough, soft sheet may also take ink better than a smooth, hard sheet. Softness is determined by measuring the compressibility of the paper. The thickness of the sheet is determined without pressure and then under pressure, and the percentage decrease in thickness calculated. This is the percentage compressibility. Bekk [3] has developed two instruments, one for measuring compressibility under static pressure and the other under dynamic pressure. The instrument using static pressure permits the measuring of thickness under increasing loads. The instrument for dynamic pressure uses a pendulum with a hammer having a slightly rounded head. This head can be inked and then dropped from a definite height against a paper sample mounted on a steel block. As the hammer strikes, it rebounds and the rebound can be measured on a graduated arc mounted back of the path of the hammer head. The inked portion leaves a circular mark on the paper specimen. The diameter of the circle is the measure of the softness of the paper. A soft paper will compress more than a hard paper and the circle will be larger. The cushioning action of the paper is correlated to the rebound of the hammer. The greater the cushioning action, the less the rebound. The Gurley-Hill S.P.S. tester [4] has an attachment which measures the softness of the paper. This instrument works on the air-flow principle. A specimen of paper is clamped between two smooth circular rings. The bottom ring has on its face four steel pins which rise 0.002 inch above the surface of the ring. These pins press into the surface of the paper. The air-flow between the two plates without a paper specimen is constant. As the pins press into the surface of the specimen, the air-flow is decreased, and the farther the test reading is from the standard air-flow, the softer the paper. Strachan and Hanshaw [5] have developed a thickness gage for the measurement of the softness of paper under static pressure.

Porosity. The ease with which air passes through a sheet of paper is considered by some papermakers as a measure of the oil absorption factor or ability of the paper to absorb oil. Larocque,[6] in his studies has shown that paper has a large number of blocked capillaries into which oil can penetrate, but which do not pass entirely through the sheet of paper and, therefore, are not accounted for in a porosity test.

This conception of the relation of porosity to oil penetration is refuted when we consider that a highly filled sheet has very low porosity but still may have excellent ink receptivity. A coated paper has practically no porosity and yet the paper can have a very high rate of oil absorption due to the pigments present in the surface of the sheet.

The Gurley Densometer [7] and the Gurley-Hill S.P.S. tester are the standard instruments for measuring density or porosity of a sheet. The Bekk smoothness tester has an attachment for measuring porosity. Other instruments have been developed but they have not found favor in the trade.

FIGURE 45. *Hoe color convertible newspaper press* (Courtesy of R. Hoe & Co., Inc.)

Opacity. In printing, the ability of a sheet to prevent show-through is important especially when both sides of the sheet are to be printed. Opacity is also necessary to prevent printing on the succeeding sheet from showing through the first sheet. Show-through, caused by oil penetration around the printed areas, is often blamed on lack of opacity.

Some pulps have more opacity when made into a sheet than others. Ground-wood pulp is the most opaque pulp; bleached sulfite is the least. The use of secondary stock in printing papers helps increase the opacity, but it tends to give a soft and sometimes fuzzy sheet. The addition of mineral fillers is probably the best manner to increase opacity. Hydration of pulp reduces its opacity. The type of filler used is important. The opacity of the filler depends upon its refractive index.

China clay talc and calcium carbonate are the common fillers used today. Titanium dioxide is also used. Clay has a specific gravity of 1.55 and an opacity of 2.60 while titanium dioxide has a specific gravity of 2.55 and an opacity of 3.90. The addition of titanium dioxide produces opacity with less filler than when clay is used. This factor is important when high opacity is desired and at the same time maximum strength is needed. The addition of filler, as mentioned before, promotes the smoothness by permitting easier calendering of the sheet. Crush and blackening produced by overcalendering the sheet causes the paper to lose some of its opacity, but the addition of fillers helps to prevent this. Filler in paper also improves the printing quality, producing better ink receptivity of the surface of the sheet. All the beneficial effects of fillers are present also in coated papers since coating pigments are similar to filler pigments and produce the same effect except that they are placed on the surface of the paper instead of in the body stock. The Bausch and Lomb Opacimeter [8] measures opacity by the contrast ratio method. There are several new instruments on the market which have adopted this method of measuring opacity.

Grit. This characteristic of paper is detrimental to printing plates and good printing. A gritty paper may produce scratches in fine halftone plates. Grit also causes wear of the face of type and halftones. It is extremely bad when it shows up in rotogravure printing. A scratch on one of the expensive rolls manufactured for rotogravure printing may require the replacement of that roll.

A mineral coated paper, although smoother, is harder in finish than an uncoated paper and may exhibit extreme abrasive qualities. Coated paper also tends to wear printing plates and type faster than an uncoated sheet.

Bekk [3] draws a strip of paper under pressure over a smooth microscope slide. The scratches produced on the glass indicate grit.

A very simple method of checking the abrasive nature of a filler or coating is to rub the surface of the paper with a silver coin such as a dime. A gritty or abrasive surface will be evidenced by the formation of a black spot on the paper. The rapidity and darkness with which the spot develops indicate the degree of abrasiveness of the paper.

Surface Strength. The surface strength of uncoated papers depends on the beater treatment of the fibers and the sizing. With coated papers, surface strength depends on the coating adhesive used as well as the body strength of the base paper. Surface strength is the resistance to pick or lifting of the paper surface during printing. If the mineral coating is weak, it will flake and pick during printing, but if the body stock is weak, fibers and whole sections of the sheet may pull free from the paper. These particles cling to the type and halftones causing them to fill in and carry ink in the nonprinting areas. Loose particles on the surface of type will produce black dots with white halos around them.

The test generally used to determine surface strength is the wax pick test. It consists of melting a series of waxes having graded adhesive strength and sticking them to the surface of the sheet. The waxes are cooled 15 minutes, then pulled vertically with a quick jerk. These waxes are numerically graded according to strength and are sold by the Dennison Mfg. Co.[9] The paper is said to pass the highest number wax which does not break or injure the surface of the paper. Additional information may be registered, such as surface pick, surface broken, or body pick when making this test. These factors are considered important in determining where the picking occurs. The first or surface pick on coated paper indicates a weak coating adhesive resulting in breaking away of the coating. The second indicates a weak link between the coating and the body stock and the third a weak body stock. These, of course, are relative observations. Uncoated papers may also be graded as to surface strength. Case or K & N Laboratory waxes are also used but are fewer in number and have wider ranges between waxes. They are classed according to the color of the wax.

Some printing plants require that the paper does not pick when using certain inks. The paper is given a press test using the various inks and the printed sheets are examined for picking. The proof press is also recommended for determining pick resistance.

Bekk has developed an instrument [3] for determining pick which registers the force necessary to strip a sheet of paper from a brass plate to which one end of the paper has been attached by an adhesive. The results are given numerical values.

Comparative tests can be made by placing two sheets of paper under a template with two narrow parallel slots which permit a section of each paper to be inked. A standard ink is then rolled out with a brayer and when the proper film is obtained, the brayer is rolled over the paper samples with one motion and with a fair amount of pressure. If the paper shows picking, it does not pass this test.

The pick tests, thus far developed, do not indicate one important factor of picking which causes considerable trouble, and that is the fine flaking of a poorly bound coating. The test area in relation to a full-sized printing sheet is so small that fine picking does not show with any test except possibly the press or roller test.

It has been the experience of most printing shops which make pick tests that every now and then a paper which picks with a low number wax will print without picking, while a paper which has a pick test which rates well above that normally required for printing, will pick badly in press operation.[10]

The proof press is advocated as a means of measuring the pick of paper. The ink which is to be used in printing the particular paper is placed on the proof press. Proofs are pulled, using the test paper and a printing plate which includes a solid area. If the paper fails or picks under this test, it will probably pick when run on the printing presses.

Oil Absorption. This test is an attempt to anticipate the ink receptivity, or resistance of the paper to ink penetration. The oil-drop method is satisfactory only on papers which are of a uniform construction and fairly slack-sized. It indicates the capacity of the body of the sheet to absorb the ink vehicle but is not a measure of the surface ink receptivity. When inks, which dry by absorption, are used in printing, this test is quite accurate in determining the ink and paper relationship.[11]

On coated papers or hard sized papers, a test which applies only a thin film of oil to the paper surface can be used. A method reported by Wehmhoff [12] uses a composition roller of a definite weight to spread a measured volume of oil over the surface of the sheet. The instant of break in the oil film, due to penetration, is taken as the end point. Vallindigham [18] has refined this test by spreading the oil drop with a stainless steel roll of known weight which rolls down an inclined plane. The change in gloss reflectance of the oil film is read, using a photo-electric cell. A curve can be plotted showing the rate of oil absorption.

These tests are indicative of the effect of the ink and paper relationship, but do not show at all times the press relationship. When ink is applied to a sheet of paper, it is under considerable pressure and the rules for hydraulic pressure apply in addition to the action of capillary attraction.

Some papers are made with a carbonate filler. In general, the addition of a carbonate filler precludes the use of sizing in the paper due to the acid nature of the sizing. A paper with carbonate filler has excellent ink receptivity and makes an excellent book paper, but cannot be used for offset printing because of the acid nature of the fountain solutions.

There are many coated papers which are made with calcium carbonate as the mineral part of the coating. Calcium sulfite is another pigment sometimes used as a filler or coating. They are both very white and of good ink receptivity.

Extensive calendering of the paper reduces the bulk of the sheet and increases the density. This slows the oil-absorbing of the paper. In process printing or where two or more colors are to be superimposed upon each other, it is necessary that the surface strength of the paper is greater than for a single impression. The surface strength required must be greater for each succeeding color.

Cobb and Lowe [14] recommend the contact angle as a means of determining the wettability of the paper surface.

FIGURE 46. *Web offset press* (Courtesy of The American Type Founders Sales Corp.)

Ink Receptivity. In printing, it is the surface ink receptivity which is important rather than the ink receptivity of the body stock. Ink receptivity is an interfacial relation between the paper and the ink film impressed upon it. Due to the large variety of inks manufactured and the variety of finishes and kinds of paper used in printing, the ink receptivity varies greatly and is expressed for any paper as the relation between that paper and the particular ink being used for printing.

A paper which will receive the ink uniformly with a very light impression is said to have a good ink receptivity. A paper with good ink receptivity does not need extra pressure to cause the ink to adhere to or penetrate into the surface of the paper. The ideal condition is a paper which receives the ink readily, but is so constructed that the ink is absorbed completely on the surface without permitting the oil to penetrate into the body of the sheet. Excessive absorption of the ink into the sheet may produce two faults. (1) The ink may lose gloss, become flat and appear weak; (2) the vehicle may filter out of the ink, leaving the pigment in a semidry condition known as "chalking." The pigment, in this last condition, does not have sufficient vehicle to bind it to the paper. A condition of this kind is often mistaken for nondrying of the ink.

It is with smooth coated sheets of paper that we are particularly interested in ink receptivity. In letterpress printing, the strength of color of the impression is related to the amount of ink carried. With smooth coated papers, it is not necessary to carry an excess of ink in order to get proper coverage. Coverage, therefore, is a function of the relation between the ink receptivity of the surface of the paper and the impression. If the paper is not ink receptive, the pressman usually increases the printing pressure to force the ink into the paper. In the case of a rough-finished paper, it is necessary to carry more ink in order to fill the depressions. A light impression on a rough paper tends to produce an uneven coverage giving a mottled appearance. If a large amount of ink is used on a paper with poor ink receptivity, a squashed or mottled appearance of the impression may be the result. The ink is slow in setting because it does not penetrate into the paper and offset may occur.

A paper which has a mottled finish may produce a mottled print because this condition indicates an uneven or nonuniform ink-receptive surface. The hard or shiny spots are not receptive while the dull or soft spots are quite receptive to the ink. In order to overcome this imperfection, the pressman will usually add a stiffer varnish or ink to keep the ink from penetrating into the soft spots, thus creating a uniform lack of penetration into the paper. Here again added printing pressure may help overcome uneven ink absorption.

Papers for use in high-speed printing must show uniformly good ink reception. The short space of time in which the plate and paper are in contact makes it important that the paper accepts the ink from the plate readily.

The methods developed for determining ink receptivity are

also used for the determination of oil absorption. They vary only in that they endeavor to use a very thin coating of oil to determine the surface effect of the oil absorption. H. N. Case [15] developed the K & N testing ink which is used comparatively with a standard sample. Annis [15a] has recommended the use of the brightness test to give a numerical value to this test. Brightness is read on the paper before testing and then on the ink spot after testing. The loss of brightness is calculated as percentage. The spreading of an oil drop with a roller and determining the time for a break in the surface of the oil film as well as the complete absorption of the film have been used as a measure for ink receptivity. Prior and Weymouth,[16, 17] recommend the proof press. The proof press gives a direct relationship between the paper, ink and press and, if properly manipulated, can approach the operating speed of the high-speed printing presses. With a split fountain, comparison can be made of two inks under identical conditions. Two papers can be tested at the same time.

Moisture in Paper. The moisture content of paper is related to the atmospheric conditions under which the paper is stored or used. Today, when many of the larger pressrooms are air-conditioned, it is important to manufacture paper with a controlled moisture content. Paper which does not have a moisture content in equilibrium with that of the pressroom tends to curl, show wavy edges or belly in the middle of the sheet. The term loose edges is used when the sheet is taking up moisture from the atmosphere. This condition usually results in a wavy edge due to the fact that the edges of the paper are longer than the center of the sheet. The opposite is true of a tight edge. The sheet is giving up moisture to the air and the edges become tight and cause the center to belly. Roll paper on taking up moisture becomes longer on the ends. If absorption takes place too rapidly, the ends of the roll may split the outer laps of the roll. The same is true when paper is losing moisture. The end and outer laps tighten and if the change is too rapid, the roll may split clear across its width.

When the roll is placed on the web press, in the case of increased moisture, the edges are longer than the center and are floppy when run on the press. When the paper is losing moisture the center is longer and the edges tight and the sheet may wrinkle or the edges may break.

High moisture in paper retards ink absorption. It is generally understood that water and oil do not mix, and a fiber with high moisture content may resist the penetration of the ink. There are, however, many ingredients in printing ink which act as wetting agents and so help to overcome this effect.

A high moisture content in the paper has been blamed for slow drying of printing ink. It is generally known that in offset printing, high moisture content in the ink due to emulsification of water and ink will prevent drying of the ink. This condition will also give a mottled appearance of the printing due to striations of water and ink.

Preconditioned paper is a common order today. The paper is conditioned or manufactured to contain a known amount of moisture. It is then packed in waterproof paper or containers to prevent this moisture from changing in the package or skid. Preconditioned paper is advantageous when the paper is to be stored and used in air-conditioned plants.

Moisture content can be determined in all papers by oven drying.[18] This is slow and cumbersome. Therefore, the sword

FIGURE 47. *Two-color offset press* (Courtesy of Harris-Seybold Co.)

hygrometer [19] is designed to determine the moisture content of a pile of paper. There is also an electrometric method [20] of determining the moisture content of paper. This method determines the moisture content of a sheet of paper in a few seconds. The instrument has to be standardized, however, for each grade of paper.

Expansion and Contraction. These factors are dependent upon the moisture content of the paper. The paper fibers are hygroscopic and expand and contract with changes of moisture content. There is also an expansion of paper due to mechanical stresses set up during printing. An expansion of this kind is usually permanent while that due to moisture depends upon the atmosphere and is reversible.

It is possible to reduce the expansion and contraction due to moisture by the proper treatment of the fibers in the manufacture of the paper. The addition of certain sizing agents prevents the immediate absorption of moisture by the paper and helps reduce the expansion and contraction.

In ordinary black and white printing, changes in dimensions are not important but in four-color printing, where exact register is required, expansion or contraction is disastrous. Where exact register is required, it is customary to have the grain of the paper run the long way of the sheet to prevent fanning due to mechanical stress across the length of the press cylinder. Paper expands less in the machine direction than it does in the across-machine direction and is, therefore, more resistant to mechanical stretch in that direction.

When four-color work is printed, one color at a time by a single impression press or by a two-color press, expansion or contraction is important in obtaining good register.

There have been a number of instruments built to measure the expansion and contraction of paper under controlled humidity.[21]

The introduction of heat-set inks has increased the effect of contraction of paper in printing. Heat used to dry the inks also dries the sheet and, on presses where cutting and folding are done at the delivery end of the press, it often happens that the two outside ribbons are so narrow that they cannot be trimmed in the cutters.

Grain. The grain of the paper is important in papers which must be folded. In sheet paper, it is customary to run the sheet, when possible, with the grain lengthwise of the cylinder. This prevents mechanical stretch due to the squeeze of the impression. The sheet has more flexibility in the across-machine direction and, therefore, hugs the curve of the cylinder better.

In folding paper, the fold is smoother along the grain than when the fold is across the grain. This permits a thinner edge at the back of a book and permits easier smashing in the bindery.

Having the grain lengthwise of the book also prevents sagging of the pages when the book is standing on the shelf.

In the case of magazines printed from roll paper, the size of the magazine does not permit the fold to lie along the grain and the back of the magazine will be parallel with the across-grain direction of the paper. When the magazine is saddle-stitched, this condition gives a stronger binding and the sheets are less easily torn out.

FIGURE 48. *Seven-color rotogravure press with folder* (Courtesy of C. B. Cottrell & Sons Co.)

Color. Color of the paper has a decided effect on the shade of ink to be used. On dark-colored papers, it is necessary to use an opaque ink to cover the base color of the paper and permit the color of the ink to predominate. If transparent colors are used, the entire shade of the ink may be changed by the color of the base paper.

Two-sided papers are usually at their worst on dark colors. It often becomes necessary to change the shade of the ink in order to produce a uniform printing job on both sides of the sheet. This two-sidedness of the paper may also produce varying ink absorption on the two sides of the sheet, requiring changes in the consistency of the ink. In coated papers the two-sided effect is materially reduced by the addition of the coating.

Acidity and Alkalinity. These factors in both coated and uncoated papers are important in determining the permanence value of the sheet and enter into the printing operations in offset printing. Acidity and alkalinity have their effect on the fountain solutions used in printing by offset and these in turn, may affect the plates and presswork. Acidity is measured by the pH or hydrogen ion range.[22]

Uniformity. The most important quality which the printer requires of a sheet of paper is uniformity. Most of the other factors can be overcome by an adjustment in the ink, but a nonuniform paper will cause trouble every time. The pressman must balance his press conditions against the extremes of the paper and hope for the best.

Ink Coverage. This factor in printing is directly related to many properties of the paper already listed. Cramer [23] lists smoothness, oil absorption, and ink receptivity as the prime factors in paper affecting the ink coverage. It is well known that when it becomes hard to obtain a good, solid print on a paper due to roughness of the paper, the first change is to add more ink. The second is to increase the pressure in order to force the ink into the sheet. In other words, if the sheet is rough, it takes more ink to fill the depressions, but if the ink receptivity is not satisfactory, it may take pressure to force the ink on the paper. The rate of oil absorption will also determine the amount of ink necessary to obtain a given color.

Varnishing. Paper for varnishing must be fairly oil-resistant. The inks used in printing on a sheet which is to be
varnished must not bleed in varnish or alcohol. Varnishing is

FIGURE 49. *Double five-color sheet-feed rotary press with pile
feeder* (Courtesy of C. B. Cottrell & Sons Co.)

done by spot varnish or spirit varnish. Spot varnish is applied
by a regular press operation and usually increases the brilliance
of inks over which it is printed. Varnish placed over ink has
no loss of gloss, but in the open spots the varnish may penetrate
and the surface becomes flat and dull.

Spirit varnishing is usually a second operation performed
after printing. It is applied by roll or spray and then dried by
heat to prevent sticking or piling.

Varnishing is done to protect the printed surface under special use conditions such as wear on cover stock or to resist
moisture.

Laminating of printed work between layers of synthetic
plastics accomplishes the same effect, but is usually more expensive.

Printing Papers

Printing can be applied to almost any surface. It is done on
metal, glass, cloth, ceramics, plastics, and paper. Paper can

be grouped in several classes. In each class, the papers bear a similarity to one another and can be printed under similar conditions.

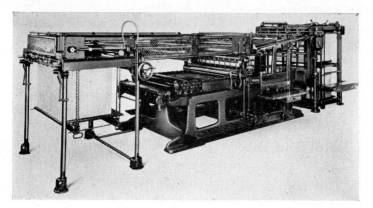

FIGURE 50. *Single-color letterpress* (Courtesy of Miehle Printing Press & Manufacturing Co.)

Absorbent Papers. This class includes rag or wood fibers specially treated to make an absorbent felted sheet which is soft and spongy. The fibers are loosely bound and must be printed with an ink having a soft body and very little tact. The ink usually dries by absorption. Blotting paper is probably the main item of this class on which printing is done.

In many cases blotting paper is faced on one side with a sheet of coated or other printing paper.

Bag and Wrapping. The papers in this class are mostly kraft papers. Bags and wrapping are also made from glassine, Cellophane, tissue, and wood or sulfite manila papers. In most cases, printing can be done by any of the three processes. There are large quantities of wrappings printed by gravure. Cellophane and glassine may be printed by the aniline process and letterpress and offset may also be used.

Board. This group includes binders board, pulp board, container board, chip board and boxboard. Container board and boxboard constitute the bulk of the printed work. Most boards used for printing are of the lined variety. Container board is usually lined with kraft paper. On boxboard, other grades of paper are used as liners. Printing must use inks which correspond to the liner. Printing on containers and boxes is usually done by letterpress. Moisture-set inks are extensively used in carton and container printing.

Paperboard is 0.009 inch or more in thickness. Boxboard and container board must be strong, flexible, and durable to resist wear and handling. The inks used must be soft and fluid, but dry rapidly to a hard finish resistant to scuffing and chaffing. It must also be permanent to fade.

Coated Book Paper. The major quantity of printing papers falls into this class. They may be made from rag or wood, and exhibit antique, machine, supercalendered, dull and glossy coated finish. They are usually not hard finished although supercalendered coated book paper may have a fairly hard finish.

A great variety of inks can be used in printing book papers. Inks generally known as book inks are formulated with a minimum tack and some penetrating qualities, depending upon the stock used and the speed of the press.

Book papers especially formulated for use on the high-speed heat-set presses must be very uniform in formation and ink receptivity. Inks for these presses are very thin and dry mostly by evaporation.

Coated paper is used in large quantities for printing halftone illustrations. The ink is made with enough tack to give a good transfer without squash in the print, but not sufficient tack to lift the surface of the paper. Casein and starch are the adhesives used to bind the coating to the body stock.

Book Jackets. These are made of a heavy paper for the protection of books. Several grades and finishes from a rough cover stock to a high-finished coated cover are used. The last type lends itself very well to four-color printing.

Bread Wrappers. A bleached, waxed sulfite paper is used for wrapping bread. This paper is very often printed with several colors of ink and then waxed. Inks for use on this kind of work must be quick-setting and must not bleed in wax. Moisture-set inks are finding considerable use for printing bread wrappers.

Car Blanks and Railroad Board. These are coated boards used in printing. Car blanks are coated on one side and can be used in four-color printing for car advertising.

Railroad board is coated on two sides and in a variety of brilliant colors. This type of paper is used for labels on freight cars and this application accounts for its name.

The inks used are the same as those used in printing coated paper, but may be letterpress or offset inks.

Chart and Map Papers. Chart papers are heavy rag papers or coated papers. They must be extremely clean and have minimum expansion and contraction. Map paper is similar, but of lighter weight and must be strong and resist folding. Much of the printing of charts and maps is done in several colors. Map paper is usually made with a high wet strength. Since register is paramount, a minimum dimensional change due to moisture is important.

Magazine Paper. This class takes in most of the book grades from antique through coated book depending upon the quality of the printing of the magazine. Pulp magazines use a bulky newsprint. Illustrated magazines may be in black and white or in four colors on supercalendered paper and coated book paper. Many of the illustrated magazines are printed on the high-speed web presses in four-color heat-set inks.

Poster Paper. This paper is available in several grades. It must be sized to permit pasting. Much of the work is done by offset printing. Some high-grade four-color work is done on poster paper.

Cigar Labels. This is a paper coated on one side. It may be printed with halftones and gold ink. The finished work is very brilliant.

Label Paper. A paper sized for labels may be coated or uncoated. It should have a high pick resistance, a hard surface, and withstand varnishing. Labels are printed in many colors and may be varnished after printing.

Cover Paper. This is a grade which varies from a soft, thick, bulky paper through hard sized papers resembling bonds and ledgers to coated papers. Here again many grades of paper are included which require a corresponding variety of inks. Colors vary from light pastel and white to the deep shades.

An ink which is called cover ink usually has a fairly soft body to prevent picking. The pigments used in most cases are of an opaque nature to cover the darker colored papers.

Newsprint Paper. This is a low-grade printing paper made with 70 to 80% of ground wood. It has had little or no beating and the paper is not calendered to too high a finish. It is soft and requires only enough strength to permit it to run smoothly over the presses. Halftones are seldom of a higher screen than 60 lines. The ink dries entirely by absorption.

Some newspapers are being printed by offset.

Rotogravure Paper. This is a bulky paper with an English or supercalendered finish or a coated smooth finished paper. The paper must be smooth in order to accept the gravure ink evenly and must be free from grit and hard particles.

Inks for this process are very thin, short, have very little tack, and dry by penetration and evaporation.

Tag Board or Bristols. This grade of boards is used in making tags. There are a number of varieties of board which fall in this class, such as bristols, bottle cap paper, and tickets on which printing is done.

REFERENCES

1. Brecht and Pfretzschner. "Filler Content and Technological Properties of Paper." *Papierfabr.* **35**—Tech. Teil 73, 80, 85, 92 (1937).
2. TAPPI, Suggested method T479 sm—48. "Printing Smoothness of Paper." *Paper Trade J.,* p. 62, 63, 64 (April 15, 1948).
3. J. Bekk. "What the Printing Process Demands of Paper." An address before the Technical Section of the Papermaker's Association in London, March 13, 1935. Published by the London School of Printing and Kindred Trades.
4. W. Gurley and L. E. Gurley. "Gurley-Hill S.P.S. Tester." *Paper*

Trade J. **106,** No. 14, 31 (1938) Institute of Paper Chemistry. Instrumentation Studies XXXVI. The Gurley-Hill S.P.S. Tester Paper Trade J. 110, No. 23:27–33 (June 6, 1940).

5. Strachan and Hanshaw Ltd. "Ink and Paper Testing Machine." *World's Paper Trade Rev.* **110,** No. 9, 636 (1938).
6. G. L. Larocque. "The Oil-paper Relationship in the Printability of Paper." *Pulp and Paper, Canada.* **38,** No. 2, 77–84 (1937).
7. TAPPI T-460 M-46. "Air Resistance of Paper."
8. TAPPI T-425 M-44. "Opacity of Paper."
9. TAPPI T-459 M-45. "Wax Test for Surface Strength of Paper."
10. F. A. Weymouth. "Some Observations on the Relation of Coated Paper to Ink." *Paper Ind.* **22,** No. 4, 398–400 (1940).
11. TAPPI T-462 M-43. "Printing Ink Permeation of Paper" (Castor-oil Test).
12. B. L. Wehmhoff. "Evaluation of the Printing Quality of Paper." *Paper Trade J.* **100,** No. 6, 41–44 (1935).
13. V. V. Vallandigham. "Forecasting Printability by Oil Absorption Measurements." *Tech. Assn. Papers.* **28,** 523–525; discussion 73–74 (June 1946); Paper Trade J. **123,** No. 17:39–41 (Oct. 24, 1946).
14. R. M. Cobb and Donald V. Lowe. "A Sizing Test and a Sizing Theory." *Paper Trade J.* **98,** No. 12, 43–46 (1934).
15. William A. Kirkpatrick II. "The Use of Waxes and Case Testing Ink in Testing Printing Papers." *Paper Trade J.* **109,** No. 12, 36–38 (1939).
15-A. H. Annis. Tech. Assn. Papers. 1936—P. 46.
16. P. H. Prior. "The Approach to the Problems of the Printing Quality of Paper." *Paper Maker.* International Number 1938.
17. F. A. Weymouth. "Testing Printability of Paper with Ink." *Tech. Assoc. Papers.* **25,** 247–250; discussion 71–72 (June, 1942) Paper Trade J. 114, No. 15:37–40 (April 9, 1942).
18. TAPPI T-412 M-42. "Moisture in Paper and Paperboard."
19. Robert F. Reed. "Modern Paper-conditioning Methods and the Paper Hygroscope." *Lithographic Technical Foundation Tech. Bull. No. 1* (Research Series 9), 1937.
20. D. C. Culver. "Electronic Measurement of Moisture in Paper." *Instrumentation.* **1,** No. 6, 18–20 (1945).
21. TAPPI T-447 M-45. "Moisture Expansivity of Paper."
22. TAPPI T-435 M-42. "Hydrogen Iron Concentration of Paper Extracts."
23. G. Cramer. "Paper Characteristics versus Ink Coverage." *Tech. Assn. Papers.* **25,** 170–172; discussion 72–73 (June 1942) Paper Trade J. 114, No. 12:50–52 (March 19, 1942).

Chapter XIV

FILMS

by W. H. Aiken

S ELF-SUPPORTING plastic films in continuous lengths were produced in this country before the turn of the century but developments in thin films were very slow for the first quarter of this century. The real growth of the thin-film industry as we know it today has taken place in the last two decades and at a tremendous rate. In 1947, the production of film in the United States was approximately 235,000,000 pounds. This production was broken down as follows:

	Pounds
Cellophane	137,500,000 [1]
Cellulose Acetate and Mixed Ester Plastics	
Continuous Sheets under 0.003 inch	7,200,000 [2]
Continuous Sheets over 0.003 inch	7,800,000 [2]
Cellulose Nitrate Sheets	9,000,000 [2]
Vinyl Resin Sheeting and Film Including Safety	
Glass	63,000,000 [2]
Miscellaneous (Estimated)	10,500,000 [2]
	235,000,000

The growth of Cellophane production from its introduction in 1924 to 137,500,000 pounds in 1947 indicates the rapid pace at which the film industry has grown. Even more phenomenal is the growth of the vinyl film industry. In 1939, only about

1,200,000 pounds of vinyl resin were used in this country for *all* uses.[2] Yet only eight years later, *vinyl film alone* used thirty-five times this much vinyl resin.

In the rapid growth of the film industry, numerous items have appeared on the market, such as plastic foil, plastic film, plastic sheet, and plastic sheeting. Before going farther into a discussion of self-supporting film, the terminology to be used should be clarified. For the packaging trade, plastic materials have been classified on a basis of thickness as follows: 0.005 inch and below is called film; above 0.005 inch is called sheet. This classification has been used regardless of whether the material is supplied in roll form or as individual sheets. While this definition is probably satisfactory for packaging materials, distinction appears necessary between materials that are flexible, semirigid, or rigid when used in thicker sections. The Society of the Plastics Industry has appointed a Technical Film Committee to establish nomenclature for film material. This committee has not yet made its recommendations, and no attempt will be made here to give a detailed classification. For the purpose of this discussion, film materials of all ranges of thickness and flexibility will be referred to as film. However, the major part of the discussion will be limited to thin films that are available in continuous lengths.

Materials Used for Films

Numerous materials are used for the production of self-supporting films. All of these materials are polymers of high molecular weight, and, with the exception of Cellophane, all of the films discussed here are made of thermoplastic resins. The composition of materials used for films are classified as cellulose and cellulose derivatives, rubber derivatives, vinyl and substituted vinyl derivatives, and polyamides. In each class, many materials of various compositions and molecular weights are possible and in most cases several are commercially available. For example, cellulose acetate resins are commercially available which contain from 36.5 to 44.5% acetyl; however,

films are usually prepared from resins with an acetyl content
of 39.5 to 41.5%.

Cellulose and Cellulose Derivatives

Regenerated Cellulose. Cellophane is prepared from cellulose xanthate which is soluble in alkalis. The film is cast
from an alkaline solution and then regenerated to cellulose.

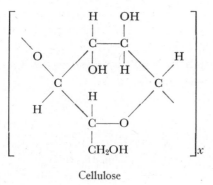

Cellulose

Cellulose Esters. Cellulose acetate, cellulose acetate-butyrate, cellulose nitrate, and cellulose propionate are all esters of
cellulose. They are prepared by the reaction of cellulose in the
form of purified cotton linters or wood pulp with acids or acid
anhydrides and may be represented by the formula:

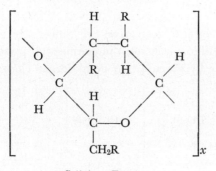

Cellulose Ester

The radical R in this formula is as follows:

Resin	R
Cellulose Acetate	—OOCCH$_3$
Cellulose Acetate—Butyrate	$\begin{cases} \text{—OOCCH}_3 \text{ and} \\ \text{—OOCC}_3\text{H}_8 \end{cases}$
Cellulose Propionate	—OOCC$_2$H$_5$
Cellulose Nitrate	—ONO$_2$

This formula represents an ester in which all three of the hydroxyl groups of the cellulose have been reacted. In the cellulose esters used for preparing films, however, not all the hydroxyl groups are esterified.

Cellulose Ether. Ethyl cellulose is the ethyl ether of cellulose of the following formula:

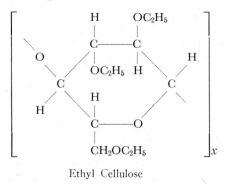

Ethyl Cellulose

Rubber Derivatives

Although several derivatives of rubber are produced, only rubber hydrochloride is used in commercial plastic films. This resin is made by the addition of hydrogen chloride to rubber:

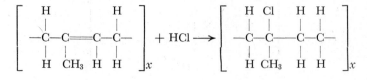

Rubber   Rubber Hydrochloride

Vinyl and Substituted Vinyl Resins

The largest class of materials used for the production of films are the vinyl and substituted vinyl compounds. The basic vinyl reaction is as follows:

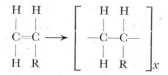

Vinyl Monomer   Vinyl Polymer

Most vinyl resins are prepared by reaction of the monomer to produce the polymer. Exceptions to this are polyvinyl alcohol and polyvinyl butyral, which are prepared from polyvinyl acetate. The substituted vinyl resins are prepared from monomers in which one or more of the hydrogens are replaced by a radical.

Polyvinyl chloride is prepared by polymerizing vinyl chloride. The vinyl chloride copolymers are prepared by polymerizing a large amount of vinyl chloride with small amounts of other monomers, such as vinyl acetate or vinylidene chloride.

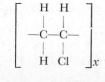

Polyvinyl Chloride

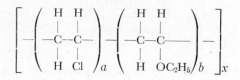

Polyvinyl Chloride—Acetate

Polyvinylidene chloride is prepared by polymerizing vinylidene chloride, which is unsymmetrical dichlorethylene. The commercially available materials of this class are actually copolymers obtained by polymerizing large amounts of vinylidene chloride with small amounts of other materials, such as vinyl chloride.

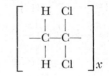

Polyvinylidene Chloride

Polyethylene is prepared by the polymerization of ethylene. It may be considered a vinyl compound in which the R is hydrogen.

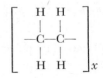

Polyethylene

Polyvinyl alcohol is prepared by hydrolysis of polyvinyl acetate.

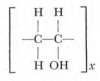

Polyvinyl Alcohol

Polyvinyl butyral is prepared by condensation of polyvinyl alcohol and butyraldehyde.

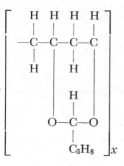

Polyvinyl Butyral

Polystyrene is prepared by the polymerization of styrene, which is a vinyl benzene.

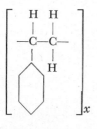

Polystyrene

Polytetrafluoroethylene is prepared from tetrafluorethylene, a substituted vinyl compound in which R is fluorine and in which the three hydrogens are replaced with fluorine.

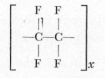

Polytetrafluoroethylene

Polyvinyl carbazol is prepared by the polymerization of vinyl carbazol.

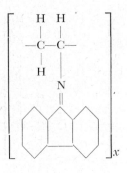

Polyvinyl Carbazol

Polyamides

Polyamide resins are derived from the reaction of aliphatic dibasic acids with diamines. For example, adipic acid and hexamethylenediamine are used to prepare the so-called 6–6 polymer.

$$\left[\begin{array}{c} H \\ | \\ -N-(CH_2)_6-N-C-(CH_2)_4-C- \end{array} \right]_x$$

6–6 Polyamide

Methods of Manufacture

The principal processes for preparing films may be divided into two categories:

1. Those in which the film is formed from a solution or dispersion of the resin by coagulating or drying.

2. Those in which the resin is formed by application of heat and pressure, the thermoplastic nature of the resin causing flow.

Many film-forming materials can be converted into usable film by one of several modifications of these two general processes. The processes in use today for preparing films from any given type resin are used either because they give desired characteristics, such as appearance, physical properties, surface characteristics, or low cost, or because the resin has certain limitations which allow it to be manufactured into a film only by certain methods.

FIGURE 51. *Casting machine used in the production of plastic films* (Courtesy of John Waldron Corp.)

Film from Resin Solutions and Dispersions

Solution Castings. Casting of resin solutions on polished drying surfaces is perhaps the oldest methods used for the commercial preparation of plastic films. The first surface used was plate glass, but continuous films were also produced by casting on large metal wheels, on endless belts, and on coated papers.

Nickel on chrome plated wheels up to 35 feet in diameter are used. The resin solution may be applied to the wheel through a hopper, and the distance between the bottom of the hopper and the wheel constitutes an orifice which gages the amount of solution deposited on the revolving wheel. As the film progresses around the wheel, the temperature is increased and circulating air is used to aid in the removal of the solvent. Shortly before the wheel completes its revolution to the casting hopper, the dried or partially dried film is stripped from the wheel.

The casting belt is essentially an endless belt supported by two drums. The belt may be a highly polished metal surface such as stainless steel, or, it may be composed of a material such as fabric or rubber which has been given a smooth coating of some material which is not affected by the solvent to be used, and from which the film may be readily stripped. The solution is cast on the belt above one of the drums in a manner similar to that used in wheel casting. The film is dried by heating elements placed in the drying tunnel and by the circulation of hot air around the belt. The film remains on the belt until it has almost completed its revolution back to the head drum where it is stripped off. The stripped film may be returned through the length of the machine for further drying.

Paper to be used as the surface for film casting is first coated with a thermosetting resin which is then cured. The solution of film-forming resin is applied to the coated paper and allowed to dry in contact with it. The film leaves the oven free of solvent, and is rolled up together with the backing paper. Later the film is separated from the paper and the paper used again.

For economical operation, casting machines are provided with solvent-recovery equipment. Semirigid film, such as cellulose acetate, may be stripped from the casting surface while the film still contains a considerable amount of solvent, and further drying accomplished either in a tunnel or in a festoon dryer. However, elastomeric films, such as are prepared from plasticized vinyl chloride resins, must have most of the solvent removed from the film before stripping, or they will be too soft to handle.

Cellulose acetate, cellulose acetate-butyrate, cellulose propionate, cellulose nitrate, ethyl cellulose, rubber hydrochloride, nylon, polyethylene, polyvinyl alcohol, vinyl chloride copolymers, and polystyrene films can all be prepared by solution casting.

Dispersion Castings. In recent years, a technique has been developed for preparing dispersions of vinyl chloride copolymer resins of high vinyl chloride content and high molecular weight. These resins give the most durable film, but because they are

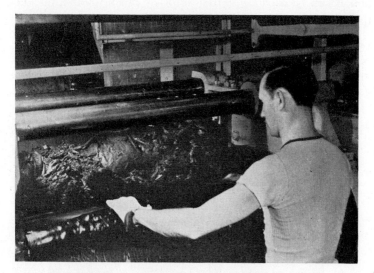

FIGURE 52. *Milling compounded plastic resin prior to calendering* (Courtesy of Bakelite Corp.)

of limited solubility, they have not usually been converted into film by casting. The recently developed dispersions (called organosols) are prepared by dispersing finely divided resin powder in plasticizers. The plasticizer solvates or swells the surface of the resin particle sufficiently to disperse it in the plasticizer, but solution of the particle does not take place. In order to increase the mobility of the dispersion, the plasticizer is usually diluted with a volatile organic liquid such as a liquid hydrocarbon, which is not a solvent for the vinyl resin. Such dispersion usually contains 60 to 70% resin and plasticizer and 30 to 40% volatile thinner.

Films are laid down from organosol by the conventional methods used in casting solutions. After the volatile thinner has been removed from the film, it must then be heated at elevated temperatures for a short time, e.g., at 350° F. for 1 minute, to fuse the resin and plasticizer into a continuous film. Organosol casting is more economical than solution casting, and it can be used to prepare films of much greater thickness than can economically be prepared by solution casting.

FIGURE 53. *Rear view of film calender* (Courtesy of Bakelite Corp.)

Extrusion of a Solution into a Nonsolvent Liquid. Films may be prepared by extruding a solution of plastic material into a liquid which is miscible with the solvent, but which is a nonsolvent for the resin. For example, vinyl film can be prepared by extrusion of a solution of the resin in methyl ethyl ketone into water. In order to obtain a clear, transparent vinyl film by this process, all of the solvent should not be removed from the resin by the precipitating liquid, but a certain portion of the solvent should be removed by subsequent drying. The general principles of this process may also be adapted to the preparation of films of cellulose derivatives, which may later be regenerated into cellulose.

Extrusion into Acid Coagulating Bath. Regenerated cellulose (Cellophane) is not a plastic material, but it is produced in the largest volume of all thin transparent films in the United States today. Unlike the plastic films which undergo no chemical change in their preparation, regenerated cellulose is manufactured by converting the derivative back to cellulose after it has been formed into a film. Either purified wood pulp or cotton linters are treated with concentrated alkali and carbon disulfide to convert it to cellulose xanthate. The alkali solution of cellulose xanthate, or viscose, is forced into an acid coagulating bath through an orifice, and is either pulled forward under its own strength or is carried on a support. Depending on the salt concentration in the coagulating bath, the cellulose xanthate may be precipitated and then regenerated in a separate bath, or both precipitation and regeneration may be carried out simultaneously. Following regeneration, the cellulose film is freed of sulfur in a hot caustic bath, is bleached, and finally passed through a bath that adds glycerin or some other hygroscopic agent to the film to serve as a plasticizer.

Both flat sheets and special-purpose tubes are made by this process. Special devices for escape of the gases formed have been perfected for use in regeneration of seamless tubes without rupture or weakening of the film.

Film Production by Application of Heat and Pressure

Calendering. In recent years, large quantities of nonrigid vinyl film have been prepared by calendering. In this process, the resin, plasticizers, resin stabilizer, color, and calender lubricant are either kneaded in a mixer or mixed in a Banbury and then transferred to a heated two-roll mill for further mixing. The hot mass is carried to the top of the calender stack, which consists of three or four rolls. The thickness of the film is controlled by the distance of the nip between the calender rolls. The rolls may be finished to give a smooth film, or may be etched to give a mat surface. Films stripped from the calender may be cooled in air, on cooling rolls, or by submerging in a cooling liquid. If desired, the films may be oriented by the tension put

FIGURE 54. *Front view of calender producing unplasticized vinyl film* (Courtesy of Bakelite Corp.)

on the hot film as it is pulled from the calenders. For preparing good film from resins of high vinyl chloride content, a calender roll temperature of about 320°F. is necessary, but resins of lower vinyl chloride content and of a lower molecular weight can be successfully calendered also at lower temperatures.

Plasticized polyvinyl chloride, plasticized and unplasticized vinyl chloride copolymers, polyvinyl butyral and polyethylene can be converted into film by calendering. It is not practical to prepare calendered film thinner than 0.003 inch.

Heat Extrusion. In recent years, there has been increased production of thermoplastic film by heat extrusion. Films have been prepared by this method from polyvinyl chloride, vinyl chloride copolymers, polyvinylidene chloride, polystyrene, polyethylene, cellulose acetate and cellulose acetate-butyrate. In this process, strips of resin, granular or compounded resin, are carried forward by a screw to heated areas where the resin is softened and forced out through a circular or slit die. Depending upon the resin being used, the hot film may or may not be oriented in one or two directions. The film is cooled either by contact with air or by submersion in a cooling liquid. For the extrusion of polyvinyl chloride copolymers and polyvinylidene chloride, the extruder must be made from corrosion-resistant metals. Films in a wide range of thickness can be made by extrusion.

Wet Extrusion. This process, which has made possible the production of cellulose nitrate sheets in continuous lengths, is similar to heat extrusion with the exception that a small amount of volatile solvent is present in the extrusion mass to facilitate extrusion at temperatures that are safe for the cellulose nitrate. The resin is put in a large mixer with suitable plasticizer and volatile solvent and worked into a gel-like colloidol mass. The mass is then worked on heated rolls where dye and color pigments may be added and the solvent is allowed to evaporate until the correct consistency is reached. The material may then be formed into a cylinder known as a "jelly roll" or it may be cut into strips which are then cut into chips. In one type of extruder, the jelly roll is forced into the front of the cylinder, the die clamped on, and steam applied to the nozzle. When the stock has been softened, a hydraulic ram forces the material through the die. This process is somewhat slow and costly on account of the time consumed in cooling the die, opening the cylinder, and then reheating the die after the head has been closed. More economical is a continuous screw-type extruder into which chips are fed. The sheets from either type extrusion are hung in heated rooms to allow evaporation of the solvent.

Block Skiving. For this process, the stock is prepared in a manner similar to that used in wet extrusion. Then it is removed from the heated roll and stacked into a slab, which is pressed in a heated press into a block 6 inches thick and approximately 22 inches by 52 inches large. The block is then cut into sheets 0.005 inches thick and up, and the sheets seasoned at elevated temperatures to remove residual solvent. Seasoning may be from a few days to several months. The sheets are then surface-finished by pressing between heated platens. This process is used on cellulose nitrate and cellulose acetate.

Roll Skiving. Because of its chemical inertness and heat resistance, polytetrafluoroethylene does not lend itself to fabrication into films by the conventional processes. Film has been made from this resin by preparing a molded cylinder from powder by application of heat and pressure, and then skiving a film from this cylinder in a manner similar to that used in plywood manufacture.

Properties of Films

The various films will be discussed from the standpoint of their inherent properties and the uses for which they are best suited. No attempt is made to give numerical comparisons of physical properties for a number of reasons. In the first place, test procedures are not sufficiently standardized to obtain data on all films on the same basis. In the second place, there is insufficient background to correctly evaluate the test results in terms of end use. For example, a film to be used for packaging must possess a certain amount of inherent toughness which can probably be best evaluated by an impact strength measurement. The toughness required of a film for many fabrication applications is of a different order from that required for packaging, and it can probably best be evaluated by a number of tests including impact strength, tearing resistance, elongation, and recovery from stretching.

The approximate yields of several commercial films for various thicknesses are given in Table XI.

Cellophane. Regenerated cellulose film, usually called Cellophane, was first manufactured in this country in 1924, and today accounts for about 55% of the total film production in this country.

Table XI

Approximate Yield in Square Inches per Pound of Various Commercial Films

APPROXIMATE SQUARE INCHES PER POUND

Thickness in Inches	Plain Cellophane	Waterproof Cellophane	Cellulose Acetate	Ethyl Cellulose	Pliofilm	Saran	Polyethylene	Vinyl Chloride Copolymer
0.00020					100,000			
0.00040					55,000			
0.00075					30,000			
0.00080	23,400							
0.00088			25,000					
0.00090		21,000						
0.00100	16,600		22,000	23,800	24,000			
0.00120			18,300		20,000			
0.00125						11,800		
0.00130		15,300						
0.00140			14,600					
0.00150				15,800	17,000			
0.00160	12,400						20,100	
0.00170		11,600			14,000			
0.00200			11,000	11,900			15,200	11,000
0.00225					10,750	7,000		
0.00250					9,500			
0.00300				4,700			10,100	7,300

Regenerated cellulose film without addition of plasticizer is a rattly, brittle material that would be of little commercial interest. Flexibility is obtained by the addition of suitable plasticizers, the most efficient of which is water. Water would, of course, be lost rapidly from the film, but the same end result is accomplished by the use of hygroscopic materials, such as glycerin and glycols, which not only take up water from the atmosphere but have some plasticizing action in themselves. A commercial Cellophane film, then, consists of regenerated cellulose containing perhaps 15 to 20 parts of glycerin to 100 parts of cellulose and a varying amount of water, depending upon the relative humidity with which it is in contact.

Cellophane has excellent transparency and is inherently greaseproof. The uncoated sheet has certain limitations due to the hygroscopic nature of the cellulose and its plasticizer. Chief among these is the lack of water-vapor resistance and the fact that water in contact with the film tends to leach out the plasticizer. The dimensions of the sheet also vary considerably with changes in relative humidity of the surrounding atmosphere. The strength characteristics of the film vary with its moisture content, which, in turn, depends on the relative humidity of the air in contact with the film. The durability of the film depends on a combination of many factors, but its elongation is very important. Therefore, a Cellophane film will lose tensile strength as its water content is increased because its elongation is increased. A Cellophane film that has been conditioned at a high relative humidity is very durable and will stand much abuse, even at low temperatures, while an oven-dried Cellophane film may be brittle at room temperature.

Many variations have been made in the basic uncoated Cellophane sheet to increase its utility. These include additions to make it colored, opaque, fire-resistant, and resistant to the passage of ultraviolet light, for retarding development of rancidity in some products. The most important variation was the introduction of water-vapor resistant coatings in 1927. These coatings, which consist essentially of nitrocellulose, a plasticizer such as dibutyl phthalate, a resin such as ester gum, and a wax such as paraffin, are applied from solvent solution to the film. These coatings are approximately 0.00006 inch thick and add about 10% to the weight of the base sheet. For sheets that are to come in contact with water, an intermediate coating or "anchor coat" may be applied between the Cellophane sheet and the nitrocellulose coating. The water-vapor resistant coating reduces the normal water vapor transmittance of the uncoated base sheet several hundredfold. It also reduces the tendency of the plasticizers to leach from the sheets and minimizes fluctuation in water content (and with it strength and dimensional changes) with variations in relative humidity. The coating may also be compounded so that it will heat-seal to itself.

Cellophane is designated by letters which denote the properties of the finished sheet. The system used by one manufacturer is as follows:

A—Anchored (Water-repellent)
C—Colored
D—Moistureproof coating, one side only
H—Partially resistant to blocking in humid atmosphere
J—Flame-resistant
L—Less moistureproof than standard
M—Moistureproof
O—Opaque
P—Plain (Non-moistureproof)
R—Rancidity-retardant
S—Heat-sealing
T—Transparent (Uncolored)
U—Low surface slippage

Thus, the designation MSAT means that the sheet is transparent and has a water-vapor-resistant coating which is heat-sealing and can be used in contact with water.

The thickness of most unsupported films is expressed in mils, which is equivalent to thousandths of an inch; or gage, which is equivalent to ten thousandths of an inch. The gage of

Cellophane is not defined as a measure of thickness, but was originally a measure of weight. The gage of Cellophane originally designated the weight in milligrams of a square meter of uncoated film. Variations in plasticizer compositions and concentration and in the composition of coatings cause deviation in the weight of the finished film even though its cellulose content remains constant. Therefore, it is possible that several sheets with the same gage designation may vary considerably in weight and thickness.

The thickness and yield for plain and moisture-proof Cellophane of one manufacturer are given below for the three common gages:

Plain Cellophane	Approx. sq. in. per pound	Approx. Thickness in inches
#300	23,400	0.0008
#450	16,600	0.0012
#600	12,400	0.0016
Waterproof Cellophane		
#300	21,000	0.0009
#450	15,300	0.0013
#600	11,600	0.0017

Cellophane is the lowest in price for a given area of all the transparent films. It is used in a wide variety of applications, chiefly for packaging. It is used to wrap such greasy products as fats, oils, bacon, sausage, and other meats. Animal casings for sausages, wieners, and lunch meats have largely been replaced by Cellophane tubing. It is used in packaging frozen foods and in wrapping bread, macaroni, noodles, and other paste products. Cellophane is used extensively in the packaging of tobacco products such as cigarettes, cigars, plug, and cut tobacco. It is used to package candies, cut flowers, and as hoods for milk bottles. Cellophane is finding use in the packaging of fresh vegetables, either as bags, as wraps, or as overwraps for cardboard trays.

Cellophane has also been used as flame-resistant winding on wire and electrical cables and for separator and circuit identification purposes in cable fabrication. It has been used as ribbon, as cord, and in the millinery trade. Cellophane has been used extensively as the base for preparing pressure-sensitive tape. Colorless, as well as colored, sheets are used for general wrapping purposes. During the war, large quantities of gas-resistant capes made from a special grade of lusterless, opaque, colored, fireproof, or gasproof Cellophane were procured for the Armed Forces.

Cellulose Acetate. Cellulose acetate is the cellulose plastic most widely used in films. Cellulose acetate flake of high viscosity and high acetyl content is used in order to obtain best durability. For general-purpose film 10 to 15% phthalate plasticizer is used and triphenyl phosphate plasticizer is used where fire-resistant film is desired. Thin cellulose acetate film is produced in continuous lengths by casting from solvent solution on a moving, polished surface. Continuous lengths of thicker film may be produced by laminating cast film or by heat extrusion. Standard sheets 20 x 50 inches in thicknesses of 0.005 inch and up are produced by skiving from pressed blocks.

The cellulose acetate film is characterized by good transparency, clarity, and brilliance. It is moderately resistant to outdoor aging, but is much more resistant to aging than is usually required for the purposes for which it is used. The elongation of cellulose acetate film is usually 25 to 40% and the tensile strength varies from 4,000 psi for thick skived sheets to three or four times this value for cast films. A cellulose acetate film transmits large quantities of water vapor rapidly, although special water-vapor-resistant grades have been produced by application of proper coatings. The water absorption of the sheet is increased at high relative humidities, but the dimensions of the sheet change only 1 to 2% in going from 30 to 100% relative humidity. Fabrication of cellulose acetate film has long been limited because it could not be heat-sealed, but had to be fabricated with adhesives. Recently, heat-sealing machines have been built which will heat-seal cellulose acetate film, and this development promises to expand its uses.

Cellulose acetate film is used to a considerable degree in packaging. Its properties of greaseproofness and waterproofness combined with its good dimensional stability and excellent clarity make it durable for certain specialized application. One large use is in transparent windows in bags and boxes and as a tight wrap over rigid boxes, where its good dimensional stability insures that it will not be ruptured or delaminated owing to humidity changes. In recent years, it has found increasing use as a laminate for aluminum foil for water-vapor-resistant packaging of such items as beverage powders and dehydrated soups. Excellent multicolor printing is done in reverse on cellulose acetate film, and the printed sheet then laminated to a backing, such as paper or fiber board. Washable wallpaper has been made by laminating a thin sheet of cellulose acetate film over the printed wallpaper.

Cellulose acetate film is used as the base for producing pressure-sensitive tape of good dimensional stability. It has recently received increased recognition as an electrical insulation material. The development of a mat finish applied on continuous rolls of film has helped to eliminate static and the necessity for a lubricant to increase the use of the material for insulation. A few years ago, large quantities of cellulose acetate film were used as the inner layer material for safety glass, but it has been largely replaced for this use by polyvinyl butyral. Some photographic film for home and hospital use is made from cellulose acetate and law requires that amateur and educational movie film is made from a material of the slow-burning characteristics of cellulose acetate.

Thin cellulose acetate films have found considerable use as a tight wrap and in bags for prepackaged vegetables. Cellulose acetate sheets are used for a variety of applications, including boxes, instruments, drawn and blown objects, etc.

Cellulose Acetate-Butyrate. Cellulose acetate-butyrate film is produced in limited quantities by heat-extrusion and by casting from solution. This film has a tensile strength roughly the same as that of cellulose acetate and an elongation of 40 to 60%. Its impact strength is better than that of cellulose acetate both at room and at subzero temperatures. It has less than half the water absorption of cellulose acetate and its dimensional stability is excellent. Its chief uses are for electrical insulation and for lamination to paper and foil.

Cellulose Nitrate. Cellulose nitrate was probably the first plastic film used commercially. It has long been used for photographic film and was used extensively as windows in car curtains. It was the first material used as an interlayer for safety glass; however, because of several defects, the most important of which was poor aging, it is no longer used for this purpose.

Cellulose nitrate of medium viscosity and 8 to 10% nitrogen content is used for film preparation. Many plasticizers have been proposed for nitrocellulose, but camphor is the best all-round plasticizer. Continuous film is prepared by casting from solution, and thick sheets are prepared by wet extrusion and by skiving from blocks. A cellulose nitrate film has an elongation of 25 to 35%, a tensile strength from 4,000 psi for very thick sheets to 13–16,000 psi for cast film, good impact strength, low water absorption and good dimensional stability.

Although there are a multitude of uses for thick rigid sheets of cellulose nitrate, the high flammability of this material prevents its use in thinner sections for general purposes, such as packaging. Because of the inherent toughness of cellulose nitrate film, it is used in large volumes for commercial movie film.

Cellulose Propionate. Commercial films have not yet been made from cellulose propionate, but preliminary studies indicate that film and sheet made from this material should have advantages in flatness, dimensional stability, and toughness.

When a curve is plotted relating the impact strength of cellulose propionate to flexural strength, it is found that the curve is unusual for cellulose plastics in that the impact strength rises rapidly to give high values in the region of flexural strength which is still very desirable. The material has good dimensional stability, giving an increase in length of 0.4% in going from 0 to 90% relative humidity.

Ethyl Cellulose. Ethyl cellulose film is prepared by casting a solution of ethyl cellulose of medium viscosity and medium ethoxy content. Ethyl cellulose is an ether and requires less plasticizer than the cellulose esters; 10 to 15% of one of a number of esters may be used as plasticizers. Ethyl cellulose gives a clear, transparent film of good toughness. It has a tensile strength of 8 to 10,000 psi and an elongation of 25 to 30%.

The ethyl cellulose film is characterized by resistance to discoloration on exposure to sunlight, and it is unaffected by edible fats and oils. The film shows low water absorption, but is not inherently water-vaporproof. An ethyl cellulose film does not heat-seal. Most of the uses which have been found for ethyl cellulose film are of thicker sections.

Rubber Hydrochloride. Rubber hydrochloride, which is prepared by the reaction of pale crepe natural rubber and hydrogen chloride, is made into a film by casting from solutions on a moving belt. It is supplied both in "normal" grades which are recommended for those packaging applications in which high water vapor protection is a prime requisite, and in "plasticized" grades for specific applications. Both grades are available in thickness from 0.00075 to 0.0025 inch.

Rubber hydrochloride was the first plastic film used in the general fabricating trade, and much of the art of fabricating items of plastic film was learned on this material. It can be fabricated by stapling or sewing and is easily heat-sealed at 110 to 120° C. During and following the war, owing to the rubber shortage, rubber hydrochloride film was replaced in the fabricating field by vinyl films which offer greater toughness and sunlight stability for many applications. Rubber film can be stretched to give very thin "tensilized" films of very great area per pound. This film is used for a number of specialized applications, such as decorative wraps and ribbons.

Rubber hydrochloride film was the first water-vapor-resistant plastic film used for packaging, and has continued to be the outstanding plastic film for this application. It is offered in a range of flexibility from material of no plasticizer content, which has very high resistance to the passage of water vapor, to highly plasticized film, which is desirable for frozen-food packaging. The water-vapor-transfer rates of the various grades at 100° F. with 5% relative humidity on one side of the film and 95% relative humidity on the other side are given in Table XII.

TABLE XII

The Water-vapor Transmission Rates of Various Grades
of Pliofilm

Grade of Pliofilm	Gage	WVTR, g./100 sq. in./24 hr.
NO	100	0.55
NO	140	0.40
NO	170	0.35
N1	100	0.70
N1	140	0.50
N1	170	0.45
N2	100	1.18
N2	140	0.70
N2	170	0.60
P4	120	1.35
P4	140	0.90
P6	140	1.40
FF	75	4.27
FF	120	3.04
FF	140	2.20

A rubber hydrochloride film offers a combination of water-vapor resistance, transparency, dimensional stability, toughness, heat-stability, and machine-handling characteristics not found in other films. Its aging characteristics have been found adequate for packaging applications. The tensile strength values vary from 4300 psi to 5100 psi and elongation from 400 to 800, depending on the type of film.

Rubber hydrochloride film is resistant to dilute acids and alkalis. It is oil- and greaseproof and nonflammable. It shows very low water absorption and excellent dimensional stability over the entire humidity range. Rubber hydrochloride film is, therefore, useful for windows in bags and boxes and for over-wraps for boxes.

Rubber hydrochloride films are used to package both dry products to protect them from moisture pickup and to package moist products to prevent their drying out. Products containing liquids, such as pickles in brine and fruits in syrups, have been successfully packaged in rubber hydrochloride film. The material can be stretched after heating to permit stretch wrapping of such irregular objects as fruits and vegetables. The highly plasticized grade of film is used extensively in the packaging of frozen foods.

Because of its unusual characteristics of high resistance to oxygen transmission but low resistance to the passage of carbon dioxide, rubber hydrochloride film makes a useful package for coffee. It is combined with Cellophane, paper, and metal foil for a variety of packaging applications.

Polyvinyl Chloride and Vinyl Chloride Copolymers. There has been greatly increased production in recent years of flexible films from vinyl chloride type resins. For the production of the best quality film, polymers of high vinyl chloride content and high molecular weight are used. However, tough sheets have been prepared from resins of medium vinyl chloride content and medium molecular weight. The composition of vinyl chloride type film can be varied, depending on the properties desired. The lower the vinyl chloride content of the resin, the less plasticizer is required to obtain a given flexibility. Usually a flexible film made from vinyl chloride type resin contains 20 to 35% plasticizer. Dioctyl phthalate is perhaps the best all-round plasticizer for use in vinyl chloride type films, but many other ester-type plasticizers, as well as Buna N rubber and petroleum derivatives, have been successfully used.

Before the war, vinyl chloride film was produced principally by calendering. This process is still in use for the manufacture of the major amount of this type of film, but much film is also produced by casting from solution or organosol on a continuous, moving surface, by extrusion of solvent solution into a precipitating liquid, and by heat extrusion. Calendered film is available in thicknesses of 0.003 to 0.040 inch, while cast film is usually less than 0.003 inch thick. The most desirable flexible film from the standpoint of "hand," "drape," and freedom from blocking or tackiness is made on calender rolls which have been etched to give a film with a rough surface. Highly plasticized film with smooth surfaces has the tendency to cling to itself. This can be overcome by incorporation of suitable antiblock agents in the formulation.

The properties of vinyl chloride films depend a great deal on composition and properties of the resin, plasticizer, and resin stabilizer used. In general, flexible vinyl chloride films are tough and durable and retain their properties at subzero temperatures. For the same composition, calendered and cast films give about the same tensile strength and elongation, but cast films offer higher tearing strength. Typical strength values are 3000 to 4000 psi tensile and 225 to 300% elongation. Vinyl chloride film is waterproof and has low water absorption, but the resistance to water-vapor transfer is mediocre. The material is inherently resistant to chemical attack. Vinyl chloride films can be prepared that are unaffected by oils, greases and fats and which have no effect on these products when packaged in the film. The film can be made transparent, translucent or opaque, in pastel shades or brilliant hues. It can easily be fabricated by heat-sealing.

Thin vinyl chloride film has been used very extensively in the fabrication trade for the production of such items as shower curtains, garment bags, raincoats, bowl covers, umbrellas, waterproof cases and covers, aprons, curtains, tobacco pouches, and industrial tapes. It is the most widely used flexible plastic film for such purposes. A special grade of vinyl chloride film plasticized with Buna N rubber is used for the packaging of oleomargarine.

Thicker vinyl film, either press-polished to make it smooth or embossed to give it a design, has been used for handbags, shoe uppers, wallets, luggage, and furniture upholstery.

Polyvinylidene Chloride. Polyvinylidene chloride film, which has been offered commercially in recent years, has the greatest resistance to the passage of water vapor of all the commercial plastic films. Because of its limited solubility, rather short softening range, and limited stability at elevated temperatures, the resin has not been fabricated into a film by either casting or calendering. It is made by nearly simultaneously heating the resin and forcing it at high pressure through a circular orifice. The tube is then cooled, oriented, and slit into a flat sheet. Polyvinylidene chloride is presently available in thickness of 0.00125 and 0.0025 inch.

Polyvinylidene chloride film is resistant to dilute acids, to alkalis, and to oils, fats, and waxes. It is resistant to most solvents. Its water absorption after 1 week is less than 0.01% and its dimensions are not affected by changes in relative humidity. Its tensile strength is 7,000 to 11,000 psi and its elongation is 20 to 40%. The film is nonflammable.

When exposed to temperatures above 90° F., the polyvinylidene chloride film shrinks due to release of stress present in the material as a result of its orientation. This shrinkage amounts to over 20% above 250° F. Because of this shrinkage, the polyvinylidene chloride film cannot be heat-sealed on conventional packaging equipment and this has limited its use somewhat. However, special techniques have been developed for heat-sealing this film at 285° to 305° F.

Polyvinylidene chloride film has been used for packaging metal parts and assemblies, for packaging some food products, such as cheese, and as bottle-cap liners.

Polyethylene. Production of polyethylene resin was started in this country during the war for use as an extruded sheath for insulation of electrical wiring. When sufficient quantities became available for other uses, films were among the first items produced. Polyethylene can be calendered, heat-extruded, skived from pressed block, and cast from solutions on a continuous moving surface. Commercial film which has been made to date has all been prepared by heat extrusion. It is available in thicknesses of 0.0015 to 0.015 inch. Since the specific gravity of polyethylene is 0.92, it gives more area of a given thickness per pound than is obtained with any of the other films.

Polyethylene film has a tensile strength of about 2000 psi and an elongation of 200 to 300%. The first 100% of the elongation is reversible, but above this amount cold drawing takes place. Polyethylene has the best toughness at low temperatures of all the commercial plastic films. Although the film stiffens considerably upon decrease in temperature, its rate of stiffening is not nearly so great as that of many other plastic materials. It does not become brittle until temperatures below —50° F. have been reached. It has been noted on many commercial polyethylene films that tear resistance actually increases with decrease in temperature, at least to 0° F. This may account in part for the good toughness of polyethylene at low temperatures, because most plastic films show decrease in tearing strength with decrease in temperature.

Polyethylene film has very low water absorption and its dimensions and electrical properties are practically unaffected by changes in relative humidity. The dielectric and power factors remain constant over a wide range of frequencies and the dielectric constant changes little over a wide temperature range. Polyethylene film shows good resistance to the passage of water vapor, but its resistance to the passage of most gases is mediocre. Polyethylene film is odorless, tasteless, and contains no plasticizer to be lost. Prolonged exposure to heat and ultraviolet light does not discolor the film, but may impair its chemical and physical properties. However, polyethylene film is one of the most resistant to outdoor aging.

Polyethylene film softens in the range of 228° to 234° F. and can be heat-sealed at 250° F. to make a joint of good strength. However, because of its somewhat sharp softening point, polyethylene film is more difficult to seal than some of the other plastic films. This, together with the fact that the gage of polyethylene film available today is somewhat variable, has caused difficulties in heat-sealing the film on conventional equipment.

Considerable quantities of polyethylene film have been produced for the fabrication trade for such uses as tablecloth covers, food bags, bowl covers, shower curtains, etc. It is also used in increasing quantities for packaging, especially for frozen foods. See Figure 55.

FIGURE 55. *Typical examples of polyethylene film used in form of a tube and a package liner for food packaging* (Courtesy of Plax Corporation)

Polyvinyl Alcohol. Polyvinyl alcohol film has been produced on a limited scale in this country for a number of years. The film is exceptionally clear and brilliant and has excellent chemical resistance. It is very resistant to oils, greases, and organic solvents and is very resistant to the passage of oxygen. Its uses are confined to applications where it will not come in contact with water, as the film is water-soluble. Although it is possible to reduce its water sensitivity by a number of different treatments, these treatments do not change the water solubility of the plasticizers used, e.g., glycerin, which can still be leached from the treated film and cause stiffness.

The strength of polyvinyl alcohol film depends a great deal on the relative humidity of the surrounding atmosphere. At high relative humidities, the film is exceedingly tough; however, with decreasing relative humidity the film loses water and gains in tensile strength, but loses in elongation, flexibility, tearing strength and toughness. Typical strength values for the film after conditioning at 65% RH and 70°F. are 4,000 psi tensile strength and 270% elongation. Polyvinyl alcohol film is used extensively for gloves, aprons, and capes to give protection against solvents and greases. The film can be fabricated by heat-sealing after first moistening the film with water.

Polyvinyl Butyral. Polyvinyl butyral film in thicknesses of 0.015 to 0.030 inch is used extensively as the interlayer for safety glass. This film has largely replaced other materials for this purpose because of its clarity, excellent adhesion to glass, toughness over a wide range of temperatures, and because it does not discolor upon prolonged exposure to sunlight. Polyvinyl butyral film for use in safety glass contains about 40 parts of plasticizer to 100 parts of resin. It is made by calendering or by extrusion through a slit orifice. In both methods of preparation, the film is immediately chilled to hold its shape.

Calendered polyvinyl butyral film in thicknesses of 0.010 to 0.030 inch has been used for artificial leather. Formulations for this purpose usually contain 30 to 50 parts of plasticizer and 50 parts of pigment. Clear stocks are not used because they are too soft and tacky. The tensile strength of the film is 1800 to 3200 psi. The pigmented film can be embossed to give a hard, dry surface. It has excellent abrasion resistance and a leathery feel that makes it valuable as a leather substitute.

Although thinner films of polyvinyl butyral have been used for crib sheets, baby pants, etc., its relatively poor tear strength limits its use for these purposes.

Polystyrene. Polystyrene film is prepared both by casting on a continuous moving surface from a solution of aromatic hydrocarbons and by hot extrusion. Polystyrene film prepared by either method is very brittle, but this property can be improved by stretching the heated film in one or two directions. Upon heating, polystyrene remains relatively hard up to the transition point, then passes to a rubbery state having a strong elastic memory, and then becomes a viscous fluid. Stretching the film while it is in the rubbery state increases the tensile strength parallelly to the direction of flow and reduces it perpendicularly to the direction of the flow. Heat-extruded film is available in thicknesses of 0.003 to 0.25 inch and cast films in thicknesses of 0.0006 to 0.003 inch. Even the stretched film is somewhat brittle as no effective plasticizer has been found for polystyrene. When flexed, the film gives a metallic sound. It has extremely low water absorption, but only mediocre resistance to water-vapor transmission. Polystyrene film is resistant to acids, alkalis, and alcohols. The tensile strength of the stretched film is 5500 to 7000 psi and the elongation 7 to 50%.

Polystyrene film has outstanding electrical insulation properties and it is widely used in electrical condensers. It has also been used as a cable wrapping material.

Polytetrafluoroethylene. Polytetrafluoroethylene film is exceedingly resistant to a wide variety of chemical agents and to extremes of heat and cold. Tests indicate that the material withstands the attack of all materials except molten alkali metals. Its brittle temperature is less than —100°F. and it is useful up to 480°F.

This film, which is skived from a cylinder, has a tensile strength of 2000 to 4500 psi and an elongation of 300 to 400%. Polytetrafluoroethylene is available only in experimental quantities, but it has been found to be valuable as a covering for heat-sealing irons to prevent their sticking to plastic films, coated papers and coated Cellophane.

Polyvinyl Carbazol. Polyvinyl carbazol film has been manufactured in this country on an experimental scale. The film is rather brittle, but it has outstanding electrical insulation characteristics. In Germany, a solution of the resin in tetrohydrofuran was cast to give thin films that were used as a substitute for mica in condenser dielectrics.

Polyamides. Polyamide films have not been produced extensively in this country, although there has been limited production of solvent-cast films. In Germany, extensive work has been done on polyamide films. Cast film made from a copolymer of regular 6–6 polyamide and poly-epsilon-amino caprolactam, using isododecylphenol as plasticizer, was used extensively by the German army as mustard gas protective sheets. This film has a tensile strength of 2,000 to 3,000 psi and an elongation of 230 to 260%. Artificial leather was made by calendering the same resin plasticized with sulfonamide plasticizers. Poly-epsilon-amino caprolactam film, prepared by heat extrusion and then stretched, exhibited tensile strengths up to 28,000 psi in the direction of stretching.

Polyamide film is resistant to fats, oils, most solvents, and a variety of chemicals. At high relative humidity, the film is exceedingly tough, but as it is water-sensitive its toughness decreases at low relative humidities. Polyamide film is easily heat-sealed.

Use of Films in Laminated Structures

Films are often laminated to themselves or to other materials, such as paper and metal foil. The reasons for preparing such laminations are numerous, but include the following:

1. To improve resistance to passage of water vapor
2. To give a structure that is both resistant to grease and to water vapor
3. To provide a surface which will heat-seal to the backing material
4. To provide strength to the film materials
5. To provide strength to the backing material, and
6. To provide a bulky backing to the film.

Laminants used include flexible waxes, natural and synthetic rubbers, and natural and synthetic resins. The choice of adhesive will be governed by the strength of bond desired, the nature of the materials to be bonded, the clarity desired in the laminant and various economic factors, as well as other properties that may be desired in the laminated structure.

Lamination of a film to itself makes possible the production of a thickness which could not be produced economically in the manufacturing process for the film. For example, cast films cannot be produced economically in a thickness much greater than 0.025 inch, but multiples of this thickness may be obtained by lamination. A film may also be laminated to itself to improve a given property. For example, when extremely good resistance to the passage of water vapor is desired, rubber hydrochloride film may be laminated to itself; by proper choice of the laminate, the resistance may be further improved.

Lamination of specific films to paper and metal may be used rather than a coating of the same material for reasons which may include the following:

1. It may be more economical to apply the thickness desired as a film than as a coating.
2. Better adhesion may be obtained by the use of adhesives than by applying the plastic material directly to the paper or foil as a coating.
3. The film material may be available only as a film.
4. Better strength and flexibility may be obtained because the film will not penetrate into the paper, as might be the case with the coating.

There are numerous applications for laminated structures containing films. Cellulose acetate and rubber hydrochloride are laminated to metal foils to add strength and a heat-sealing surface to the foil. Cellophane is laminated to paper to provide a strong, water-vapor-resistant pouch-package for tobacco. Cellulose acetate, Cellophane and rubber hydrochloride are all laminated to cardboard to improve appearance, give protection, and to provide windows in cut out portions of the cardboard. Cellophane is laminated to rubber hydrochloride to give a package for bacon that is resistant to the passage of water vapor, air and grease.

Printed Films

Films are often printed to enhance their utility or appearance. Most often printed are Cellophane, cellulose acetate, rubber hydrochloride and films produced from vinyl chloride resins. The first three films are printed in single or multiple colors for many packaging applications. Such printing may provide decorative effects as well as give a description of the properties of the product and directions on its preparation and use. These films may also be printed in reverse and the printed surface laminated to a backing material such as paper. The printing is then viewed through the transparent film to give a very pleasing effect, and a printed surface which cannot be abraded away in use.

FIGURE 56. *Typical home uses of printed plastic films—aprons and curtains* (Courtesy of Bakelite Corp.)

All of the films mentioned above have been printed for fabrication uses. In recent years, increasing amounts of the vinyl films have been printed for such uses as curtains, shower curtains, and tablecloths. Printing of this film in multiple colors and in many varied designs including flowers, fruits, checks, and stripes greatly improves its appearance.

Plastic films present the printer with a number of problems. Adhesion to some films is difficult, either because the ink does not sufficiently attack the film material or because the plasticizer of the film affects the bonding strength of the ink. If inks are used which are very good solvents for the film, they may cause swelling and puckering of the film. In elastomeric films, such as vinyls, precautions must be taken to insure good register.

REFERENCES

1. Anon., "Outlook For '48." *Modern Packaging.* **21,** 71 (1948).
2. Anon., "Looking Toward 1948." *Modern Plastics.* **25,** 59 (1948).

Chapter XV

METAL-FOIL PAPERS

by J. H. Davies

ALUMINUM-foil papers are different in many respects from other coated papers, such as flints, pyroxylins, etc., in that the "coating" is actually a solid sheet of aluminum foil. Aluminum foil is manufactured by rolling operations in much the same way as other thin-gage metals. A billet or slab of aluminum is passed through breakdown mills and then transferred to finishing mills set to produce the desired gage. In thicknesses greater than about 0.006 inch, aluminum is known as strip or sheet, but when rolled below this thickness, it is known as foil. Other materials such as acetate films and Cellophane have incorrectly, at times, also been called foil, but these films should not be confused with genuine aluminum foil which is an actual metal foil.

The aluminum that is used for rolling into foil is of approximately 99.5% purity, the balance being principally iron and silicon. Usual standard gages are 0.00025, 0.00035, 0.0004 0.00045, 0.0005, 0.00065, 0.0008, 0.001, 0.0015, 0.002, 0.0025, 0.003, 0.004 and 0.005. Each of these gages has a calculated square-inch yield per pound with a rolling tolerance of plus or minus 10%.

The standard width is 26 inches. Other widths, however, are being made and can be used. The greatest width of foil in a single web that is in extensive use today as metal paper, is 36 inches. Rolling mills in the future may be able to commercially produce webs of foil up to 40 or 50 inches wide.

The gage of foil to be used in manufacturing the metal-covered paper depends upon the final consumer use and the requirements of the completed product. Both light and heavy gages can be readily laminated to all weights of paper from boards to tissue. The selection of the paper or board for lamination is one of the most important phases of manufacturing the completed article. The paper should not contain any ingredients that will reject the acceptance of the adhesive. It should be free from impurities and foreign matter that will result in blemishes on the surface of the foil-paper. The surface of the paper on the side to which the foil is mounted determines, to a great extent, the finished appearance. This is particularly true of the lighter gages of foil, which are so thin and pliable that they tend to conform exactly to the contours of a rough paper surface, producing a surface on the foil which diffuses light, instead of giving a mirror reflection. Commercial grades using a calendered or machine-glazed sheet usually have an appearance between these two extremes.

The foil itself as delivered from the rolling mill either has an absolutely smooth and glass-like finish known as "bright," or a diffusing surface, known as "satin," matte or dull. The bright surfaces result from contact with the highly polished steel rolls of the mill. The matte surface is obtained by rolling two sheets together, back to back. Selection of either the bright or satin foil surface depends solely on the finished effect desired. With heavier weights of foil, such as 0.002 and 0.004 inch, the surface of the paper does not play such an important part, since the foil tends to bridge over depressions and thus compensates for roughness of the paper surface.

The finished appearance of the mounted foil is also affected by the adhesive used in pasting the foil on the paper. One of the most widely used types of laminating adhesive is based on sodium silicate or water glass. This will produce and excellent bond between foil and paper and results in a finished product with good adhesion. However, this adhesive contributes little if anything to smoothing out any roughness in the paper. Although water-resistant, it is not waterproof and tends to become brittle on aging. Another general type of adhesive is based on starch. This has the advantage of producing a somewhat softer and smoother sheet than the silicate-type adhesive. Other types of laminants that may be employed include the waxes and various hot melts based on vinyls, polyamides, etc. Recently, experimental work has been directed at the development of thermosetting resins for foil lamination, in order to produce a sheet which is boilproof and will not delaminate at heat-sealing temperatures. Some casein adhesives are useful

FIGURE 57. *Pack rolling can be used with foil in its thinner gages; two layers of aluminum foil are passed simultaneously through the rollers* (Courtesy of Aluminum Corp. of America)

in approaching these specifications and recent developments
have stressed the application of synthetic resin and rubber base
latex adhesives. All of these specialized laminants involve
higher cost than either the silicate or starch types, since the
adhesive is more expensive per pound and in many cases more
of it must be used. Each of these adhesives has its place in
producing a finished product for a particular need or specification.

There are several methods of bringing together the web of
metal foil and the web of paper to form the metal-paper product. The most commonly used method is carried out in the
tunnel-type laminator which consists of a mounting head, a
heated and ventilated tunnel approximately 35 feet in length,
and a rewind unit. The webs of aluminum foil and paper are
brought together at the head of the machine, the adhesive being applied by pickup and applicator rollers from the glue pan
directly to either the web of metal or the paper. Whether the
adhesive should be applied to the foil or to the paper depends
upon the type of paper as well as the type of foil and the adhesive being used. After the webs are brought together between pressure rolls, they travel through the tunnel or over
steam heated drier drums to drive off the moisture contained
in the adhesive, so that the moisture will not be trapped within
the roll after rewinding. Good automatic control of this operation is important, since the incorrect moisture content may
cause curling. Excess moisture in the finished sheet may also
cause corrosion of the surface of the foil. This corrosion
usually takes the form of minute, irregular white spots, which
appear much as if little worms had eaten out the surface of the
foil. It is also important that after the metal paper has been
put into stock, it is kept in a dry and ventilated place and handled in the same manner as fine printing paper, so that the
paper will not reabsorb any moisture from the air. If this does
occur, corrosion may appear within the roll because the moisture
picked up will remain in the paper unless again driven off by
heat. Curling is due to the fact that the paper backing expands

and contracts with changes in moisture content, whereas the metal foil remains dimensionally stable and cannot pick up or lose moisture. The combined metal paper will curl in the same way as cover or printing papers and should be handled as such.

FIGURE 58. *First pass in a series of breakdowns in cold-rolling mills by means of which coiled aluminum sheet is converted into form of foil* (Courtesy of Aluminum Corp. of America)

Coloring of the foil may be accomplished by staining or lacquering or by dyeing the surface after an oxidizing and etching process such as an anodic treatment. Anodic treatment yields brilliant colors, but is not in commercial use in this country. The usual coloring operation is similar in principle to a coating or over-all printing operation in that the color is picked up from the pan by means of rollers and applied uniformly to the foil surface. The foil then travels through a ventilated tunnel over a heated bed to drive off the solvents. The lacquer may be applied either before or after the laminating process and is often applied on an aniline or gravure printing press.

Although there is a very wide choice of synthetic lacquer bases which can be used, none of the newer plastics has been able to supplant nitrocellulose as the principal base for foil coloring. The colors or color combinations are unlimited, as is the number of possible formulations of bases, resins, solvents, and plasticizers which can be used to obtain the desired decorative effect. Clear lacquers are sometimes used to minimize finger marking and to facilitate printing. In all of these lacquering operations, the foil acts as a complete barrier to the solvent so that all evaporation must take place from the surface. In view of this, and because of the short time available in the tunnel for drying, considerable skill is required in blending the solvents to avoid bubbles or blushing.

Color shades may be commercially matched from other papers to foil. To run a special shade other than the mill's standard line, a 24 ream minimum quantity is usually requested, because special mixes have to be made and a special run of the color is required. The initial matching of a color is usually time-consuming and expensive because of the scrap produced before the proper color density, hue, and shade are obtained. Therefore, various orders for a given color are combined whenever feasible to produce the longest possible run.

The most generally used paper and foil lamination consists of an 0.00035 inch foil mounted on a 30 pound paper. Foil of this thickness is the most economical on a ream basis. The same is true of the 30 pound paper, which has proved through use to be best weight for most purposes. This combination of foil and paper is the most economical for many purposes.

In addition to the usual laminations of one layer of foil against a single layer of paper, aluminum foil has found a considerable market when laminated to form specialized products designed to take advantage of its excellent heat insulation properties and its moisture-vapor resistance. Some of these laminations consist of foil on both sides of a sheet of kraft paper.

Others involve paper on both sides of the foil or foil laminated to plastic films. Where combinations of properties are desired, as, for example, a moisture-vapor barrier, heat-sealable on one side, with a decorative color and high tear resistance, as many as five plys may be specified without unreasonable production cost. In later paragraphs various combinations of foils laminated to films and papers are discussed and some of the uses for these combinations are listed.

FIGURE 59. *A strip of heavier gage aluminum foil undergoes another breakdown pass* (Courtesy of Aluminum Corp. of America)

Most of the combinations of foil and paper can be readily embossed to produce attractive decorative patterns. Embossing designs are limited only by quantity and variety of the embossing rolls available. Embossing is done in the same way as on other types of coated and uncoated papers. From the selected design the engravers will engrave a blank steel roll to the specification of the embossing machine. The expense involved for a special design on a small order is prohibitive, but for a design already available the production cost is reasonable. Because of the high cost of special rolls and of the engraving operation, it is usual to have only one of the two embossing rolls engraved, the second being a special paper roll, having exactly twice the diameter of the steel roll. This paper roll is operated wet against the engraved roll, using high pressure, until its surface becomes an exact negative of the embossed design. If desirable, print attachments can be used so that the foil can be print-embossed or topped during the embossing operation.

In selecting a design for embossing, attention should be paid to obtaining the greatest number of highlights or reflecting areas on the embossed sheet in order to give the finished product sparkle and life. Many orders for paper and foils have been lost or obtained by the purchaser liking or disliking a particular design or pattern. There is no definite rule as to what a certain class of trade may like or dislike in embossing designs as this is a matter of individual taste.

The basic ideas of embossing, more or less, hold true for printing of foils. It should be kept in mind that in either embossing or printing designs, the beauty of foil rests in its clean, sparkling, bright finish and that an embossing that tends to dull the surface or an over-all opaque printing that hides much of the surface of the foil detracts from its eye appeal. Printing on foil has had a tremendous appeal to the buying public and there has been great advances made in this field in the last few years. Many types of printing inks may be used and to print foil surfaces, it is wise to discuss the details with a good ink house so that they may determine the best ink for a particular type of press. Generally, when there was any difficulty in printing on foil, this difficulty has been overcome by referring the problem to the ink supplier.

The standard width of metal paper, as previously mentioned,

is 26 inches. From this width, the basic ream of 278 yards by 26 inches is produced. The ream basis for quoting is usually 20 x 26 inches—500 in 26 inch two-ream rolls. The grain of the paper backing, therefore, would run parallelly to the 20 inch dimension and if it is kept in mind that the grain of paper always runs in the length of the paper, one can always determine how the grain will run in a sheet of metal paper by determining which dimension is the length.

There are three general weights of metal paper and these are specified as 30 pound, 45 or 60 pound papers. The weight refers to the weight of the paper without the foil lamination and this paper weight is basis 24 x 36—480. When a bond paper is used in the 30 pound classification, the paper is basis 13 pounds (17 x 22—500) or on the basis of 24 x 36—480 will weigh approximately 30 pounds. When converted to metal paper basis of 20 x 26—500, the paper itself on this basis will weigh approximately 18 pounds. The combined foil and paper weight, basis 20 x 26—500, is approximately 28 to 30 pounds. The same calculations can be made for the other weights of metal paper. The standard put-up is a 2-ream roll, basis: 20 x 26—500, in 26 inch rolls. This basis may be also specified in large mill rolls containing 6 reams. The mounted paper may also be sheeted and the sizes will depend upon the limitations of the sheeting machine.

Metal paper may also be slit on slitting equipment into narrow rolls and it is generally requested by the mills that a width or combination of widths in the narrow rolls is specified that will cut evenly from the standard 26 or 36 inch width or any other width that may be available at that time from the particular mill.

Applications of Foils and Foil Mounted on Paper

There are many uses for metal paper and the 0.00035 foil solid-glue-mounted to a 30 pound paper, as mentioned previously, is one of the most widely used types.

This is used by the greeting card manufacturers in various colors, either plain or in a suitable embossed design for their greeting cards. The metal paper is usually ordered by them in large sheets of a predetermined size which will allow them to recut to smaller sizes without waste to fit the dimensions of certain cards. These small cut pieces will then be either tipped to the card or used as an insert. When it is used as an insert, only a small portion of the metal paper shows as a border around the card. The color and embossing design is very important in that it must fit in with the theme of a particular card for special occasion. For instance, one design and color that might be suitable for a Mother's Day or an anniversary card may not be suitable for a Christmas design. The selection of both the design and color usually rests with the art director or designer of the card.

The box makers also use this paper for their box coverings. It is generally the manufacturer who uses the boxes to package his product who selects the design or the color to be used for the boxes. Here again the color and embossing design play an important part in the actual sale of the metal paper and are usually selected to conform to the item to be packaged. When the design and color are selected, the box maker will then purchase metal paper for covering the box. There are many types and kinds of boxes that have been made with metal-paper cover. In some cases, the complete box is covered with one paper and in others only the top or bottom section is covered with one color metal paper and the other part coated with a contrasting metal paper. The metal paper may be used plain, embossed, or printed. The foil may be printed on high-speed rotary machines, by the silk-screen method, or by regular flat-bed press. Some very beautiful effects have been obtained by both embossing and printing on the foil in one, two, or possibly more colors. Here again embossing designs and printing designs are limited only to the embossing and printing rollers available at any one of the mills. Metal-paper-covered boxes have been made for such products as jewelry, food, candy, cosmetics, liquor, writing equipment, etc. In fact, almost any manufacturer that uses a decorative box in packaging his product is a potential user of metal paper as a box covering.

FIGURE 60. *Aniline type press for coating or printing foil*
(Courtesy of Kidder Press Co.)

The same type of metal paper is also being used by the makers of spiral wound containers. In this operation, the metal paper is used as one of the plies in making the container. The ply of foil may be on the outside of the container or it may be used as the inside liner of the container or both. These containers range from the very small sizes which are sometimes used for lipsticks or other small products to larger containers for use in packaging food stuffs or greasy or hygroscopic materials. Manufacturers of the spiral wound containers may use this paper for several purposes. One is, of course, the decorative feature on the outside of the container; another would be the protective quality of the foil. Depending upon the product to be packaged, a heavier weight of foil and paper backing may be specified depending upon what the manufacturer requires of the package. It is, therefore, a wise precaution, when dis-

cussing an order with a potential user, to find out two important facts: What is the product to be packaged and what does
the user expect the finished package to accomplish? Does he
wish it just for its decorative feature or for its protective qualities? In many cases it may be necessary to change completely
the specifications of foil, paper, and even the adhesive between
the foil and paper according to the end use.

The field of gift wrapping papers is another large outlet for
the same type of metal paper. It is used also here in the plain,
embossed, printed, and both printed and embossed form. These
gift wraps may be put up in a small roll consisting of one, two,
or more sheets in the roll. The roll may then be overwrapped
and banded or just banded depending upon the packaging specifications of the user. It is also sold in small rolls of 25, 50
or 100 foot length. When it is sold by the sheet, the usual size
is 20 x 26 inches. These sheets are also sold in a fourfold flat
package in the same manner as the printed gift wrap tissue
papers are folded.

The display field also uses large quantities of metal paper.
It is used by the display people in making back drops for window display, for winding around columns, and in various other
ways to decorate the display window or inside store or counter
display. It is used by this trade also in the plain, embossed, or
various fancy printed designs. It may also be used for silk-
screening special designs in one or several colors. It is also
sold in this field in rolls of 25, 50, or 100 yards or as sheets by
the ream. Metal paper is also used to make up small display
items such as stars, little figures, etc., from the stock. The
spiral-wound container people also use metal paper for spiral
winding to large tubes which are used as display columns and
stands. This is spirally wound to the outside of the tube for
its decorative effect. The 0.00035 foil laminated to board stocks
has various applications in the display field. This foil laminated
to about a 6 to 7 point board, both plain and colored, and sometimes with a colored board back is used for die cutting of
leaves. These leaves are formed in sprays or are incorporated

into other display items. Heavier weights of board, such as 10 and 15 point board are used for counter display and show cards and also find application in making the shadow-box type of display unit. Duplex metal paper, which is foil laminated to both sides of either paper or a board stock, is also used in the display field much the same ways as described previously. In making show cards or heavier weights of board up to 30, 40, or 50 points in thickness, the lightweight metal paper is also relaminated by sheet laminators or mounters to the heavy gages of board. These are used where a very rigid show or display card is required.

The commercial printers use this weight of metal paper in printing many items. One item that has gained in popularity in the last years is the food can label. Many other types of labels, where a gummed backing is not required or where a labeling machine is used, utilize the same weight. Metal paper has been printed and used as book jackets and as advertising mailing pieces relaminated to blotting stock as blotters. The same weight is used for beer labels which do not require a pregummed backing but are put on by the bottlers' own gluing machine. The bottlers of soft drinks also use these labels.

The most commonly used heavier metal papers are the 45 pound and 60 pound weights. Here again the weights refer to the paper backing, and with a 45 pound paper as mentioned, actually on a book basis, the paper itself would weigh 20 pounds (17 x 22—500). These heavier metal papers are used in many of the applications listed previously, depending upon the specifications of the user. Here again it is well to ask, when discussing metal paper with a potential user, how is it to be used and what is expected of the product. This will enable the mill to suggest the proper paper.

Light-weight foil of 0.00035 gage, when laminated to a 45 or 60 pound pregummed paper, is used by the seal and label trade for printing, embossing, and die cutting seals and labels. The weight of 45 or 60 pounds refers to the paper on the same basis as previously mentioned. To this weight there is approximately 10 to 13 pounds of gumming. The foil is laminated to the ungummed side of the paper so that when a seal or label is printed, the foil surface is the surface on which the label is printed, and having a gummed back, it may be attached to either a box or other item which is to be labeled. The adhesive used on this pregummed paper may be either an animal glue or a dextrin glue depending upon how and where the seal or label is to be used. Dextrin-pregummed paper is used, e.g., for hosiery labels. Dextrin is used for these labels because the stripping of the label by the actual consumer is easier than if an animal glue were used. The dextrin is sufficiently strong to hold the label on the stocking until it reaches the consumer. Another use is in the Christmas seals or labels where the taste of the dextrin is not as objectionable as that of the animal glue. This holds true for any other type of label which is applied by the consumer by wetting the adhesive with the tongue. Pregummed metal paper is used mainly in silver and gold with either bright or mat finish, depending upon the specifications of the seal or label manufacturer. The silver may be used with a lacquered or plain finish on the foil. Some label makers prefer a lacquered finish to prevent finger-marking and to have a printing surface. This lacquered finish, however, is not essential for printing although it facilitates printing in some cases. If the seal or label is to be heavily embossed in a bas-relief design heavier gage of foil will usually be specified. This gage of foil may be 0.0005, 0.001, 0.002 or 0.004 inch thick and can be laminated to 45 pound or 60 pound pregummed paper. The actual specification rests with the seal maker as to the gage of foil needed to obtain the results desired in making the seal. The 0.00035 inch foil when laminated to board of varying thickness has special uses such as lamp shades for which the foil is laminated directly to the board. Match box folders of the same makeup enjoy a wide popularity as an advertising medium and also, imprinted with name or initials, as a gift item.

The 0.00035 inch foil laminated to 30 pound paper is also

used by sheet liners to laminate to lightweight board stocks for use in making party hats, party favors, ash trays, and various other novelty items. It is also used by toy manufacturers for various items.

It was mentioned previously that it is important in the manufacture of metal paper that all excess moisture is driven from the laminated paper. It is well to bring this up again here since the sheet laminators of the light-weight metal paper to board sometimes do not pay sufficient attention to moisture when they laminate to heavier boards. In their operation it is important to drive off also the moisture contained in the adhesive that they use. The foil being on one side forms a moisture barrier and if the sheets are stacked, there is no way for the moisture to escape. If there is excessive moisture present it may eventually result in a corrosion of the foil surface as previously described.

Metal papers in various combinations of foil and paper have

FIGURE 61. *Embossing calender for foil* (Courtesy of B. F. Perkins & Sons, Inc.)

some specialized uses. Some of the specialized items are handled as direct mill sales and do not travel through the usual paper channels. Nevertheless, in passing, it would be interesting to note some of these uses. The 0.00035 inch foil on 30 pound paper has one extremely wide use which has escaped the notice of most people since it is so common and this application is in the cigarette package. Most of the popular brands of cigarettes now on the market have a light-weight foil paper as a liner. A special paper is used which is nontoxic and taste-free so that the cigarette will not pick up any foreign odor or taste. This foil or metal paper, for many years, has been commonly known as "tinfoil" and this is probably due to the fact that most of the cigarettes, several years back, were packaged in a composition foil which was made from tin and lead, although some aluminum was also used. Today most packages of cigarettes contain the aluminum metal paper as described.

Another large industrial use of light-weight metal paper is in the insulation field. The metal paper, in various forms, may be used in back of home radiators to reflect the heat and to insulate the walls behind the radiator from excessive drying. It may also be used in other specified forms for insulation of walls and ceilings of homes. It is being combined with building and insulation boards to act in conjunction with these boards for insulation purposes.

The 0.00035 inch foil laminated to a 15 pound tissue paper has been used and is now being used as a bottle-neck foil. It is used in silver or colored finish, embossed, and cut in rectangular shape or die-cut to a specific shape. This is a small band that goes around the neck of the bottle and is used by the brewers and also by the soft-drink bottlers. The embossed pattern is usually a stock design or can be a brand name embossing by arrangement with the mill producing the material.

Special label stock may be made by using the 0.00035 inch foil on a 30 pound paper and coating the paper side with a heat-sealing or a pressure-sensitive coating. The stock with heat-sealing coating is also used in fabricating heat-sealable bags.

These bags are used for potato chips, popcorn, etc. In special laminations of foils, films, and papers, with a heat-sealing coating, bags are used for packaging dehydrated soup mixes, etc. Foils coated with a protective coating and laminated to various types of paper may be used as soap wrapping and for the wrapping of shaving sticks. They may also be used for packaging cream cheese and other processed cheese.

The 0.00035 inch foil, when combined with a light-weight wax paper, is used extensively in the confectionery field. It is used for the packaging of chocolate bars and patties. A glassine paper may also be used as a backing. The use of the wax or glassing paper with the foil is to aid stripping the wrapper from the chocolate since most other types of paper have a tendency to adhere to the chocolate surface. Lollypops and other hard candies are being wrapped in this light-weight waxed paper and the foil surface is being printed with a decorative design or with a brand name. Chewing gum for many years has been packaged in a combination of foil and waxed paper.

The applications of the foil and paper combination are so varied that, when discussing metal paper with a prospective purchaser, several questions should be specifically answered for the benefit of the mill supplying the base sheet. These questions have been mentioned previously but cannot be over-stressed as to their importance:

1. How is the metal paper to be used?
2. What is expected of the metal paper?
3. Is it to be processed in a form other than as it is received?
4. What are the widths, sizes and quantities that would be involved?

It is usually wise to submit samples to the customer for his definite approval prior to actually having the mill process the order if there is anything special in the way of specifications.

The field of uses for foil without paper backing is quite extensive. The foil can vary in thickness between 0.00025 and 0.006 gage. The very lightweight foils are used in electrolytic condensers. Heavier weights may be used for protective purposes in the home by the housewife in various ways and can be handled in much the same way she has previously used waxed paper. Aluminum foil utilized in this manner will preserve foods much longer than would waxed paper. It may also be used in cooking, in the broiler or the frying pan to help in keeping these utensils clean, or in pressure cookers to separate foods while they are cooking. It is also used in the florist trade and is known as "pot foil." This foil is colored, embossed, or printed and is used mostly during the holiday seasons for wrapping around flower pots for its decorative effect.

Heavy gages of foil in a hard high-polished finish are used extensively in the display field in much the same manner as metal paper, i.e., as backgrounds, columns, etc. It is generally used in the plain silver, or colored unembossed finish. Lighter gages in the soft finish are used in the display field for backgrounds that require material that will mold and adapt itself to irregular surfaces.

Based on the specific gravity of aluminum, the aluminum foil has a calculated square inch yield per pound with a rolling tolerance of plus or minus 10%. The various gages mentioned previously with their approximate square inch yield per pound are listed in Table XIII.

TABLE XIII

Approximate Yield in Square Inches per Pound of
Aluminum Foils of Various Thicknesses

Gage	Square Inches
0.00035	29,200
0.0005	20,500
0.0008	12,800
0.001	10,250
0.002	5,100
0.003	3,400
0.004	2,560
0.005	2,050

Some Properties of Aluminum Foil and Foil Laminates.

In this section are quoted selected passages and tables of data from a series of papers on aluminum foil by Junius D. Edwards and D. B. Strohm of Aluminum Company of America.[1]

With constantly increasing interest in the storage of products at low temperatures, it is important to know that aluminum foil does not become brittle at low temperatures. In fact, recent measurements show that aluminum increases in strength and ductility as the temperature is lowered, even down to —320°F.

Aluminum, the metal, is impervious to gases and this characteristic offers an important advantage to the package designer. It must be recognized, however, that not all gauges of aluminum foil have zero water-vapor transmission. In thicknesses below about 0.0015 in., foil will contain minute pinholes. In the very thin gauges of foil, such as 0.00035 in., these pinholes will be of sufficiently frequent occurrence to permit an appreciable rate of moisture diffusion. However, as the foil thickness increases, the number of pinholes in any given area decreases and the size of pinhole also decreases. These pinholes seem to be an inevitable result of rolling metal to such a thin gauge; the best of rolling practices seem able only to control their size and number.

An idea of their effect upon water-vapor transmission is given by the data in Table XIV, which presents characteristic WVT values for foil of four different gauges. In making this test, 100 sheets (12 in. square) of each gauge of foil were taken and every tenth sheet tested for WVT. In the case, however, of the 1-mil foil, only eight of the 100 sheets showed pinholes in the test; in the case of 0.0007-in. foil, only 15 of the 100 sheets showed pinholes. In the two heavier gauges, only three pieces of the 0.001-in. foil and eight of the 0.0007-in. foil, respectively, had pinholes in the center area, where their effect on WVT could be measured. The data of Table XIV clearly illustrate the fact that there is considerable variation in the WVT of different test pieces of the same gauge aluminum foil. This is to be expected, of course, since any pinholes present are uniform neither in size nor in distribution. The averages, however, clearly indicate the trend toward lower permeability as the thickness of the foil is increased. The sample test area for the permeability measurements shown in Table XIV and elsewhere in this paper was approximately 10 sq. in.

The method employed in measuring the permeability of these materials to water vapor is essentially that described previously.[2] A glass test dish, filled with calcium chloride desiccant, is closed by the test membrane which is wax-sealed at the edges. The test dish, after weighing, is supported in a chamber

TABLE XIV

Water-vapor Transmission of Aluminum Foil			
Thickness of foil(in.)	WVT (g. H_2O per 100 sq. in. per 24 hr. with air at 100°F. and 100% R. H.)	Thickness of foil (in.)	WVT (g. H_2O per 100 sq. in. per 24 hr. with air at 100°F. and 100% R.H.)
0.00035	0.62	0.0007	0.07*
	0.11		0.08
	0.20		0.06
	0.23		0.05
	0.15		0.04
	0.69		0.08
	0.29		0.01
	0.34		0.04
	0.18		
	0.07		
	Average 0.29		
0.0005	0.08	0.001	0.02*
	0.05		0.03
	0.06		0.02
	0.12		
	0.15		
	0.09		
	0.13		
	0.31		
	0.17		
	0.04		
	Average 0.12		

Gauge of foil (in.)	Number of 12 in. square sheets with pinholes	Number of sheets with no pinholes
0.00035	100	None
0.0005	100	None
0.0007	15	85
0.001	8	92

* WVT values not averaged because majority of the 100 sheets examined had zero permeability.

filled with air of the required temperature and humidity; the air is maintained in positive circulation with a fan. After a measured period, the water-vapor transmission is determined by weighing.

Untreated papers, as a rule, offer very little resistance to water-vapor passage. As a result, combining paper with aluminum foil, particularly when it is attached by glue lines and not an over-all adhesive, results in very little change in the permeability of the foil. In the case of one particular lot of 0.00045-in. foil which was laminated to 35-lb. bond paper by widely spaced glue lines, the permeability of the composite product was only 15% less than that of the foil alone. That the reduction in permeability was not greater is not surprising since the paper alone, under standard tests, had a WVT of 325 g. per 100 sq. in. per 24 hr.

In Table XV are given data showing the water-vapor transfer of foil laminated with two different types of plastic. These are commercial materials and examination showed that adhesion was generally good, though not complete. For comparison with these values another series of tests was run showing the permeability of the same foil and plastic simply laid one over the other without a laminating adhesive between. These data show that while good adhesion between foil and plastic is necessary for the most efficient barrier, water-vapor transfer is quite limited even when the foil and plastic are not laminated but form two barriers "in series," so to speak.

TABLE XV

Effect of Adhesion between Foil and Sheeting on Permeability of Laminates

Description of material	Permeability (g. H_2O per 100 sq. in. per 24 hr. at 100°F. and 100% R. H.)	
	Laminated with all-over adhesive	Foil laid on plastic film—no adhesive
Aluminum foil (0.00035 in.) in	0.019	0.136
combination with moisture-	0.019	0.117
proof Cellophane sheeting	0.011	0.058
	0.012	0.083
	0.013	0.107
	0.019	0.110
	0.020	0.100

TABLE XV (*Continued*)

Effect of Adhesion between Foil and Sheeting on Permeability of Laminates

	Permeability (g. H_2O per 100 sq. in. per 24 hr. at 100°F. and 100% R. H.)	
	Laminated with	Foil laid on plastic
Description of material	all-over adhesive	film—no adhesive
	0.021	0.041
	0.014	0.040
	0.021	0.043
Average	0.017	0.084
Aluminum foil (0.00035 in.) in	0.004	0.254
combination with acetate sheet-	0.012	0.019
ing	0.024	0.015
	0.027	0.153
	0.018	0.050
	0.005	0.005
	0.015	0.200
	0.029	0.203
	0.029	0.413
	0.012	0.183
Average	0.018	0.150

NOTE: Permeability—foil, 0.3; Cellophane, 0.45; acetate, 48.0.

The data of Table XVI show that with proper laminating techniques and proper selection of materials, foil-plastic laminates having WVT values as low as 0.00 can be secured. To secure a laminate of uniformly low permeability, it is desirable to use one of the heavier gauges of foil, such as foil 0.001 in. in thickness.

TABLE XVI

Water-vapor Transmission of Aluminum-foil Laminates

		Permeability (g. H_2O per 100 sq. in. per 24 hr. at 100°F. and 100% R. H.)	
Material	*Thickness (in.)*	Flat	Creased*
Aluminum foil laminated with	0.00035	0.00	...
moistureproof Cellophane	0.0009	0.01	0.03
		0.01	0.01
Aluminum foil laminated with	0.00035	0.01	...

TABLE XVI (*Continued*)

Water-vapor Transmission of Aluminum-foil Laminates

Material	Thickness (in.)	Permeability (g. H_2O per 100 sq. in. per 24 hr. at 100°F. and 100% R. H.) Flat	Creased*
cellulose acetate	0.0012	0.02	0.07
Aluminum foil laminated with	0.00035	0.01	0.01
rubber hydrochloride	0.0008	0.01	. . .
Aluminum foil laminated with	0.00035	0.01	0.02
vinyl polymer	0.0012	0.02	0.01
Aluminum foil laminated with	0.00035	0.00	0.04
wax to 30# glassine			
Aluminum foil 2S-O	0.00035	0.07	0.42
Aluminum foil laminated with	0.001	0.00	0.00
moistureproof Cellophane	0.0009		
Aluminum foil laminated with	0.001	0.00	0.00
vinyl polymer	0.0012		
Aluminum foil laminated with	0.001	0.00	0.02
wax to 25# glassine			
Aluminum foil 2S-O	0.001	0.00	0.40

NOTE: Each value in this table is the average of measurements on two or three test pieces. In some cases, two or more lots of laminates were tested.

* These test pieces were creased with four equidistant parallel folds and then with four more folds at right angles to the first; there were thus 16 crease intersections on the face of the test pieces.

Permeability of Foil Laminates to CO_2

Because of the interest in the use of carbon dioxide as an inert atmosphere in packaging, a series of measurements has been made on the permeability of two aluminum-foil laminates to this gas; these data are presented in Table XVII. For comparison with the data on the laminates, permeability figures are presented for the plastic films alone. The evidence is quite convincing that although the plastic films alone show an appreciable permeability, the foil laminate is quite impervious to penetration by either carbon dioxide or water vapor. These data supplement the information presented in Table XVI.

The fact that aluminum does not produce any toxic effects makes it an entirely safe packaging medium. This fact has been established not only by scientifically controlled experimental investigations, but also by long experience, particularly with aluminum cooking utensils. Carefully controlled tests have proved that contact with aluminum, in contrast to a number of other metals, does not accelerate the loss of vitamins in cooking. The loss of vitamin C during pasteurization of milk in an aluminum container was no greater than when pasteurized in contact with glass. The loss due to heating under these conditions was about 30%, while pasteurization of milk in copper completely destroyed vitamin C. This is only one reason why aluminum foil caps have proved so satisfactory in the bottling of milk.

TABLE XVII

Permeability to Carbon Dioxide and Water Vapor of Aluminum Foil Laminated to Films and of Films Alone

	Permeability (g. per 100 sq. in. per 24 hr.*)		
Material	CO_2†	$CO_2 + H_2O$	H_2O
Aluminum foil (0.00035 in.) laminated to moistureproof Cellophane	0.001	0.004	0.000
Aluminum foil (0.00035 in.) laminated to vinyl polymer	0.001	0.005	0.001
Cellophane alone	0.030	0.193	0.197
Vinyl polymer alone	1.78	4.18	2.72

* Recorded values are the average of concordant measurements on four different test pieces at a temperature of 77 to 81°F.

† Permeability to carbon dioxide measured at 760 mm. pressure difference; carbon dioxide in next column was saturated with water vapor.

Another advantage of aluminum foil is the sterile character of the surface which results from annealing at a temperature of about 700°F. Aluminum foil is also odorless, tasteless and does not absorb odors from the surrounding atmosphere.

Chocolate and chocolate candy bars are products which should reach the consumer in the freshest possible condition. This means the appearance should be appetizing, the texture correct and the flavor free from staleness or rancidity. In Table XVIII are data on storage tests of 1-lb. chocolate fudge nut bars wrapped in six different types of wrappers and stored for 25 days. The performance of these wrappers was judged in several ways: by the weight loss after 25 days' storage, by the flavor and by the appearance. The flavor and appearance ratings were appraised independently by three different inspectors.

Wrapping in plain waxed paper with a glassine outer wrap (No. 1) showed the largest weight loss after storage. This poor performance also coincided with the lowest flavor rating and appearance. The chocolate bar with the No. 1 wrapper was distinctly stale in taste and appeared hard and dry with surface crystallization along the edges. Mold was not observed on any of the chocolate bars. Wrapper No. 5, which was a laminated-foil wrapper, heat sealed, showed the best performance on all counts. However, the chocolate bars in each of the five wrappers which employed aluminum foil had a soft, creamy texture and were free from staleness. In the case of chocolate and other products, where volatile essential ingredients play such an important part in flavor and palatability, even a very small weight loss may be significant of loss in quality.

TABLE XVIII

Wrappers for Chocolate Nut Candy Bars

Description of wrapper	Weight loss in g. after 25 days' storage at 85–90° F.	Flavor rating	Appearance rating
1. Waxed paper (0.002 in.) separate inner wrap; glassine paper (0.0015 in.) overwrap	11.0	4	4
2. Aluminum foil (0.00045 in.) laminated to glassine paper (0.0015 in.); glassine next to chocolate	2.5	3	3
3. Aluminum foil (0.00045 in.) laminated to waxed glassine paper (0.0015 in.); waxed glassine paper next to chocolate	2.5	2	3
4. Waxed paper (0.0022 in.) separate inner wrap; overwrap of aluminum foil (0.00045 in.) wax-laminated to glassine paper (0.0015 in.)	2.5	2	3
5. Aluminum foil (0.001 in.) coated with heat-sealing lacquer and laminated on opposite side to acetate sheeting; lacquer coating next to chocolate. This wrapper was heat sealed at seams and ends	0.5	1	1
6. Aluminum foil (0.001 in.)	1.5	2	2

In flavor and appearance, No. 1 is the highest and No. 4 the lowest rating.

It is also important to employ a wrapper which will prevent absorption of foreign odors by chocolates. A severe laboratory test was carried out in which sweet milk-chocolate bars wrapped in various ways were stored in desiccators containing, in one case, cotton moistened with turpentine and, in the other, strong peppermint candy. At periodic intervals, bars were removed, unwrapped and tasted by two or more inspectors in order to detect the first trace of turpentine or peppermint vapor absorption. These tests, presented in Table XIX, showed quite definitely that while it was only a matter of hours before the paper wrappers permitted penetration and absorption of foreign odors, the aluminum foil wrappers kept the odor out for days.

There are many fine articles made of steel which require special wrapping to make sure that the customer will receive them free from rust; these may range from surgical knives to polished steel bearings. Generally such articles are treated with a rust-inhibiting oil prior to packing. This oil treatment, however, is not proof against rusting, as the following tests will show. The wrapper employed should be proof against penetration by the oil. Aluminum-foil wrappers can be very effectively used, both to prevent rusting and to prevent oil penetration.

The results of a series of tests on wrappers for polished

TABLE XIX

Efficiency of Wrapper in Preventing Foreign Odor Absorption by Sweet Milk-Chocolate Bars

(Chocolate bars stored in glass desiccators, one containing cotton moistened with turpentine and the other containing peppermint candy)

| | Time to taste | |
Description of wrapper	Turpentine	Peppermint
1. Aluminum foil (0.0007 in.) coated with heat-sealing lacquer; wrapper heat sealed along side seam and ends	6 days	7 days
2. Aluminum foil (0.0007 in.) coated with heat-sealing lacquer and laminated one side to moistureproof Cellophane; coated surface heat sealed along side seam and ends	20 days	19 days
3. Plastic bleached greaseproof paper 22½ #; side seam and folds not sealed	5 hours	3½ hours
4. Opaque greaseproof paper 30#; side seam and folds sealed	5 hours	3½ hours
5. Control—no wrapper	½ hour	1 hour

carbon steel bearing races are presented in Table XX. The two wrappers (1 and 2) employing aluminum foil were very effective in protecting the oiled bearings during storage in a hot, humid atmosphere. Even wrapper 1, which was not heat sealed, did a good job on the oiled bearings; the same wrapper around a dry bearing (7) was not completely protective.

TABLE XX

Wrappers for Polished Steel

(Polished carbon steel bearing races, dipped in antirusting oil, excess oil drained and bearings wrapped. Packages stored at 106° F. and 90 to 92% relative humidity)

Description of wrapper	Degree of tarnishing after	
	Storage 180 hr.	Storage 1,000 hr.
1. Aluminum foil (0.00035 in.) laminated to 25# red paper with wax; foil next to bearing	0	0
2. Aluminum foil (0.00035 in.) laminated to 25# red paper with wax; foil next to bearing; steel bearings wrapped in foil laminate and heat sealed in bag made from aluminum foil (0.001 in.) with lacquer coating	0	0
3. Red paper 25#	1	7
4. White glassine paper	10	10+
5. Waxed paper 40#	2	9
6. Kraft paper waxed	2	7
7. Aluminum foil (0.00035 in.) laminated to 25# red paper; same as No. 1, except bearings were dry (not oiled); foil next to bearing	1	2

The degree of rusting after storage is indicated by code numbers from 0 to 10. Zero indicates no rusting, while the degree increases from 1 to 10; No. 5 indicates appreciable rusting, while No. 10 indicates a surface which is about 90% rusted.

It would appear that wrapping paper will take up moisture and stimulate the corrosion of steel with which it is in contact. However, the foil laminated to paper greatly reduces the rate of moisture pick-up and prolongs the protective life of the wrapper.

The beautiful finish on sterling silver when it leaves the maker's factory is a difficult finish to preserve untarnished. Mere traces of hydrogen sulfide in the atmosphere, particularly in urban districts, form silver sulfide on silverware and produce the familiar tarnished-silver appearance. This is a matter of considerable concern to the silver distributor, as well as to the housewife. One large distributor of silverware has spent many thousands of dollars in repolishing silverware in order to make it acceptable for delivery. This repolishing can be avoided by means of a suitable wrapper of aluminum foil.

The data in Table XXI present the results of wrapping individual silver teaspoons in the regular double tissue-paper wrappers in comparison with a single tissue wrapper and an overwrap of aluminum foil. Neither of the foil wrappers tested was heat sealed, but the deadfolding characteristics of the foil helped it cling closely to the teaspoon and so limit the access of air that in a storage period of 11 weeks no tarnish occurred. A very noticeable tarnish was produced on silverware wrapped in the regular way with plain tissue and stored for only two weeks under the same conditions.

TABLE XXI

Wrapping to Prevent Tarnishing of Silverware

Description of wrapper on silver teaspoon	Period of storage and degree of tarnish *					
	1 week	2 weeks	4 weeks	6 weeks	8 weeks	11 weeks
1. Unwrapped spoon	1	2	3	4	4	4
2. Regular double tissue paper wrapper	0	1	2	2	2	2†
3. Aluminum foil (0.00035 in.) + one-ply tissue paper	0	0	0	0	0	0
4. Aluminum foil (0.0005 in.) + one-ply tissue paper	0	0	0	0	0	0

* Code for degree of tarnish:
  0–No detectable tarnish.
  1–Trace of tarnish.
  2–Noticeable tarnish.
  3–Severely tarnished.
  4–Tarnished black.
† Also showed pitting of the silverware.

Table silver is customarily shipped in packages containing one dozen or more table knives or forks. It is a simple matter to place a heat-sealed aluminum foil wrapper around such a carton and protect its contents against tarnish for a very long period. Special articles such as bowls, trays, vases and the like can be placed in heat-sealed aluminum envelopes, so that when the article is wanted for use or display no polishing will be necessary. Once the trade understands the advantage of such a package, it will be in great demand.

The success of aluminum foil wrappers with tableware suggests its use for wrapping surgical sterling-silver sundries, such as silver cranium head plates, bone plates and screws, silver joint overlays, etc.

Summary

Aluminum foil finds a wide variety of uses in the packaging field. The principal technical characteristics of foil which recommend it for these applications may be summarized as follows:

1. Impervious to moisture and gases (in certain gauges).
2. Greaseproof.
3. Non-sorptive.
4. Shrinkproof.
5. Odorless and tasteless.
6. Hygienic; non-toxic and sterile.
7. Resistant to corrosion; non-aging.
8. Dead folding.
9. Strong.
10. Functions well in laminates.
11. Appearance; brightness and glitter.
12. Reflects radiant heat; opaque to light.

Selected laboratory data point the way to the most efficient and economical ways to use aluminum, alone and with other wrapping materials, to solve difficult problems in the packaging of such varied products as foods, drugs, cigarettes, steel and silverware.

The uses of both laminated and unlaminated foils are limited only to the imagination. Many more applications than have been mentioned for foils mounted and unmounted exist and in the next few years the consumption will most likely be doubled.

REFERENCES

1. J. D. Edwards and D. B. Strohm. "Aluminum Foil." *Modern Packaging.* **21,** No. 6 :143 (1948) ; **21,** No. 7 ; 150 (1948) ; **21,** No. 8 :186 (1948).
2. J. D. Edwards and D. B. Strohm. "Measuring Permeability to Carbon Dioxide and Water Vapor." *Modern Packaging.* **19,** No. 2 :157 (1945).

Chapter XVI

GLOSSARY

ABRASION RESISTANCE. The resistance to scratching or wearing away of a sheet of paper or board, through contact with another sheet of paper or board, or with some other object.

ABRASIVENESS. That property of a sheet which causes it to abrade surfaces. Emery paper is an example of extreme abrasiveness, whereas lens paper probably has minimum abrasiveness. This property is of importance in the use of paper, e.g., abrasiveness in printing papers causes undue wear of type.

ABSORBENCY. That property of a material which causes it to imbibe or take up liquids with which it is in contact.

ACCELERATE. To hasten or quicken the natural progress or process of an event or a series of events. An accelerated test of a coated material is a severe test that determines the comparative durability in a shorter length of time than required under service conditions.

ACCELERATED WEATHERING. Machine-made means of duplicating or reproducing weather conditions.

ACID DYES. A class of aniline dyes, stable in acid solutions, in which the color is associated with the negative radical; usually sodium salts of sulfonic acids. As a class they have a lower coloring power than basic dyes, but they are much faster to light.

ACID NUMBER. The amount of free acids in fats, oils, waxes and resins, expressed as the number of milligrams of potassium hydroxide (KOH) required to neutralize one gram of the material being tested.

ACIDITY. Either hydrogen-ion concentration (pH; less than 7) or total acidity. Both are determined on the water extract of the paper. Total acidity is measured by extraction of the paper with boiling water, followed by titration of the extract with standard sodium hydroxide solution to a specified end point, normally the phenolphthalein end point, and is expressed as percentage of sulfur trioxide (SO_3) on the weight of the paper extracted.

ACRYLATE RESINS. Glass-clear flexible thermoplastics made by polymerizing esters of acrylic acid.

ACTINIC RAYS. Those rays of light which cause chemical changes in a paper or plastic film. The actinic rays of sunlight are strongest in July in the United States and weakest in January.

ACTIVE SULFUR. Sulfur which is present in paper in the form of compounds which will react with metals to cause tarnishing.

ADHESION. The act or state of adhering or, in more specific words, the sticking together of substances in contact with each other.

ADHESIVE. A substance that causes two similar or dissimilar surfaces to adhere to each other.

AGALITE. See Asbestine.

AIR BRUSH. See Air Knife.

AIR-DRYING. Capable of drying hard at room temperature and without the aid of artificial heat.

AIR IMPACTER. Similar to an air knife except that it does not supply or remove any of the coating material; it acts as a spreading and smoothing device, producing a smoother surface than an air brush.

AIR KNIFE OR AIR BRUSH. The air knife acts on the principle of a doctor blade and uses a thin flat jet of air for removing the excess coating from a wet, freshly coated sheet. In practice, the air-knife coater applies a large excess of semifluid coating by means of an applicator roll which contacts the paper. The excess coating is immediately removed by means of the air knife, which also serves to trowel the remaining coating to a smooth surface.

ALABASTER. See Calcium Sulfate.

ALBUMEN (ALBUMENIZED) PAPER. Paper used in photography, which is coated with albumen (albumin) from the whites of eggs mixed with ammonium chloride and then treated with silver salts. Such a paper is light sensitive.

ALCOHOL-RESISTING. This expression is used in connection with a dried film of coating material which does not dissolve in contact with alcohols.

ALIPHATIC HYDROCARBONS. Hydrocarbons having an open chain structure, e.g., methane, ethane, propane, etc.

ALKALIPROOF PAPER. A paper used in wrapping alkaline materials, such as soaps, alkaline adhesives, etc. Paper which does not show appreciable discoloration when wetted with 1 per cent sodium hydroxide (caustic soda) or 40° Baumé sodium silicate is normally considered alkaliproof.

ALKYD RESIN. Synthetic resin of the glycerol phthalate type.

ALUMINUM PAPER. A base paper of ordinary wrapping weight coated with aluminum powder. It is used particularly for wrapping food products and tobacco.

ALUMINUM SILICATE. A white inert pigment of poor hiding power. Obtained from certain natural deposits of china clay, feldspar and similar materials.

ANHYDRITE. See Caleium Sulfate.

ANHYDROUS. Free from water.

APPARENT DENSITY. The weight per unit volume of the sheet. It is commonly calculated by dividing the basis weight by the caliper, although it must be recognized that the numerical value thus obtained is dependent upon the definition of the ream.

AROMATIC HYDROCARBONS. Hydrocarbons characterized by the benzene ring, e.g., benzene, naphthalene, toluene.

ASBESTINE. Mineral (nearly pure magnesium silicate in fibrous form), occurring in the eastern part of the United States and southern Germany, which is intermediate in physical properties between talc and asbestos. It is sometimes called agalite.

ASH. The inorganic residue obtained by completely burning a pulp or paper. Ash content is the percentage of such residue (corrected for any water lost during calcination) on the basis of the weight of air-dried pulp or paper.

AUTOCHROME PRINTING PAPER. Coated paper suitable for multicolor printing.

AZEOTROPIC MIXTURE. Liquid mixture which exhibits a maximum or minimum boiling point.

BACTERIAL COUNT. The number of bacteria in a paper or board determined by a definite technique; all organisms, both pathogenic and nonpathogenic, which will grow under the conditions set up by the technique used, will be counted.

BAKING. The process of drying a coating material by the application of artificial heat. A baking product is one which requires the application of artificial heat to become hard and dry. Lacquers are not baking products, but a small amount of heat is sometimes used to hasten the evaporation of volatile solvents from the lacquer film.

BALANCED SOLVENTS. A combination of solvents designed to give a specified performance.

BALL MILL. Nonlined pigment mill in which steel balls inside a revolving cylinder reduce the size of pigment particles.

BARIUM SULFATE. A filler used as such or in combination with other pigments; obtained from mineral barytes or synthetically. The artificial product is called blanc fixe, fast white, pearl white, or permanent white.

BARYTA PAPER. Paper coated with barium sulfate to obtain a smooth matte finish. This paper is frequently used as the base for photographic emulsions, in which case the paper must be free from agents injurious to such emulsions.

BARYTE. Inert pigment which is prepared by grinding under water crude mineral barite. It is unaffected by acids and alkalis but has no opacity and is used either as a base for other color or as a bodying medium or extender. Baryte is practically pure barium sulfate.

BASE. The metallic salt upon which coloring matter is precipitated to form the insoluble pigments called lakes. A tinted paste is also called a base.

BASIC. Of alkaline nature. Capable of uniting with an acid to form a salt.

BASIC DYES. A class of aniline dyes which are stable in alkaline solutions. The color base is insoluble in water but may be rendered soluble by transformation of the base into a salt (such as the oxalate, chloride, etc.). These dyes are characterized by great tinctorial strength and brightness, but as a rule they are not fast to light. Fastness to light may be improved by using basic dyes as topping colors. In this case, acid or direct dyes are used as the bottom colors and the basic dyes produce a relatively fast-to-light color lake with these dyestuffs.

BASIS WEIGHT. The weight in pounds of a ream (480 or 500 sheets) of paper cut to a given size. The U. S. Government Printing Office uses a unit of 1,000 sheets. The standard size for record and comparison of physical properties in the specialty paper industry is 20 x 26 inches; the ream contains 500 sheets. The basis weight of wallpaper is expressed arbitrarily in ounces and may be converted into basis weight on a 24 x 36—500 basis by multiplying the ounce weight by four, and adding two.

BENDING CHIP. A paperboard used for the manufacture of folding cartons. It is made of waste papers and, by definition, must endure a single fold up to 180° without breaking or separating the plies.

BENDING STRENGTH. Resistance to deformation and breaking under bending stress. It is judged in terms of both the stress and strain that causes failure. This property is of importance only in stiff papers or paperboards.

BENTONITE. A type of clay, occurring principally in the western United States, characterized by its high absorptive power and colloidal properties. Some varieties will absorb more than three times their own weight in water, swelling to a jelly-like mass.

BINDER. A component of a coating composition which is primarily responsible for the adhesive and cohesive forces.

BITUMEN. Mixture of hydrocarbons, particularly asphalt, and crude petroleum, are said to be bituminous.

BLACK PHOTO PAPER. A paper, usually of the duplex type, which is used to protect or wrap sensitized photographic materials. It must be free from pinholes and from chemicals harmful to a photographic emulsion. The basis weight is about 40 pounds (24 x 36—500).

BLACK TONER. A black pigment usually consisting of black lake, aniline black dye, or purified bone black.

BLACKENING. Darkening of paper caused by crushing at the calenders or supercalenders, which is associated with a decrease in the opacity of the sheet. It may be caused by excessive pressure, excessive moisture in the paper, or a combination of these factors.

BLANC FIXE. An artificially prepared barium sulfate which is finer, bulkier and more opaque than barytes.

BLEEDING. Discoloration caused by the diffusion of a stain or other substance into succeeding coats. A nonbleeding color is one which is not soluble in materials used over it. Certain shades of aniline oil colors will bleed through any number of finishing coats applied over it.

BLENDING. The word "blending" is often used almost synonymously with the word mixing, i.e., when two materials are blended they are intimately mixed together. At other times, blending refers more particularly to gradually shading off from one color to another, as for example: blending stains are those which are used to make certain parts of a finished work have different or darker color than other parts and the color change is gradual.

BLISTERING. This term refers to the formation of bubbles or blisters on the surface of the finished work, usually after the film is dry.

BLOCK RESISTANCE. The resistance of a coated paper to blocking.

BLOCKING. Tendency of two coated sheets to adhere to each other. This adherence tears the paper or picks off portions of one or both faces when the sheets are separated. Blocking is affected by the pressure, temperature, time of contact, and affinity of the two faces for each other. Blocking may occur when the sheet is tested face to face, or face to back and both are equally important.

BLOWN OIL. Oils which have been bodied and partially polymerized or oxidized by blowing air through them. Blown castor oil is used frequently in lacquer manufacturing.

BLUSHING. When a lacquer film takes on a white or grayish cast during the drying period it is said to "blush." Blushing is caused directly by the precipitation of a portion of the solids content of the lacquer. Blushing is caused by the high relative humidity of the surrounding atmosphere and/or by small traces of moisture which are always present in freshly applied lacquer films and unless the solvents used are of the type that form evaporating mixtures with water, the film is likely to blush. Blushing may also be caused by the solvent combination becoming unbalanced by evaporation so that the nonsolvents for nitrocellulose or for some other constituent of the lacquer become more concentrated and allow one or more of the constituents to be precipitated.

BODY. Consistency. For Newtonian liquids, body is the same as viscosity.

BODY STOCK. The base stock or coating raw stock for plain or decorated coated papers. It is also used in connection with industrial papers before they are treated. On account of the wide range which body stock may cover and also on account of the fact that it is usually made to order under special specifications, it cannot be described as containing certain amounts of any particular kind of pulp nor is there any way of referring to weights and colors. It is also termed base paper.

BODYING ACTION. Tendency of a lacquer to take on a thicker consistency upon standing. Bodying action in a lacquer may be attributed to evaporation of volatile materials and/or to acidity of ingredients.

BOILING POINT. The temperature at which the vapor pressure of a liquid equals the air pressure, that is, the temperature at which boiling begins.

BOILING RANGE. The temperature range within which a liquid boils to dryness.

BOND COAT. A coat of finishing material used to improve the adherence of succeeding coats.

BONDING ACTION. The condition of adhering or bonding between coatings or surfaces.

BONDING STRENGTH. Resistance of a sheet to the removal of coating or fibers from it. This property is of particular importance in printing papers. If, where tacky inks are used, small bits of the surface are "picked" by the type leaving the paper, the debris of fibers and surface coating clog the type and leave a nonuniformly inked surface. The force with which fibers adhere to each other within a sheet of paper or with which plies in a board or laminated sheet adhere to each other.

BOWL. (1) A British term for calender roll. (2) Paper used in the construction of supercalender rolls.

BOX-COVER PAPER. A light-weight paper used for covering paper boxes. It may be plain, antique, embossed, ink-embossed, glazed, flint-glazed, coated, decorated, or otherwise embellished to add to its usefulness or attractiveness. It may be made of chemical wood pulp, chemical wood and mechanical pulps, rag, or rag and chemical wood pulps. Strength is not always essential. It is usually made in basis weights of 25 to 40 pounds (20 x 26—500) or 40 to 60 pounds (25 x 38—500).

BOX ENAMEL PAPER. White or colored coated paper, used for covering boxes. It is coated on one side only and highly glazed.

BOX LINERS. Papers used for the inside of boxes containing food or meat or crates containing celery, lettuce, or other vegetables, to keep the products fresh through the retention of moisture and to protect the contents from contamination. Almost any grade and any weight of paper may be used, depending upon the product in question.

BREAKING. Passing a coated or gummed paper over the edges of a bar which cracks the layer of adhesive and eliminates the tendency to curl.

BREAKING UP. When thinning lacquer pastes, it is necessary to add thinner or base to obtain a uniform mixture. This process of stirring the lacquer paste with only a small amount of lacquer thinner or nitrocellulose base is called "breaking up" of the paste. This process is repeated until the desired consistency is finally reached.

BREAKS. Tear in a roll of paper which occurs while the paper machine is running. Such breaks are generally spliced and marked by a protruding flag.

BRIGHT ENAMELS. Papers highly polished by calendering and brush polishing, coated on one side only, and chiefly used for labels.

BRIGHTNESS. As commonly used in the paper industry, the reflectivity of a sheet of pulp or paper of blue light measured under standard conditions on an instrument designed and calibrated specifically for the purpose. Strictly speaking, brightness is not a colorimetric quantity.

BRILLIANCY. The brightness or apparent strength of a color to the eye. This attribute of color corresponds to the loudness of sound. Brilliant is also used to describe a glittering surface. For example, a very high luster is sometimes spoken of as a brilliant luster.

BRISTLE MARKS. Indentions in the surface of coated paper caused by bristles that have come off coating brushes and adhered to the calender roll.

BRITTLE. A dried lacquer film is said to be brittle when it is easily broken or is not tough or tenacious, especially when bent rapidly or scratched as with a knife blade or the finger nail. The opposite of tough. Resistance to abrasion.

BRITTLENESS. That property of a material which causes it to break or fail when deformed by bending. It is of practical interest only when the deformation causing failure is small. A sheet of badly aged paper which cracks and breaks when bent only slightly is said to be very brittle.

BROCADE PAPER. A type of paper which has been subjected to a heavy embossing. Both cover and box weights are produced.

BRONZE CREPE. Crepe paper which has been coated with gold or copper powder or given a metallic color.

BRONZE PAPER. A paper or board coated on one or both sides with a solution containing a finely divided metallic powder and a binder, e.g., pyroxylin, casein, glue, etc.

BRUSH COATING. The process of applying a semifluid mixture of the pigment and the binder by means of a revolving cylindrical brush and smoothing the coating so applied by means of oscillating flat brushes which contact the coated sheet as it is being drawn tightly over a moving rubber apron or a revolving drum.

BRUSH ENAMEL PAPER. A paper coated on one or both sides and brush polished previous to calendering to produce a smooth, even, and brilliant surface. It is used largely for cigar labels, illustrations, and box coverings.

BRUSH MARKS. Marks left on the surface of coated paper by the brushes used in spreading the coating material. They may be due to defects in the brushes, in the coating material, or in the adjustment or operation of the brushing machinery.

BRUSH POLISHING. Polishing a coated paper having a high wax content by means of cylindrical brushes revolving at a higher peripheral speed than the linear speed of the paper.

BRUSHLESS COATING. Any kind of coating applied without the use of brushes, examples are air-knife, drum, flow-on, knife, print-on, roll, and spray coatings.

BUBBLE TEST. In comparing the viscosity or consistency of a lacquer with that of another lacquer or unknown solution of known consistency, the lacquer is placed in a vertical tube beside a similar tube of the known lacquer. By inverting the tubes quickly and noting the comparative rate of rise of the bubbles the comparative consistency or viscosity of the new lacquer is established. This test is known as the bubble test and offers a rapid comparative method of observing the consistency of a clear lacquer.

BULK. Thickness of a pile of a specified number of sheets when measured under a specified pressure.

BULKING VALUE. Ability of a pigment to add volume to a liquid when ground in it. The bulking value depends upon the specific gravity of the pigment, although the oil absorption, fineness of grind and other conditions also have some effect upon the results in actual practice. The bulking value is usually expressed in increase in volume in gallons obtained when grinding 100 pounds of the pigment.

BURNISHED FINISH. Another term for glazed finish. It is sometimes restricted to flint and friction glazing.

BURST FACTOR. Bursting strength in grams per square centimeter divided by the basis weight of the sheet in grams per square meter.

BURSTING STRENGTH. The pressure required to rupture a specimen when it is tested in a specified instrument under specified conditions. It is largely determined by the tensile strength and extensibility of the paperboard or paper. Bursting strength is commonly taken as an important measure of the strength of paper or paperboard, and it is important in certain uses of paper, such as in packaging, where the contents tend to burst the sheet from the inside.

CABLE PAPER. A strong rope or kraft paper, made on a Fourdrinier or cylinder machine, generally acid free, used for winding electrical cables. Strength is essential, as the paper is cut into very narrow widths ($\frac{3}{16}$ to $\frac{5}{8}$ of an inch) for winding round the individual wires which make up the cable. Significant properties are freedom from holes and electrically conducting particles (especially iron particles). The basis weight varies from 50 to 125 pounds (24 x 36—480). After wrapping, the cables are treated with various impregnating (waterproofing) agents and encased in lead sheaths.

CALCIUM CARBONATE. Filler and coating agent. It is occasionally called whiting. It is obtained as the reaction product of lime and carbon dioxide or as a by-product of caustic soda manufacture. Chalk is natural calcium carbonate and is used, to a limited extent, in paper making. Precipitated calcium carbonate, which is an artificial chalk, has a smaller particle size than the natural product.

CALCIUM SULFATE. Found in nature as anhydrite ($CaSO_4$), also called alabaster, calopone, pearl filler, tissue filler, and gypsum.

CALENDAR BOARD. A paper board upon which calendars and displays are printed. It is made usually of white patent-coated or clay-coated board with a surface finish to take fine printing designs. Stiffness and nonwarping properties are important characteristics.

CALENDER. A set or "stack" of horizontal cast-iron rolls with chilled, hardened surfaces, resting one on the other in a vertical bank at the end of the paper machine. The paper is passed between all or part of these rolls to increase the smoothness and gloss of its surface.

CALENDER CRUSHED. A term applied to a sheet of paper in which the fibers have been pushed out of position and the formation disturbed by excessive pressure in the calendering operation. Calender-crushing usually causes a decrease in opacity and a dulling of the color.

CALENDER CUTS. Defects in paper caused by wrinkles in the paper as it passes through the calender rolls, appearing as slits, or glazed or discolored lines across the sheet.

CALENDER DYED. A term applied to paper or paper boards dyed or stained at the calender rolls. The dye solution is supplied from calender boxes to the calender rolls, which transfer it to either one or both sides of the paper or board.

CALENDER FINISHED. A term applied to any paper with a surface glazed by means of calenders; it does not include plate finish but refers to machine finish, English finish, supercalendered, and calender-friction-glazed.

CALENDER MARKED. A term applied to paper on which marks from the calender rolls are impressed.

CALENDER SCALES. Small particles of pigment that gather on the calender rolls and are pressed on the paper.

CALENDER-SIZING. Application of an emulsified wax to paper or boards at the calender. The paper or board may be treated at one or both sides with the sizing agent, depending upon whether one or two water boxes are used. Calender sizing increases the water resistance of the product and, in some cases, the oil resistance also.

CALENDER STREAKS. Continuous streaks of darkened paper occurring parallel to the grain, caused by uneven pressing and drying prior to calendering.

CALENDERING. The operation of finishing a sheet of paper by passing it through a calender or supercalender.

CALIPER. The thickness of a sheet measured under specified conditions. It is usually expressed in thousandths of an inch (mils or points).

CANDY-SLAB PAPER. A heavy waxed paper with a high finish, in a basis weight of 55 pounds (24 x 36—480), which is used in the manufacture of candy while the individual pieces are cooling and setting. The paper must strip from the candy when cold without removing the coating from the candy or leaving any paper on the candy. The wax used must have a higher melting point than the hot candy. A manila sheet or a highly glazed sheet varnished on one side may also be used. It may be embossed with the name of the manufacturer in reverse and thus leave the name in the candy on cooling.

CARBON BLACK. Finely divided carbon obtained by burning natural gas in a regulated air supply, the carbon particles being deposited on a metallic surface.

CARBONATE PAPER. A printing paper largely used in the magazine publishing field. It is made of chemical wood pulps heavily loaded with calcium carbonate, generally not sized, with an English finish and of good color and opacity. It is usually made in basis weights of 40 to 50 pounds (25 x 38—500).

CARDBOARD MIDDLES. Coarse boards made from mixed waste papers and mechanical pulp and used as fillers for cardboards. The chipboards or newsboards are cylinder made, nonfolding, and with fairly smooth surfaces, to which is laminated cardboard lining paper for the production of special surfaced boards.

CASE-HARDENING. Surface-hardening without thorough drying of the film.

CASEIN. A protein obtained from milk and used in the sizing of paper and as an adhesive in the manufacture of coated papers.

CASEIN-COATED PAPER. A coated paper in which casein has been used as an adhesive.

CAST-COATING. Process in which the coated paper is pressed against a solid surface while the coating is in a highly plastic condition. For most coatings, a steam-heated drum is used. When dried, the finish is similar to the contacted surface.

CATALYST. A substance which alters (increases or decreases) the velocity of a reaction and which is unchanged at the end of the reaction.

CELLULOSE ACETATE. Acetic ester of cellulose, which is a polyhydric alcohol. Together with plasticizers, it can be coated from volatile solvents as a tough, clear, colorless sheet.

CENTIGRADE. The temperature scale on which the freezing point of water is 0° and its boiling point is 100°.

CENTIPOISE. One hundredth of a poise (unit of viscosity).

CHINA CLAY. See Kaolin.

CHIPBOARD. See cardboard middles.

CHLORINATED RUBBERS. Resin-like rubber derivative obtained by passing chlorine gas into a solution of rubber in chloroform, carbon tetrachloride, etc. Contains about 65% combined chlorine.

CHLOROBROMIDE PAPER. A photographic base paper which is coated with an emulsion of silver chloride and silver bromide in gelatin.

CHOKE-ROLLER DESIGN. A paper design in which the background is solidly printed.

CHROMO PAPER. A term applied to any paper or board especially suited to accept colored printing. Chromo paper is usually defined as a coated paper of good quality, color, and surface with sufficient strength to take many colors.

CLAY. A finely divided, siliceous material, usually derived from the decomposition of aluminous minerals. It is used in the paper industry as a filling and coating agent. Freedom from grit, correct particle size, and good color are important requisites.

CLAY-COATED BOXBOARD. A high-grade folding boxboard, coated with clay, used in the manufacture of folding boxes. Distinguishing features are brightness of color, excellence of printing surface, and permanence of color and brightness. The basis weight and gage schedules correspond to those for regular folding boxboard, except that clay coating generally adds slightly to the weight of board of a given thickness.

CLOUDINESS. When a material is not clear and bright it is said to be "cloudy" or to show "cloudiness." The term cloudiness is sometimes used to denote blushing. Cloudiness can be attributed to the hygroscopic nature of some solvents used.

COATED. A term applied to paper and paper board, the surface of which has been treated with clay or a pigment and adhesive mixture, or other suitable agent, to improve the finish with respect to printing quality, color, smoothness, opacity, or other surface properties. The term is also applied to lacquered and varnished papers.

COATED ART PAPER. A paper used for high-grade printing work, especially in halftone printing, where detail and definite handling of shading and highlights are important. It is usually a high-grade coated paper having a glossy, highly uniform printing surface.

COATED BOARD. Paper board which is clay coated. This board is used for box making and miscellaneous purposes.

COATED COVER PAPER. Paper in weights used for cover paper but with a coated surface. It is usually coated on both sides and has either a dull or high finish.

COATED MAGAZINE PAPER. Coated paper used in printing magazines, especially those carrying colored illustrations. This term covers a wide range of paper, from paper-machine-coated mechanical wood-pulp-base papers to the highest grades of coated paper, and also a wide range of basis weights.

COATED OFFSET PAPER. Coated paper, with a high resistance to picking, coated on two sides and sized in the same manner as coated lithograph paper suitable for use in offset printing. The basis weights usually range from 60 to 100 pounds (25 x 38—500).

COATED PAPER. Any paper which has been coated. This term covers a wide range of qualities, basis weights, and uses.

COATING CLAY. Any clay suitable for coating paper.

COATING COLOR. The completed coating formulation ready for use. It contains the pigments, adhesives and all other additives which together make up the final coating formula.

COATING COMPOSITION. A generic term for paints, lacquers, enamels, printing inks, etc.

COATING RAW STOCK. Any paper used as a base paper for coating. The type of paper varies with its ultimate use.

COHESION. Attraction by which the particles of a body are united.

COLD FLOW. If subjected to pressure for a sufficient period of time, no organic elastic material will return exactly to its original shape. This change of shape is called cold flow. Compression set is the amount by which a small cylinder of rubber is distorted by cold flow.

COLLOID MILL. Machine for dispersing a solid or liquid in a liquid. Its essential feature is the relative motion, usually at high speed, of two very closely spaced surfaces, which produces intense shearing stresses in the liquid and solid particles flowing between these surfaces. The shearing stresses are due to forces of viscosity in the liquid, rather than to a grinding action between the moving surfaces.

COLLOIDAL. State of subdivision of matter in which particles of 1 to 100 mμ are dispersed in a continuous medium.

COLOR FASTNESS. The property of a paper, dye, or dyed paper to retain its color in normal storage or to resist changes in color when exposed to light, heat, or other deleterious influences.

COLOR LAKE. Artificial pigment prepared by precipitating a dye on an inorganic base such as alumina, barium sulfate, clay, etc. The term pulp color is also applied to these lakes but it is sometimes extended to cover pigments sold in the paste form, such as the chrome yellows. Dry lakes are made by drying and grinding color lakes.

COMMON EMBOSSINGS. Patterns in common use by manufacturers of embossed paper. For instance: Skytogen and certain leather grains, moire, basket weave, Persian lamb, and swirl designs.

CONCENTRATION. The amount of substance (weight or percentage) contained in a unit volume of solution, e.g., grams per liter.

CONDENSATE. Product which is obtained by cooling the vapors of a substance to a liquid.

CONDENSATION. The act of liquefying by cooling vapors of any substance that have been driven off by the application of heat. The process of forming liquid from its vapors.

CONSISTENCY. Resistance to flow. For Newtonian liquids, consistency is the same as the viscosity. Although "consistency" is an accepted rheological term it has qualitative meaning only, and is used with qualifying adjectives as "buttery," "thin," "high," etc., in describing plastic flow.

CONSTANT HUMIDITY. Nonchanging percentage of humidity; usually referred to as a condition of a room.

CONTACT ANGLE. The angle at which the surface of a liquid meets the surface of a solid or of another liquid. The angle is measured within the liquid so that, for example, the contact angle of water on glass is small, whereas that of water on paraffin or of mercury on glass is large. This is a quantity of interest in the discussion of penetration of liquids into paper.

CONTRAST RATIO. The ratio of the diffuse reflectance of the sheet when backed by a black body to that of the sheet when backed by a "white" body. The spectral nature of the light, the geometry of illuminating and viewing, and the spectral reflectance of the white body must be specified. There are several contrast ratios in use, the differences between them being the differences in reflectance of the white body placed behind the specimen; contrast ratio is an important measure of the opacity of paper.

CONVERTER. A plant which manufactures paper products, such as papeteries, envelopes, bags, containers, coated paper, gummed paper, etc., from paper purchased from others.

CONVERTING PAPER. Any paper which may be converted by a separate operation to produce a paper of different characteristics or to produce a product quite distinct from the original paper. Thus, kraft paper is made and sold to be converted into asphalt paper, waxed paper, gummed tape, paper bags; writing paper is converted into envelopes, etc.

COPOLYMER. Giant molecules formed when two or more unlike monomers are polymerized together. If a polymer is like a long train of box cars, a copolymer is mixed freight, box cars and tank cars alternating or arranged in any proportion such as three box cars and one tank car.

COPPER ENGRAVING. See Die Stamping.

CORRUGATING. Imparting a wave-like shape to a paper or board. It is carried out on a corrugating machine by moistening or steaming a roll of paper prior to passing it between two metal rolls cut with alternate ridges and grooves which are geared to run in complement to each other. This impresses permanent parallel flutes in the paper at right angles to the machine direction.

COVER PAPER. A great variety of papers used for the outside covers of catalogs, pamphlets, booklets, magazines, and other printed matter requiring protection from handling, for covering boxes, sometimes for photograph albums and mounts, etc. Cover papers are usually made from rag pulp, chemical wood pulp, or various mixtures of the two; other grades may contain mechanical pulp. The basis weights range from 25 to 100 pounds (20 x 26—500); the lighter weights are commonly known as box covers and are used for the outside covers of boxes. The medium weights, i.e., 50 and 65 pounds may be pasted two-ply; the 65 pound weight is the most popular in that thickness. Some of the essential features of cover paper are good folding qualities, permanence of color, an even printing surface, and a high resistance to handling and abrasion. Some cover papers are surface-sized for offset printing. Available in a wide variety of colors, surface finishes, and decorations. Some grades of cover paper are embossed with a leather design and used for folders.

CRACKING. Defect in coated paper, caused by the separation of the coating layer or the formation of fissures in the surface of the coating in printing or other converting processes. A term referring to fissures in the crease when a sheet of paper is folded.

CRACKLE FINISH. Lacquer finish resulting from applying a top coat lacquer designed to shrink and crack and expose a more flexible undercoat, usually of a different color.

CRAWLING. Defect of a finishing composition in which the adhesion to the surface is too low to prevent the finish, while still wet, from pulling together, leaving uncoated areas.

CRAZING. Film failure usually due to disrupting the continuity of the top coat resulting in fine wrinkles and minute surface cracks. In the case of coated cloth and paper, a whitening when creased or deformed, especially under compression.

CREASABILITY. The property of a sheet to resist cracking when sharply bent and to permit a smooth crease without wrinkles. This property should be carefully distinguished from brittleness, which involves a small degree of bending.

CREPE PAPER. Produced by crowding the wet sheet on the roll by means of a doctor. The paper is made from sulfite, sulfate, or mechanical pulp or a mixture of these in various basis weights. For colored crepes, the sheet is wetted in a dye solution, which contains addition agents, usually glue. Crepe paper is used for various articles, such as napkins, tablecloths, decorations, etc.

CROCKING. Removal of color on abrasion or rubbing.

CURE. Rubber and some synthetics are cured or vulcanized by mixing with sulfur and heating. Other synthetics differ from rubber in that they can be cured by heating without sulfur.

CURL. Curvature of the sheet. It may appear as a gross curl in one direction of the sheet, e.g., the machine direction, or as an uneven warping of the edges of the sheet. Curl is produced by one or more of the following factors: The moisture content of the atmosphere or of the sheet, the distribution of the moisture throughout the sheet, orientation of fibers throughout the sheet, or the internal stresses within the sheet.

DAMPERS (DAMPING ROLLS). Chilled cylinders, located ahead of the calender stacks, which condense a continuous spray of steam and transfer the moisture to the paper web as it passes to the calenders. A spray of moist steam or water playing on the web of paper.

DECORATED COVER PAPER. Cover paper with a design produced by embossing or some other process. The paper may be coated or uncoated and it may be decorated during or after manufacture.

DEEP-ETCH OFFSET. A type of offset printing in which the design is chemically etched a few thousandths of an inch below the surface of the plate and is, therefore, similar to intaglio. It is also called offsetgravure, and lithogravure. Deep-etch offset differs from real gravure in that the depth of the etch is uniform and the size of the halftone dot varies; in real gravure printing, the size of the dot is uniform, but gradations of tone are obtained by the variations in the depth of the etched dots.

DEFLOCCULATION. State or condition of a dispersion of a solid in a liquid in which each solid particle remains independent of and unassociated with adjacent particles. A deflocculated suspension shows zero or very low yield value.

DENSITY. Weight per unit volume. Density is also used as a term to denote the strength of color in speaking of colored materials. When a material covers quite solidly in one coat it is said that the color has great density. Likewise, density is sometimes used to express freedom from voids or solidity: a nonporous film is sometimes called a dense film.

DESIGN PRINTING. Immersing a sheet of paper in a color solution and subsequently passing it between design-marked rollers, so that the design stands out heavily colored or printed against the lighter background of the same color. Wrapping paper may be design marked, safety paper is also often design printed.

DEXTRIN. Carbohydrate produced from starch by hydrolysis due to the action of dilute acids, enzymes, or dry heat. It is an intermediate product between starch and the sugars resulting from starch on hydrolysis. Dextrin is an amorphous, white, or yellowish powder, soluble in water or dilute alcohol, but precipitated by strong alcohol. It is used as an adhesive in the preparation of gummed papers.

DIE STAMPING. Intaglio process for the production of letterheads, cards, etc., printing from lettering or other designs engraved into copper or steel. Ink is smeared over the surface of the die, the surface is wiped off, and the ink remaining in the design is printed under heavy pressure, which also partially embosses the paper. The terms copper and steel engraving also cover this process.

DIELECTRIC STRENGTH. The maximum potential gradient that a material can withstand without rupture.

DILATANCY. Property of certain suspensions in which the resistance to flow increases at a greater rate than the increase in rate of flow. Quicksand or wet sea sand have dilatancy: If the surface is struck sharply, the sand is rigid and solid; but slow, sustained pressure causes the sand to flow and an object to sink into the sand mass.

DILUENTS. In the manufacture of resinous and/or cellulosic type finishes volatile liquids which are not primary solvents for the ingredients are used to lower the viscosity and give certain other desirable properties. These are called diluents or thinners.

DILUTION RATIO. Ratio by which a given solvent or solution may be diluted.

DIRECT DYES. A class of aniline dyes, so called because they dye cellulose fibers directly, i.e., without a mordant. They have less tinctorial power than the basic dyestuffs; but, in general, they are much faster to light than the basic dyes and, in some cases, than the acid dyes.

DIRECT LITHOGRAPHY. A planographic printing process in which The paper (or cloth, etc.) to be printed comes into direct contact with the stone or metal plate. The design to be printed is drawn, photographed, or transferred to the surface of the stone or metal with a special crayon or ink, which is then subjected to the action of a weak acid that hardens the ink. The process of printing first requires moistening the surface with water, which is absorbed by the blank parts and repelled by the wet parts but adheres to the ink-drawn design.

DISINTEGRATION. The complete breaking down of the dried film of a finishing material. It may be caused by long continued exposure or aging or to the improper type of finishing material being used for the work at hand.

DISPERSING AGENT. A reagent which is compatible with the solvent and holds finely divided matter dispersed in that solvent.

DISPERSION. Heterogeneous system of solids, gases, liquids, or immiscible liquids.

DISTILLATE. Product obtained by cooling the vapors of a substance.

DISTILLATION. Evaporation and recondensation used for separating liquids into fractions according to their boiling points.

DISTILLING RANGE. The temperature range within which a liquid can be distilled.

DOCTOR (BLADE). A thin plate or scraper of wood, metal, or other hard substance placed along the entire length of the roll or cylinder to keep it free from paper, pulp, size, etc., and thus maintain a smooth, clean surface.

DOPE. Nitrocellulose, cellulose acetate, or other cellulose derivatives dissolved in suitable solvents.

DOPE COTTON. High-viscosity nitrocellulose, i.e., 20 to 30 second, 40 second, and 70 second nitrocellulose.

DRIERS. The salts of certain metals which hasten the drying when added to paints or varnishes. Some driers are in dry form, others are in paste form, but most of them are dissolved in oils and volatile solvents with or without the presence of gum resins. These solutions are known as driers, oil driers, japan driers, liquid driers, and japans. The action of driers in oils is not thoroughly understood, but they are thought to act as catalytic agents. The metallic salts most commonly used are those of lead, manganese, and cobalt.

DRUM COATING. The process of smoothing the coating by means of oscillating flat brushes contacting the coated side of a moving web of freshly coated paper which is drawn tightly against a revolving drum. The drum distinguishes it from the apron coater, in which the drum is replaced by a moving rubber belt or "apron."

DRY LAKE. See under Color Lake.

DRYING OIL. Oils which dry to a varnish-like film upon exposure to air and sunlight. Linseed oil, china-wood or tung oil and perilla oil are the three principal vegetable oils of the drying class used in lacquer and varnish manufacture.

DULLNESS. Lack of luster or gloss.

ELASTICITY. The property of returning to the original shape or volume after the distorting force has been removed.

EMULSIFYING AGENT. Surface-active substance that promotes the formation of emulsions and keeps them stable.

EMULSION. Intimate mixture of two immiscible liquids, one of them being dispersed in the other in fine droplets.

ESTER. Compound of an alcohol with an acid, formed with the elimination of water.

ESTER GUMS. The glycerol ester of rosin acids. It is made by heating rosin with the glycerol under pressure until condensation takes place. The gums are insoluble in water but soluble in amyl acetate, turpentine, carbon tetrachloride, and some oils. They are not synthetic resins but rather modified natural resins. They are used as substitutes for copal, damar, and kauri gums in making enamels, paints and cellulose lacquers. They are also used with tung oil for waterproof varnishes.

EXCLUSIVE EMBOSSINGS. There are several hundred different embossing designs which have been originated or purchased by individual manufacturers who own these designs exclusively. Most manufacturers have exclusive designs of their own and many such designs are protected by registration at the United States Patent Office. The Coated and Processed Paper Assoc., 1002 Union Trust Bldg., Providence 3, R. I. maintains a registration bureau of these designs for the protection of its members and to answer inquiries from customers and users.

FABRIC DESIGNS. Paper printed in designs that imitate various fabrics, commonly known as "fabric prints," or embossed in imitation of fabrics, such as rep, linen burlap, and others.

FADING. Loss of color by destruction of coloring matter through exposure to light, heat, or other agents.

FAHRENHEIT. The temperature scale in which 32° denotes the freezing point and 212° the boiling point of water.

FALSE BODY. Thixotropic flow property of a suspension or dispersion. When it "thins down" on stirring and "builds up" on standing it is said to exhibit false body. The term "false body" is also used in practice for "buttery" materials which are characterized by a relatively low viscosity and high yield value.

FATTY ACID. Organic acids of a general formula $C_nH_{2n}O_2$, e.g., stearic acid; organic acids of aliphatic or open chain structure.

FESTOON DRYING. A method of air drying in which the paper is hung in a continuous web, in short loops or festoons, on traveling poles moving through a drying chamber.

FIREPROOF PAPER. Any paper that is treated with chemicals so that it will not support combustion. It is not actually fireproof but will not carry a flame.

FLINT GLAZING. A method of imparting a hard, brilliant polish to paper, more especially to coated papers, by means of rubbing or rolling with a smooth stone or stone burnisher on a flint-glazing machine.

FLOCCULATION. Formation of clusters of particles separable by relatively weak mechanical forces or by a change in the forces at the interface between the liquid and the solid dispersed particles. Flocculation is often visible as a "Jack Frost" pattern in a flow-out of a dispersion; microscopically it appears as a lacework or reticulum of loosely clustered primary particles. A flocculated dispersion of sufficient pigment concentration shows yield value. Surface active agents are often useful in reducing the extent of flocculation and the yield value.

FLOCK PAPER. Wallpaper or cover paper prepared by sizing either over the whole surface or over special parts constituting the pattern only, and then powdered over with flock (powdered wool, cotton, or rayon), which is specially dyed. It was originally intended to imitate tapestry and Italian velvet brocades.

FLOW COATING. A coating applied in a very free manner which will permit the material to flow freely.

FLUID. Gas, liquid or a very soft solid that is capable of flowing.

FLUIDITY. The reciprocal of viscosity. Fluidity is proportional to the slope of the flow curve for a true Newtonian fluid. The unit of measurement is the rhe, which is the rate of shear induced in a liquid by a shearing force of 1 dyne/cm^2.

FOILS. Metallized papers produced by applying to paper a continuous sheet of metallic foil, usually tin, aluminum, zinc, or their alloys. The foil is bonded to the paper by some form of adhesive.

FOLDING ENDURANCE. The number of folds under specified conditions in a specified instrument which a specimen will withstand before failure. In the usual test, a specimen is subjected repeatedly to double folds through a wide angle while under tension. This property, which is related to brittleness, is of importance in several uses of paper.

FORMATION. The degree of uniformity of distribution of the solid components of the sheet with special reference to the fibers. It is usually judged by the appearance of the sheet when viewed by transmitted light. This property is very important, not only because of its influence on the appearance of the sheet but because it influences the value and uniformity of value of nearly all other properties.

FREE FLOWING. A material is said to be free flowing when it shows freedom from brush marks, sags, etc.

FRICTION CALENDER. A set usually consisting of three rolls: the bottom roll of chilled iron, the intermediate roll of cotton, and the top roll of chilled iron, bored so as to admit steam. It has a burnishing action on the paper.

FRICTION-GLAZED. A term applied to paper which has a very high finish secured by passing the sheet through chilled iron rolls revolving at different peripheral speeds. This process is used largely in finishing coated box-lining papers, waterproof papers, bronzed and silver papers, etc.

FROZEN-FOOD PAPERS. Highly moisture- and moisture-vapor-resistant papers used for inner liners in frozen-foods packaging. They are usually moistureproof glassine, or bleached sulfite papers specially treated for high moistureproofness; waxed papers and plain, coated, or waxed vegetable parchments are also used. They are pliable so as to resist cracking under the low temperatures employed in quick-freezing and storage of foods. Properties required are stripping quality, strength and flexibility, resistance to penetration of liquids and vapors, high wet tensile strength, and purity.

FUGITIVE COLORS. Colors not fast to light.

GEL. A jelly-like colloid. See also Gelation.

GELATINOUS. Having the consistency of a very soft elastic solid of the nature and appearance of gelatin.

GELATION. Process by which a fluid system develops yield value. Freundlich defines sol as a colloidal suspension without yield value, and a gel as a colloidal suspension with yield value. A gel (or jelly) is commonly considered a mass retaining appreciable quantities of liquid, which exhibits properties of a solid.

GLASSINE PAPER. A smooth, dense, transparent, or semitransparent paper manufactured primarily from chemical wood pulps which have been beaten to secure a high degree of hydration of the stock. This paper is greaseproof and when waxed or lacquered is practically impervious to air and vapors.

GLAZED FINISH. High gloss or polish, applied to the surface of paper either during the process of manufacture, or after the paper is produced, by friction calender, plater, or Yankee drier, etc.

GLAZED-COATED BOOK PAPER. Any book paper having a highly supercalendered or glossy brush-finished surface.

GLOSS. Shine, sheen, or luster of the dried film. If a surface clearly and plainly reflects an image or light it is glossy.

GLOSS WHITE. Precipitated mixture of barium sulfate and aluminum hydroxide.

GLOSSMETER. An instrument used to measure the gloss intensity of a surface.

GOLD PAPER. Metallic bronze-coated paper. There are many qualities and weights ranging from light weights used in the paperbox industry to heavy bristols.

GOLD, PLATINUM METALLICS. Produced by grinding bronze (gold), aluminum (silver), and copper with casein and other gums or with pyroxylin lacquer; the coated paper is generally stack calendered to appear smooth and brilliant.

GRAIN. Machine direction of the paper.

GRAINED PAPER. Paper embossed or decorated to imitate various grains, such as alligator, marble, Spanish leather, etc. It is available in cover or box-cover weights.

GRAINING. The operation of printing various designs on a board on one or both liners. The designs commonly used are oak, marble, and cedar graining. Other designs, such as imitation alligator, may also be obtained by using specially engraved printing cylinders; the pattern is engraved below the surface of the cylinder. In passing the board under the cylinder, the design is printed by the ink contained in the engraved depressions in the cylinder.

GRAPHITE PAPER. A paper made from stock which has been treated with colloidal graphite or which has been coated by spraying, painting, or dipping with an aqueous paste of colloidal graphite. The paper is usually gray to gray-black in color. The addition of graphite increases the opacity of the sheet, renders it less sensitive to color changes by sunlight, makes it electrically conductive, and lubricates the paper.

GREASEPROOF BOARD. Paperboard pasted over with greaseproof paper, such as glassine, or a board that has been treated to render it grease- and oil-resistant.

GREASEPROOF PAPER. A protective wrapping paper made from chemical wood pulps which are highly hydrated in order that the resulting paper is resistant to oil and grease. The basis weights range from 20 to 50 pounds (24 x 36—500). This paper is used extensively for wrapping greasy food products. Paper which has been treated or coated to render it resistant to grease or oils.

GRIT. Hard, relatively large inclusions in a coating composition.

GUMMED PAPER. Paper coated on one side with an adhesive, such as dextrin, a fish or an animal glue, or a blend of these. Gummed papers are used for stickers, labels, seals, stamps, splices, tapes, etc. They lie flat without curling and adhere firmly to the surface.

GYPSUM. See Calcium Sulfate.

HALFTONE. A printing plate (usually copper or zinc) produced by the photoengraving process. It is a reproduction of a photograph, drawing, painting, print, or other object having a gradation of tones. The surface of the plate consists of dots of various sizes uniformly placed and capable of rendering not only the high lights and shadows of a picture, but all the gradations between these. An impression or print made from a halftone plate by the letterpress, intaglio, or planographic process.

HALFTONE PAPER. A printing paper suitable for printing halftones, usually of a high finish, i.e., supercalendered or coated.

HANGING PAPER. The raw stock used in the manufacture of wall paper. The converter usually coats the sheet with clay and then prints it with a decorative design, or, in the heavier weights, embosses it, although in some grades the raw stock is simply printed with the desired pattern. The rawstock is usually manufactured with a substantial portion of mechanical wood pulp, the balance being unbleached or bleached chemical wood pulp. However, for some papers, mechanical wood pulp and bleached sulfite are used, and in other cases, the papers are made from a raw stock containing no mechanical wood pulp. The sheet is hard-sized to resist moisture in the coating and pasting, has a "toothy" surface to enable the coating color to adhere to the sheet, is of uniform surface so that the design will print uniformly, and is especially adapted to hold deep embossing. It is also soft and pliable for efficient operation in the converting plant, so that it lies flat when paste is applied. The commonly used weights are 38, 42, 50, 58, 66, 74, 82, and 98 pounds (24 x 36—480), which are respectively referred to in the trade as 9, 10, 12, 14, 16, 18, 20, and 24 ounces. The ounce nomenclature presumably arose out of the weight in ounces of a roll of wallpaper of a given length and width, but it no longer represents the weight of any standard size roll of wallpaper and at present is a purely arbitrary designation.

HAZE. Dullness of surface finish removable by burnishing, usually resulting from faulty solvent balance of incompatibility of ingredients.

HEAT-CONVERTIBLE RESIN. See Thermosetting Resins.

HIDING POWER. Ability of a pigment dispersed in a vehicle to obscure a background.

HIGH-SOLVENCY THINNER. A volatile diluent which has great solvent power and which will permit dilution to a great extent with cheaper thinners.

HOT-MELT COATING. A method of applying molten plastic materials to a base stock without solvent or other carrier, using a roll, knife, casting, or extrusion method. This process gives high brilliance and gloss.

HUMIDITY. The amount of water vapor in the air.

HYDROCARBONS. Compounds containing only hydrogen and carbon, such as acetylene, benzene, etc.

HYDROGEN-ION CONCENTRATION OR pH. The measure of actual or active acidity or basicity: the number of gram molecules of hydrogen ions present in one liter of a solution. It is usually expressed as the logarithm to the base ten of its reciprocal, called pH. Neutrality is at a pH 7, which is the pH of distilled water. Solutions having a pH less than 7 are acid and those having a pH higher than 7 are alkaline. Measurement of hydrogen-ion concentration or pH may be made colorimetrically or, more accurately, by potentiometric methods.

HYDROPHILIC. Readily wetted by water.

HYDROPHOBIC. Water-repellent; not wetted by water.

IMPREGNATION. The process of treating a sheet or web of paper or paperboard with a liquid. This may be a molten material, such as hot asphalt or wax, a solution in a volatile solvent, or a liquid, such as an oil. Pressure may or may not be used in the operation.

INTAGLIO PRINTING. Printing from plates in which the image is sunken below the surface, as distinguished from printing by letterpress (relief) or planography (flat plane). Included in this class of printing are rotogravure, sheet-fed gravure, photogravure, offset gravure, copper and steel engraving, etching, stipple engraving, aquatint, and mezzotint. The image consists of regular (screen) or irregular (grain) etched depressions of lines and dots engraved by hand. They are filled with ink, and the surface is wiped or scraped clean by a doctor blade. This feature gives gravure prints an unusually wide range of tonal expression, ranging from full, velvety depths to purest highlights.

INTENSITY. The intensity of a color is its purity of hue or color tone or the degree of hue as seen by the eye, as for example, an intense red is one which is seen as a very strong pure red color.

INTERFACIAL TENSION. Surface tension at the surface separating two nonmiscible liquids.

IRIDESCENT PAPER. Coated or otherwise treated paper (cover, book, or writing), having a mother of pearl effect. One method is to expose the paper to fumes of ammonia, having been first soaked in a mixture of gum, iron sulfate, indigo sulfate, and nut galls in solution.

JELLY. See under Gelation.

KAOLIN. "A white-firing clay which in its beneficiated condition is made up chiefly of minerals of the kaolinite type. Two types of kaolin may be recognized as follows: Residual, a kaolin found in the place where it is formed by rock weathering. Sedimentary, a kaolin which has been transported from its place of origin. Sedimentary kaolins show more pronounced colloidal properties than residual kaolins" (American Ceramic Society).

KRAFT PAPER. A paper made entirely from wood pulp produced by an alkaline process. It is a comparatively coarse paper particularly noted for its strength, and it is used primarily as a wrapper or packaging material. It can be watermarked, striped, or calendered, and it has an acceptable surface for printing. Its natural, unbleached color is brown but by the use of semibleached or fully bleached sulfate pulp, it can be produced in lighter shades of brown, cream tints, and white. It can also be dyed. Kraft paper is most commonly made in basis weights ranging from 25 to 60 pounds (24 x 36—480) but can be also made in weights ranging from 18 to 200 pounds.

LABELABLE. Coined term referring to that property of a sheet of paper which allows a gummed label to adhere to its surface. This is particularly important on coated fancy, box, and cover papers since it is often desirable to paste a manufacturer's price or legendary label on the exposed surface.

LACQUER. A solution in an organic solvent of a natural or synthetic resin, a cellulose ester, such as cellulose nitrate or cellulose acetate, or a cellulose ether, such as methyl or benzylcellulose, etc., together with modifying agents, such as plasticizers, resins, waxes, and pigments. The solvent evaporates after application of the lacquer, leaving the dissolved material as a shiny, more or less continuous protective film on the surface of the material so treated. Lacquers are used for coating paper to produce a decorative effect and a glossy appearance and to enhance the color value of the ink. They are also used for increasing the grease or moisture resistance of paper.

LAKE. Pigment prepared by precipitating coloring material on a substrate. Coloring matter rendered insoluble by precipitation as heavy metal salts or by complex acids or mordants.

LAMINAR FLOW. Viscous flow. Continuous, steady motion of particles, the motion at a fixed point always remaining constant. It is obtained in capillary tubes and rotational viscometers. If the rate of shear is too high, for both plastic and Newtonian systems, "turbulent" flow results; if the rate of shear for plastics is too low, "plug flow" results.

LAMINATED BOARD. Paperboard is laminated by (a) combining two or more plies of board; (b) combining a paperboard on one or two sides, with a thin paper with specific properties. The adhesive used may be a water solution of glue, casein, or starch, or a thermoplastic wax or resin composition. The lining papers may be of book or hanging grades, for improving the appearance and the printing surface of the board, or of a special type, such as greaseproof or glassine, for imparting some specific property which could not be built into the board itself.

LAMINATING. Combining two or more layers of paper or board with an adhesive in such a way as to form a multiply paper product with or without special properties resulting from the choice of the papers and adhesives. Originally papers and boards were laminated for the sole purpose of increasing thickness and rigidity; more lately laminating has been adopted as a means to more specific ends, for example the provision of moisture-resistance. Sheets or paper in the web is laminated, depending upon the type of machinery used.

LATEX. Aqueous colloidal dispersion of rubber or rubber-like substances. A viscous, milky juice obtained from tapping the rubber tree.

LEAFING. Orientation during drying of a flake- or plate-like pigment particle in a surface film so that the major dimensions of the particle is parallel with the surface of the dry film.

LIGHTFASTNESS. Ability of a color or film to withstand exposure to radiant energy without change from the original condition.

LITHOCOATED PAPER. A paper coated on one side to withstand the water used in the lithograph process. It is made in a wide range of basis weights. Good pick strength is essential.

LITHOGRAPHY. Printing techniqque which originally involved putting writing or designs on a stone with a greasy crayon or liquid drawing medium and the production of printed impressions from this on a flat-bed press. Today it is divided into two classes, direct and offset lithography (see).

LITHOGRAVURE. See Deep-Etch Offset.

LITHOPONE. A mixture of zinc sulfide and barium sulfate used as a loading material.

LIVERING. The progressive, irreversible increase in consistency of a pigment-vehicle combination.

LONG-OIL VARNISH. A varnish relatively low in resin content, containing usually more than 25 gallons of oil per 100 pounds of resin.

LUSTER. In the paper industry, the term gloss, luster, and sheen are commonly used to indicate the same property.

MASSTONE. The color of a pigmented film sufficiently thick to eliminate transmitted light.

MATTE OR DULL-COATED. A casein- or clay-coated paper of low finish.

MEDIUM-OIL VARNISH. A varnish of medium resin content usually containing from 10 to 25 gallons of oil per 100 pounds of resin.

MELTING POINT. The transition point between solid and liquid phases. Pure solids usually melt at a definite temperature, i.e., they have a sharp melting point; mixtures, e.g., alloys have a melting range.

METALLIC COATING. Coating for either a paper or a board, the pigment of which consists of metallic flakes such as aluminum or bronze powder and the vehicle of which is casein or a lacquer. The bronze may be uncolored to give the effect of silver, or stained to give the effect of gold, gun metal, or other special shades.

METALLIC PAPER. Paper coated with metallic substances to produce the effect of a metallic surface or paper which has been combined with metallic foils.

MIL. See Caliper.

MILDEW. Finishing materials exposed to warm, damp conditions often develop a fungus growth, called mildew.

MILLING. Mixing by passing between rotating steel rolls, called a mill. Rubbers are milled to plasticize or soften them and to incorporate compounding ingredients.

MOBILE. A material is mobile when it offers little resistance to flowing.

MODIFIED RESINS. Synthetic resins modified with oil, natural resins or gums.

MONOMER. Recurring structural unit of a polymer.

NEUTRALITY. In a chemical sense, a substance is neutral when it has neither an alkaline nor an acid reaction, but in the lacquer and allied industries the term is given a little broader meaning and includes all substances which do not enter into chemical reaction with other substances used in conjunction with them.

NEWS MIDDLE. See under Cardboard Middles.

NITROCELLULOSE. Nitric acid ester of cellulose or cellulose nitrate. For different purposes the cotton is nitrated in different degrees but for use in lacquers, nitrocellulose of about 12 per cent nitrogen content has been found most adaptable.

NONDRYING COATING. A coating that does not dry in regular conditions. Factors such as too much oil or plasticizer or drying conditions influence this condition.

NONDRYING OIL. Oil which does not have the ability to take up oxygen from the air to change it from a liquid to a solid state.

Mineral oils are nondrying oils as are a few vegetable oils. Most vegetable oils are drying oils or semidrying oils.

NONPOLAR SOLVENTS. Aromatic and petroleum hydrocarbon solvents characterized by low dielectric constants.

NONVOLATILE. That portion of a material which does not evaporate at ordinary temperatures. The total of such materials in a lacquer is called the nonvolatile matter and includes the pigment, metallic drying salts, gum or resins, oils or plasticizers and nitrocellulose.

NYLONS. Long-chain, synthetic high polymers particularly polyamides, which can be formed into a filament.

OFFSET. The tendency of a printed sheet to transfer the printing to the back of the next sheet when it is not thoroughly dry or set before being wound up in a roll.

OFFSET BOOK PAPER. A book paper used principally in the offset lithographic process. It may be coated on two sides with casein as the adhesive. The paper is processed to eliminate, as far as possible, distortion from stretching or shrinking and curling. It is made to have good pick strength. Cleanliness, uniform formation, freedom from fuzz, and a bright white color are important properties. Common basis weights are 50 to 100 pounds (25 x 38—500).

OFFSET GRAVURE. See Deep-Etch Offset.

OFFSET LITHOGRAPHY. An adaption of the principles of stone (or direct) lithography, in which the design is drawn or photographically reproduced on a thin, flexible metal plate which is curved to fit a revolving cylinder. The design from this plate is transferred to or offset on a rubber blanket carried on another cylinder, which in turn transfers the design to the paper, cloth, metal, etc., resulting in a soft effect.

OIL ABSORPTION. Quantity of oil required to wet a definite weight of pigment to form a stiff paste, when mechanically mixed.

OIL LENGTH. The gallonage of oil per 100 pounds of resin in a varnish, i.e., 25 gallon length would indicate 25 gallons of oil cooked with 100 pounds of resin.

OIL RESISTANCE. The ability of a finish to withstand the softening action of oils.

OIL SOLUBLE DYE. Oil soluble dyes are those which are commonly used for making concentrated oil stains by dissolving the
dyes in coal tar solvents such as toluol, xylol, benzol and similar
light bodied oils. These dyes are spoken of as oil red, oil blue,
oil yellow, oil black, etc.

OPACITY. That property of a sheet which prevents dark objects on,
or in contact with, the back side of the sheet from being seen.
It is usually evaluated by contrast ratio. This property is of
great importance in printing and wrapping papers.

OPAQUE. Impervious to light or not transparent.

ORANGE PEEL. Pebbled film surface similar to the skin of an
orange in appearance.

OVERDRIED. A term applied to paper which has been excessively
dried with a resulting increase in brittleness and a loss of inherent strength.

OVERTONE. The color of a thick pigmented film when viewed in
reflected light at an oblique angle.

OZOKERITE. A natural hydrocarbon wax of great flexibility having a melting point of 140° to 200°F.

PARIS WHITE. A very pure form of calcium carbonate, used as a
coating material.

PASTING. The art of uniting, by means of an adhesive, two or
more sheets of paper or board, paper to board, or coated or offset paper to blotting paper. Paper may be pasted off the reel
or in the web (roll machine) or in sheets (sheet-pasting machine).

PATENT-COATED. A term used to denote a board that has been
vat-lined on the paper machine on one or both sides with an uncoated white liner, the stock for which is of a better grade than
that used for the board itself. The board is not actually coated
in the sense of a sheet to which a coating material and an adhesive (such as casein, starch, etc.) have been applied.

PEARL FILLER. See Calcium Sulfate.

PEARL WHITE. See Barium Sulfate.

PEPTIZATION. See Deflocculation.

PERMANENCE. Resistance to changes in any or all properties through aging of a specified type. Specified types of aging are for example storage under specified temperature and relative humidity; exposure to chemically active atmosphere, etc. Folding endurance, resistance to water penetration, water absorbency, color, alpha-cellulose content, and cuprammonium viscosity are properties most frequently measured in the evaluation of permanence of pulp and paper.

PERMANENT WHITE. See Blanc Fixe.

PETROLEUM SPIRITS. The fraction distilled from crude petroleum having a boiling point higher than naphtha and lower than kerosene—usually made to have a boiling point and a distillation range that closely approximates those of turpentine. Used as a thinner in varnish and paints.

pH. See Hydrogen Ion Concentration.

PHENOLIC RESIN. Synthetic resin obtained by a condensation of phenol with formaldehyde.

PHOTOGRAVURE PRINTING. Intaglio printing in which the design is placed on the printing plate or cylinder photographically. The word "rotogravure" is a contraction of rotary photogravure.

PICK. The tendency of fibers or particles to be pulled away from the paper surface when removed from tacky surfaces, such as printing plates and pasting rolls.

PICKING. Lifting or the coating from coated papers. It occurs in printing when the tackiness of the ink used is stronger than the adhesive power of the casein used as an adhesive in the coating operation. In uncoated papers the same difficulty may also occur through the peeling of surface fibers.

PIGMENT. Powdered coloring matter that, mixed with a suitable liquid, will give a dye or enamel. A pigment is insoluble, while a dye is soluble. Many pigments are inorganic compounds, e.g., ochers, siennas, umbers, iron oxides, chrome yellow, ultramarine, and lampblack. Those used in the paper industry are principally lake colors, i.e., white pigments carrying precipitated organic dyestuffs.

PLASTIC FLOW. Type of flow which occurs in materials possessing yield value.

PLASTICIZERS. Usually high-boiling solvents added to lacquers to increase the elasticity and flexibility of the dried film; also called softeners. A substance which lowers the consistency of a mixture. Camphor is a plasticizer because it converts nitrocellulose into a plastic mass.

PLATE PAPER. Coated paper provided with a smooth finish by cold rolls through pressure in a stack calendering machine. For a very high finish, this paper is sometimes subjected to steam before calendering.

POINT. See Caliper.

POLISHED-DRUM COATING. A process in which the coating is applied in any suitable manner and immediately placed with the coated side against the surface of a highly polished, heated drum which smooths and dries the sheet without the necessity of subsequent calendering or polishing.

POLYMER. A polymer is a giant molecule formed when hundreds or even thousands of simple molecules of one and the same compound are linked together end to end like box cars in a long train.

POLYMERIZATION. Formation of a polymer by addition or condensation of simpler molecules.

POLYSTYRENE. Plastic; the polymerization product of copolymer has been defined under styrene.

POLYVINYL ACETATE. Polymer of vinyl acetate, which is prepared from acetylene and acetic acid.

POLYVINYL ALCOHOL. Oil-resistant plastic prepared by hydrolyzing polyvinyl acetate.

POLYVINYL BUTYRAL. Plastic formed by reacting polyvinyl alcohol with butyraldehyde.

POLYVINYLIDENE CHLORIDE. Plastic; polymer of vinylidene chloride.

PRESERVATIVE PAPERS. Papers for wrapping foodstuffs. They contain salicylic acid or some other preservative.

PRINTABILITY. That property of a paper which yields printed matter of good quality in any printing operation. It is judged by uniformity of color of the printed areas, contrast between printed and clear areas, legibility of the printed matter, and show-through. It is generally believed that this property is related to ink receptivity of a paper and its uniformity, compressibility, smoothness, and opacity.

PRINTED BOX-COVER PAPER. Plain or coated light-weight cover paper, or an uncoated or coated book paper, with a basis weight of approximately 25 to 40 pounds (20 x 26—500). It is commonly used by converters for decorating or embossing.

PRINTED CREPE. Crepe paper, about 8 to 20 pounds in basis weight (20 x 30—480), printed on a wallpaper machine, and used for decorative or advertising purposes.

PRINT-EMBOSSED. Embossed and printed in one operation by the application of ink to the embossing pattern.

PRINT-ON-COATING. A process in which the coating is applied to dry smooth paper by means of applicator rolls which print an accurately measured, evenly distributed film of high-density coating mixture directly on the paper.

PULP COLOR. See Color Lake.

PYROXYLIN-COATED PAPER. A paper which is coated with a pyroxylin lacquer. The coated paper is water-repellent and has a peculiar gloss. Such papers are also manufactured with gold, silver, copper, and other metallic finishes and are used for box coverings, greeting cards, book covers, labels, menus, food wrappers, tobacco wrappers, etc.

REDUCE. To reduce a finishing material is to thin its viscosity or consistency by the addition of volatile liquids usually of a lighter gravity than the finish. When a volume of reducer equal to 25 per cent of the finish being reduced is added, it is said to be reduced 25 per cent or one part of reducer has been added to four parts of the finishing material.

REFLECTANCE. The ratio of the intensity of the light reflected by the specimen to the intensity of the light similarly reflected by a standard reflector. The instrument and the conditions of measurement must be carefully specified. The spectral reflectance curve gives the reflectance of the specimen as it varies with wave length over the whole visible spectrum. Reflectance is of importance in the measurement of color and opacity.

REFLECTIVITY. The reflectance of a sample, e.g., a pile of sheets, sufficiently thick that no change in reflectance is observed when the thickness of the sample is doubled. The spectral reflectivity curve, commonly used for the color specification of pulp and paper, gives the reflectivity of the sample as it varies with wave length over the whole visible spectrum. Reflectivity is of importance in the determination of printing opacity.

REGISTER. To print a succeeding form or color so that it is in correct position with reference to matter already printed on the sheet.

REINFORCING AGENT. An essential factor in increasing the hiding power of opaque (high refractive index) pigments has been the decrease in particle size, which has tended to weaken the coating film. Accordingly, the admixture of colorless and transparent pigment particles of larger size is recommended as a means of reinforcing or strengthening the film. A pigment used for this purpose is called a reinforcing agent.

RELATIVE HUMIDITY. Percentage of the amount of water vapor in a given volume of air at a given temperature as compared to the total amount of water vapor the air could hold at that temperature. In other words, it is the percentage of saturation of air with water vapor at a given temperature. If a given volume of air contains only half as much water vapor as it could hold at that temperature it is said to be 50% saturated or to have a relative humidity of 50%.

RELIEF PRINTING. Printing from raised surfaces, such as type, woodcuts, zinc and halftone plates, as contrasted with intaglio work, such as copper, and steel plates, and lithography.

RETARDERS. Combinations of solvents, and extenders which are added to a given lacquer for evaporation.

ROTOGRAVURE PRINTING. An intaglio printing process for rotary web presses, which is used by newspapers and magazines, for printing catalogs, and also for specialty printing and paper converting.

RUBBER. Elastic substance made by coagulating the latex obtained from the rubber tree and certain plants. It was named in 1770 by Priestley, the discoverer of oxygen, after its first use—rubbing out pencil marks.

RUBBER HYDROCHLORIDE. Resinous rubber derivative prepared by treating rubber with hydrochloric acid; oil- and water-resistant.

SAPONIFICATION. Hydrolysis of oil, fat, etc., with the aid of a base.

SAPONIFICATION NUMBER. The number of milligrams of potassium hydroxide required to neutralize all the free acid in one gram of fat, oil, resin, or wax.

SATIN FINISH. Smooth, satin-like finish of paper or bristol.

SATIN WHITE. A filler produced by the interaction of aluminum sulphate and slaked lime. It is used as a pigment in coating mixtures, particularly in coated paper of high white color requiring an enamel finish.

SEEDING. Formation of pigment aggregates from small individual particles.

SEMIFLAT LACQUER. A lacquer having the appearance of having been rubbed. Usually arrived at through the introduction of an inert pigment. A type of satin finish.

SHELLAC. Natural resin, produced by the action of an insect on the twigs of certain trees which grow in India. It is called "orange shellac," "white or bleached shellac," and a variety of other names, depending upon the degree of purity and the treatment which it has undergone. It is most commonly used in making spirit varnish. White or bleached shellac is made by bleaching the orange shellac, e.g., with chloride of lime. Refined shellac is a grade from which the small percentage of natural wax has been removed. Shellac itself is used as a finishing material when dissolved in alcohol and also, to some extent, in other surface coatings.

SHORT-OIL VARNISH. A varnish relatively high in resin content, containing usually less than 10 gallons of oil per 100 pounds of resin.

SICCATIVE. Any reagent which catalyzes or promotes oxidation of oils; a drier.

SINGLE-COATED. A term used to indicate that a paper or board has been coated once, either on one or both sides. The term is sometimes used (incorrectly) to designate a paper or board that is coated on one side only; such a product should be called coated one side.

SKIPPED COATING. Defects in a coated paper caused by raising of the brushes during the coating operation.

SLACK-SIZED. A term applied to a lightly sized, somewhat water absorbent sheet. The term is also used when the degree of water resistance is below standard.

SLITTING. Cutting the web of paper of machine width lengthwise of the machine direction into narrower widths. It is performed on slitters placed at the end of the paper machine as an integral part of a rewinder. Slitting may also be performed as a separate operation in the finishing process, using a rotary cutter.

SLOW EVAPORATING SOLVENTS. High-end-point solvents used in coatings to increase the flow.

SMOOTHNESS. The property of a surface determined by its variations from an ideal plane or cylinderical surface. The smoothness of paper depends on many factors in the manufacturing process. The result of an instrumental measurement of smoothness depends on the pressure applied to the surface during the measurement and, accordingly, smoothness must be evaluated under actual pressure conditions, e.g.; "printing smoothness" is usually thought of as being the smoothness of the surface while compressed by a flat metal plate under pressures comparable with those actually involved in printing.

SOFTENERS. See Plasticizers.

SOLID. State of matter in which the molecules do not have translational motion but can only vibrate about fixed mean positions.

In the solid state, the substance has definite shape and volume and resists a deforming force.

SOLUBILITY. Amount of a substance that saturates a particular solvent at a given temperature; usually expressed in grams per 100 grams of the solvent.

SOLUTION. A homogenous intimate mixture, of variable composition, of two or more substances which can be separated by physical means.

SOUR-COATED PAPER. Coated paper which has an offensive odor resulting from the use of decomposed casein in the coating mixture.

SOYBEAN PROTEIN. The protein fraction of the soybean, which is used as an adhesive and as a sizing and coating material for paper.

SPANISHED. Color applied to the entire surface of a sheet and then scraped off with a blade, which leaves varied tones of the decorating color depending on the varied depth of the embossed surface.

SPECIALTIES. Grades of paper made with specific characteristics and properties to adapt them to definite uses.

SPECTROPHOTOMETRY. Quantitative determination of the relative intensity of the various colors of spectra.

SPECULAR GLOSS. The ratio of the intensity of light reflected from the specimen that similarly reflected from an arbitrary standard, for specified and equal angles of incidence and reflection. It is an important measure of gloss, glare, and glossiness of paper; it is usually evaluated for incident and reflected rays of light making a small angles with the surface of the paper.

SPECULAR REFLECTION. Light reflected from a surface at an angle equal to that at which the incident light strikes the surface.

SPEWING. Migration of one or more components of a vehicle to the surface during the drying process, usually because of incompatability.

SPIRIT VARNISH. Solution of resinous material in a volatile solvent.

SPOT-COATING. A coating process in which the application of the coating material is confined to certain portions of the sheet, rather than covering the entire surface.

STAINED PAPER. An old term for a printed wallpaper. A paper which has been stained with color on a coater or printing machine.

STARCH. A group of naturally occurring organic materials, of the general formula $(C_6H_{10}O_5)_n$ which is found in some part of nearly all plants, in the form of granules of varying size. It is abundant in wheat, corn, barley, oats, arrowroot, cassava, rice and potatoes.

STARCH-COATED. A term applied to a coated paper in which starch is used as the adhesive for the pigment.

STEEL ENGRAVING. See Die Stamping.

STRENGTH. The strength of a pigment is its opacity or tinting power. The maximum stress required to overcome the cohesion of a material.

STRIPPLING. Embossing paper to reduce the high gloss of a sheet by running the sheet between rollers with countergrained surfaces.

SUBLIMATION. Change of state directly from solid to gaseous; in reference to coated surfaces, the process by which the pigment is volatilized.

SURFACE-ACTIVE AGENT. A substance which modifies the physical properties of a dispersion when used in small quantities, presumably by absorption at the interface.

SURFACE-COATED. A term applied to any paper or paperboard which has one or both sides coated with a pigment or other suitable material.

SURFACE COLORING. The application of a color to paper after the paper web has been formed on the paper machine. The dyeing may be a part of the papermaking operation on the paper machine or it may constitute a separate operation.

SURFACE TENSION. The property of liquids that they try to diminish their surface. Consequently they appear to be covered by an elastic membrane under tension. It is measured as the force acting perpendicularly across unit length in the surface.

SYNERESIS. Exudation of liquid from a gel.

SYNTHETIC. Made in the laboratory from its elements.

SYNTHETIC RESIN. A complex, substantially amorphous, organic semisolid or solid material built up by chemical reaction from comparatively simple compounds and approximating the natural resins in various physical properties. Synthetic resins include the phenol-formaldehyde and urea-formaldehyde condensation products, polymerization products of acrylic acid and its derivatives (acrylic resins), reaction products of polyhydric alcohols and polybasic acids (alkyd resins), etc. These resins are finding increasing use in the paper industry, as coating, impregnating, and laminating agents or adhesives.

TACK. Pull resistance exerted by a material adhering completely to two surfaces. In liquids, tack is a function of viscosity; in nonelastic plastic materials, tack is a function of plastic viscosity and yield value. Cohesion becomes negligible since rupture occurs at very small areas. Tack is measured in dynes.

TACKINESS. The stickiness of the film of lacquer and similar materials while in the stage of drying. After a varnish sets, it usually retains a sticky or tacky feel for some time until it is practically dry. A quality of a solid having a low yield value and high mobility by means of which contact readily results in adhesion; for example, glue, varnish, printer's ink and gold size under working conditions are tacky or sticky substances. When a material drys out, sets, gels, or hardens because of chemical or other changes, it loses tack or stickiness.

TEARING STRENGTH. The force required to tear a specimen under standardized conditions in an instrument designed to simulate in a general way the tearing encountered under use conditions. The edge of the specimen is cut prior to the actual tear. It is commonly expressed in grams of force required to tear a single sheet.

TENSILE STRENGTH. The force parallel to the plane of the specimen required to produce failure in a specimen of specified width and length under specified conditions of loading. In engineering practice, the tensile strength as force per unit area. In the paper industry, it is expressed in kilogram per 15 millimeters width or pounds per inch width.

THERMOPLASTIC. Refers to a solid which becomes soft or plastic when it is heated. Common thermoplastic materials are glass, wax and unvulcanized rubber.

THERMOSETTING. Refers to a solid which changes from a plastic to a rigid form when heated; the phenolics and ureas are thermosetting resins.

THINNERS. See Diluents.

TINT. Mixture of two or more pigments.

TINTING STRENGTH. The tinting strength of a pigment or color is its ability to change the color of a lacquer. Colored pigments are usually tested for their ability to tint a white and white pigments are tested for their ability to tint an ultramarine blue or similar color lacquer.

TISSUE FILLER. See Calcium Sulfate.

TITANIUM DIOXIDE. Compound (TiO_2) manufactured from titanium ores and used as such or mixed with barium or calcium sulfate or with lithopone as a loading or coating material. It is characterized by great whiteness and brightness.

TONER. Heavy metal salt or a water-soluble dye.

TOPPED AND EMBOSSED. A two-toned decoration made by applying color through a roller to the surface of the embossing.

TOXICITY. Poisonous effect on living organisms.

TRANSMITTANCE. The fraction of an incident light which passes through a specimen. This quantity has definite meaning only when the nature of the incident light and the design of the measuring instrument are specified. The variation of this property with wavelengths of the incident light is of great importance in the case of certain wrapping papers, e.g., some wrapping papers must exclude ultraviolet light from packaged materials which turn rancid on exposure to this light. In such cases, it is useful to express opacity in terms of transmittance.

TRIM. The widest sheet of paper, trimmed to remove rough edges, that can be made on a given machine. To bring to exact size, by cutting away the edges of paper in the web or sheet.

TUNNEL DRIER. A well insulated sheet-metal tunnel or large box, through which paper or board is passed for the purpose of drying it. For lighter papers, such as wallpaper, the festoon principle of conveying the paper through the tunnel drier may be employed.

TURBIDITY. A finishing material shows turbidity when its clearness is disturbed by small particles of sediment being mixed throughout the mass.

ULTRAVIOLET LIGHT. Invisible light which has a shorter wavelength than the violet rays in the spectrum. It affects finishing materials.

UNDERTONE. The color of a thin pigmented film when viewed by transmitted light.

UNSAPONIFIABLE MATTER. The substance contained in fats, oils and resins which does not unite with caustic alkali to form a soap.

UREA-FORMALDEHYDE RESINS. Thermosetting synthetic resins, the reaction products of urea and formaldehyde in the presence of acid or alkaline catalysts.

VAPOR PERMEABILITY. That property of a sheet which allows the passage of vapors. This property must be measured under very carefully specified conditions of total pressure, partial pressures of the vapor on the two sides of the sheet, temperature, and relative humidity. Since paper has specific affinity for water vapor, vapor permeability should not be confused with air permeability or porosity.

VAPORIZE. To convert into vapor.

VARNISH. A fluid which dries in contact with air by evaporation of its volatile constituents, by the oxidation of its oil and resin ingredients, or by both methods to a continuous protective coating, when spread upon a surface in a thin film. Varnish always contains resin except in very few special cases such as patent leather varnishes or litho varnishes. It may or may not contain oil, driers, and volatile thinners, although it frequently contains all of these. It may dry either with a high lustre or with practically no lustre at all.

VARNISH-LABEL PAPER. Label paper which is to be varnished subsequently. It may be uncoated or coated on one side and may have a supercalendered finish. It is made of bleached chemical wood pulp and when uncoated resists varnish penetration and discoloration largely by virtue of its high density.

VAT LINED. A term used to designate the sheet made on a cylinder paper machine where the first and/or last vats hold a stock different from what is present in the rest of the vats. This lining becomes an integral part of the sheet when the plies are squeezed together in the presses.

VEGETABLE PARCHMENT. A paper, resembling animal parchment, which is made by passing a waterleaf sheet prepared from rag or pure chemical wood pulp through a bath of sulfuric acid, after which the sheet is thoroughly washed and dried. The properties of the finished sheet are dependent upon the furnish, the paper-making procedure used to make the waterleaf sheet, and the variations in the parchmentizing process. Vegetable parchment is odorless and tasteless, greaseproof or grease resistant, and it has a high wet strength which is substantially maintained over a long period of time. It is not disintegrated by water or salt solutions, either hot or cold, and it is highly resistant to disin-tegration by many other solutions. The sheet may be softened by the use of plasticizers, and it may be waxed, coated, embossed, or crinkled. The usual range of basis weights is 30 to 60 pounds (24 x 36—500).

VEHICLE. The liquid portion of a finishing material consisting of the binder and volatile thinners.

VELOUR COVERS. Cover papers coated with cotton, wool, or rayon flock and made in box-cover or heavier weights of cover paper. The effect is a suede leather appearance.

VELOUR PAPER. Flock-dusted paper. An adhesive waterproof varnish or lacquer is first applied to the paper. While this is tacky, i.e., before it is dried, cotton, rayon, or wool flocks are dusted on the surface. The product is then dried and wound in rolls. Various decorative effects may be obtained by embossing in patterns. It is used in box covering and as a cover stock for folders. Stocks employed are usually of chemical wood pulp. For box covering, a stock of 25 pounds (20 x 24—500) is commonly used, giving a finished weight of around 45 to 60 pounds (26 x 26—500). For cover use, stocks of from 65 pounds upward are employed.

VISCOMETER (VISCOSIMETER). An instrument for measuring flow properties. The chief types of viscometers are: rotational, capillary, out flow (Ford cup—usually called orifice-type), falling ball, Tackmeter (radical flow type).

VISCOUS FLOW. See Laminar Flow.

VULCANIZING. See Curing.

WATER VAPOR PERMEABILITY. Because of the unusually high affinity of cellulose for water vapor, water vapor permeability of paper does not correlate, in general, with permeability to other vapors and gases.

WATERPROOF. A relative property of paper or board that has been heavily sized, coated, or impregnated to resist water penetration.

WATERPROOF LACQUERS. Coated papers using pigmented pyroxylin lacquers, which produce an unmottled surface with antique or high-gloss finish.

WATERPROOF PAPER. A term for a water-repellant paper prepared by combining two sheets of paper by means of asphalt, or by impregnating or coating the paper with a suitable material.

WAX COATING. Applying a coating of paraffin or other wax to a sheet of paper.

WAX EMULSION. Aqueous emulsion, usually of paraffin wax in water, prepared by the use of a suitable emulsifying agent, such as ammonium oleate. A colloid mill may be used to secure the desired degree of dispersion. Wax-rosin sizes may be similarly prepared. Wax emulsions are used in the sizing or waxing of papers, etc.

WEATHEROMETER. Device used to determine the life of a film coating by subjection to ultraviolet light, water, etc.

WEB-CALENDERING. The process of finishing paper by passing it through the calender in web form, as distinguished from sheet calendering.

WEB-EMBOSSING. Embossing of paper by rolls in a continuous web.

WEB-GLAZING. The glazing or finishing of paper in web form, as contrasted with paper finished in sheet form.

WET TENSILE STRENGTH. The tensile strength of a specimen of paper after it has been wetted with water under specified conditions. The wet strength may be of a more or less temporary nature, as in paper towels, and tissues, or of a more permanent nature, as in bag papers, cookery parchment, etc., where the paper is in contact with water for longer periods of time.

WETTING AGENT. A substance which increases the wetability of a surface by a liquid. Typical wetting agents are sulfonic acids and their derivatives, sulfates of the higher aliphatic alcohols, pine oil, etc. Wetting agents find some use in the coating industry as aids in the wetting out of pigments; they are used for increasing the absorptive capacity of towels, blotting paper, and cleansing tissues; they may also serve as dispersing agents, as in the case of sodium silicate with clay.

WHITENESS. The degree of approach of the color of a substance to that of the ideal white. High whiteness is associated with low purity and high visual efficiency. Since white paper has definite hue and saturation, it is generally preferred to treat such papers as colored and to describe their color by complete specification of hue, saturation, and of whiteness or visual efficiency.

WHITING. See Calcium Carbonate.

WINDER WRINKLES. Long, grain-direction crease marks sometimes formed in the surface of the paper in the process of winding; these marks are caused by uneven moisture content in the paper, improper tension in the paper web, or imperfect alignment of the roll shaft. It is seldom possible to eliminate these marks.

WIRE SIDE. That side of a sheet of paper which has come into contact with the wire of the paper machine during the process of manufacture.

WRINKLING. Formation of small ridges or folds in the surface film.

ACKNOWLEDGMENT

THE author wishes to acknowledge the kind permission of the American Pulp and Paper Association in allowing the reprinting of many definitions from their book "The Dictionary of Paper." In certain cases these definitions were far broader in scope than was necessary for the limited field included in this volume. Therefore, they have been abridged so that only the material of interest in the paper-converting field has been retained. Acknowledgment is also made to R-B-H Dispersions for their kind permission to reprint certain definitions from their "Glossary for The Protective Coatings Industry" which was originally published in their monthly Technical Bulletin.

514

INDEX

515